SOLVING PROBLEMS IN
CHEMISTRY

Gary K. Himes
Phillips Petroleum
Borger, Texas

Consultants
Robert C. Smoot
McDonogh School
McDonogh, Maryland

Richard G. Smith
Bexley High School
Bexley, Ohio

Charles E. Merrill Publishing Co.
A Bell & Howell Company
Columbus, Ohio
Toronto • London • Sydney

Solving Problems in Chemistry

Project Editor: **Ellen M. Lappa**
Cover Design: **Larry P. Koons**
Project Artist: **Michael T. Henry**

Cover Photo: Dana Duke

ISBN 0-675-06399-X

Published by Charles E. Merrill Publishing Co.

A Bell & Howell Company
Columbus, Ohio 43216

Preface

Solving Problems in Chemistry is designed for use in an introductory general chemistry course. This book, through the use of *Example* and practice problems, helps to develop problem-solving skills essential to the study of chemistry. The chapters contain brief explanations of basic chemistry principles. A variety of *Example* problems are provided to illustrate these principles. The *factor-label method* of problem-solving is used as part of the step-by-step process in solving the *Example* problems. Answers to the practice problems are provided at the end of the book to enable students to check their own progress.

The authors offer a wide range of expertise in the field of chemistry. The fifth edition of *Solving Problems in Chemistry* reflects a blend of their experiences in industry as well as in the high school and college classroom. Emphasis has been placed on practical applications. Environmental concerns, career information, and some everyday uses of chemicals have been integrated into the problems where appropriate. In using this book, it is hoped that today's chemistry students will become familiar with the ways in which the principles and concepts of chemistry affect their daily lives.

Solving Problems in Chemistry can be used as a supplement to standard first-year textbooks, as a guide to independent study, or as a reference in reviewing basic chemistry principles. Students will find *Solving Problems in Chemistry* a valuable aid in achieving a better understanding of chemistry. Instructors will find it a time-saving resource for planning an introductory chemistry course in terms of the needs of today's students.

Contents_____

Conversion Factors and Problem Solving —————1

1:1 Chemistry and You

Chemistry deals with the composition and structure of matter and the changes it undergoes. These changes are studied by qualitative and quantitative methods. Since matter is anything that has the property of inertia, the scope of chemistry is tremendous. Consider the contributions of chemistry to food, medicine, clothing, and household items, and you can easily see that chemistry touches your life daily.

The logical approaches and thought processes used to solve chemistry problems are transferrable to many other areas of life. Thus, it is worthwhile to learn thoroughly the skills of logical thinking and problem solving.

1:2 Units and Prefixes

A chemist who has just made a startling new discovery must be able to transmit the discovery to other chemists if it is to be of any value. In describing a chemical reaction, the chemist may have to tell how much of each substance was used, the temperature to which the material was heated before a reaction occurred, how much of each product was obtained, or many other quantitative facts about the reaction.

If other scientists are to understand this information, units which are familiar to them must be used. **Standard units** were adopted so that scientists everywhere could communicate their findings.

Table 1-1
Some Standards of Measurement

Quantity	Unit
mass	kilogram (kg)
length	meter (m)
time	second (s)
volume	cubic meter (m³)
temperature	kelvin (K)

What is measurement? It is the comparison of a standard unit to something you wish to describe in terms of the standard unit. For instance, you measure (compare) a desk and find it is 2.0 meters long, 1.0 meter wide, and 0.90 meter high. The desk has a mass of 125 kilograms. These figures mean that the desk is 2.0 times as long as the length of a meter stick, 1.0 times as wide as the length of a meter stick, and 0.90 times as high as the length of a meter stick. The desk has a mass 125 times greater than 1 kilogram.

During the past two centuries, many versions of the metric system have been used. The modernized system, called the International System (SI), was established by international agreement. SI is used by scientists in everyday life in almost all countries.

One advantage of the SI system is that we can modify the standard units to a more useful size by adding (or changing) a prefix.

Table 1-2
SI Prefixes

Prefix	Symbol	Meaning	Multiplier (Numerical)	Multiplier (Exponential)
			Greater than 1	
giga	G	billion	1 000 000 000	10^9
mega	M	million	1 000 000	10^6
kilo	k	thousand	1 000	10^3
			Less than 1	
deci	d	tenth	0.1	10^{-1}
centi	c	hundredth	0.01	10^{-2}
milli	m	thousandth	0.001	10^{-3}
micro	μ	millionth	0.000 001	10^{-6}
nano	n	billionth	0.000 000 001	10^{-9}

*The terms **mass** and **weight** refer to two different concepts, and thus, are not interchangeable in usage. Mass is a measure of the quantity of matter in an object. Weight is the measure of gravitational attraction between the earth and an object. Only mass will be used in this book. While the standard unit of temperature is the kelvin (K), the interval of the Celsius degree (C°) is exactly equal to the kelvin.

In chemistry, the most commonly used units from the International System (SI) are listed in Table 1-3.

Table 1-3
Common SI Units

Quantity	SI Unit
mass	gram
length	centimeter
time	second
pressure	bar, pascal
temperature	kelvin
area	centimeter^2
volume	decimeter^3 *, centimeter^3

1:3 Density

Density* is the mass of a substance which will occupy one unit volume. The SI standard unit of volume is the cubic meter (m^3). However, it is more practical to express density in g/cm^3.

$$density = \frac{mass}{volume}$$

The density of a gas is usually expressed in grams per cubic decimeter (g/dm^3) because gases are much less dense than solids or liquids. Expressing the density of a gas in cubic centimeters would give extremely small numbers. The densities of gases will be discussed in detail in Chapter 9.

Table 1-4
Densities of Some Materials at 25°C (g/cm³)

aluminum	2.70	mercury	13.34
carbon (diamond)	3.51	platinum	21.47
gold	19.3	potassium	0.56
iron	7.86	sodium	0.68
lead	11.34	water	1.00
magnesium	1.38		

Example 1

What is the density of a hydrochloric acid solution which has a mass of 17.84 grams and occupies 15.00 cubic centimeters?

Solving Process:

$$density = \frac{mass}{volume} = \frac{17.84 \text{ g}}{15.00 \text{ cm}^3} = 1.189 \text{ g/cm}^3$$

---

*Cubic decimeters (dm³) will be used interchangeably with liters throughout this book. Cubic centimeters (cm³) will be used interchangeably with milliliters.

*Density varies with temperature. For convenience, we will assume that the density of solids and liquids does not vary.

Example 2

What is the density of a solid piece of iron which has a mass of 11.78 grams and is 3.00 centimeters long, 1.00 centimeter wide, and 0.500 centimeter thick?

Solving Process:

$$volume = 3.00 \ cm \times 1.00 \ cm \times 0.500 \ cm = 1.50 \ cm^3$$

$$density = \frac{mass}{volume} = \frac{11.78 \ g}{1.50 \ cm^3} = 7.85 \ g/cm^3$$

Example 3

A sample of copper has a density of 8.92 g/cm³ and measures 4.00 cm long, 2.00 cm high, and 1.00 cm thick. What is the mass in grams of this block of copper metal?

Solving Process:

$$D = \frac{m}{V}$$

$$volume = 4.00 \ cm \times 2.00 \ cm \times 1.00 \ cm = 8.00 \ cm^3$$

$$mass = density \times volume = \frac{8.92 \ g}{cm^3} \left| \frac{8.00 \ cm^3}{} \right. = 71.4 \ g$$

Problems

1. Calculate the density of the following materials:
   a. 35.0 g of a substance which occupies 25.0 cm³.
   b. 2.75 kg of a substance which occupies 250 cm³.
   c. 2.80 g of a substance which occupies 2.00 L.

2. Use the densities given in Table 1-4 to determine which would be heavier—a ball of lead with a diameter of 2.00 cm or a cylinder of iron with a diameter of 3.00 cm and a height of 8.00 cm.

   Volume of a sphere $= \frac{1}{6}\pi d^3$ Volume of a cylinder $= \pi r^2 h$

3. The first of three identical tanks is filled with water, the second with carbon tetrachloride, and the third with mercury. The densities of the three liquids are 1.00, 1.58, and 13.34 g/cm³, respectively. If the tanks measure 4.00 cm long, 4.00 cm wide, and 3.00 cm deep, what is the mass in grams of the contents of each tank?

4. 30.0 grams of each of the following acids are needed. Using a graduated cylinder, what volume of each should be measured out?

		Density
a.	hydrochloric acid, HCl	1.1639
b.	sulfuric acid, H_2SO_4	1.834
c.	nitric acid, HNO_3	1.251

1:4 Significant Digits

The accuracy of the final answer to a problem depends upon the accuracy of the numbers used to express each measurement used. The accuracy of any measurement depends upon the instrument which is used and upon the observer. The digits in an answer which imply more accuracy than the measurements justify are not significant and should be dropped so that those digits which remain truly imply the accuracy of the original measurements. The remaining digits are called significant digits. Significant digits consist of the definitely known digits plus one estimated digit.

The mass of a chemical is 15.76 grams. This measurement has four significant digits. The last digit, 6, has probably been estimated but the mass of the chemical is definitely between 15.7 g and 15.8 g.

Exact numbers have an infinite number of significant digits. Exact numbers are "counts," not measurements. Thus, you may have 24 students, exactly, in a class. You cannot have 24.1 students. Relationships, such as 1 minute = 60 seconds contain exact numbers. Exact numbers can have any number of zeros to the right of the decimal point or last non-zero digit. Exact numbers, such as the 2 in 2(3.1416), do not limit the number of significant digits in a calculation. The following rules are used to determine the number of significant digits:

1. Digits other than zero are always significant.
2. Any final zero or zeros used after the decimal point are significant.
3. Zeros between two other significant digits are always significant.
4. Zeros used solely for spacing the decimal point are not significant.

The following examples illustrate these rules:

35	two	0.246	three
3.57	three	0.004	one
3.507	four	24.068	five
0.035	two	268	three
5.700	four	20.4680	six
53.0	three	2400	two

Problem

5. Determine the number of significant digits in each of the following:

a. 6.751 g	**f.** 30.07 g	**k.** 54.52 cm³	
b. 0.157 kg	**g.** 0.106 cm	**l.** 0.1209 m	
c. 28.0 mL	**h.** 0.0067 g	**m.** 2.690 g	
d. 2500 m	**i.** 0.0230 cm³	**n.** 43.07 cm	
e. 0.070 g	**j.** 26.509 cm		

1:5   Rules for Rounding Off Numbers

1. If the eliminated digit is less than 5, do not change the preceding digit.

    2.473 becomes 2.47   3.64 becomes 3.6

2. If the eliminated digit is 5 or more, add 1 to the preceding digit.

    8.27 becomes 8.3   5.396 becomes 5.40
    8.276 becomes 8.28   0.478 becomes 0.48
    4.55 becomes 4.6   4.355 becomes 4.36

1:6   Addition, Subtraction, and Decimal Places

The least accurate measurement determines the accuracy of an answer in an addition or subtraction problem. The answer may contain only as many decimal places as the least accurate measurement.

Add		Subtract
50.23	Least	28.75
23.7	← Accurate Figure →	− 17.5
14.678		11.25
88.608		
88.6	Answer	11.2
	Least	
125.7	← Accurate Figure →	10.08
1.86		− 0.021
0.074		10.059
127.634		
127.6	Answer	10.06

1:7 Multiplication, Division, and Significant Digits

In multiplication and division, the answer should have the same number of significant digits as the factor having the least number of significant digits (the least precise measurement) in the problem.

If you are using a calculator to obtain your numerical answer, you must be very careful to observe significant digits. The calculator may give you an answer of eight or more digits, most of which are not justified.

For example, in the problem 4.8070/1.23 the number of significant digits is five and three, respectively. The calculator answer may appear as 3.908130081, but rounding the calculator answer to the correct number of significant digits (three) gives a final answer of 3.91. For example

$2.38 \times 3.1 = 7.378$ or 7.4 (3.1 has two significant digits)

$2.2 \times 0.36 \times 3.12 = 2.47104$ or 2.5

$2.5 \div 0.450 = 5.5555\ldots$ or 5.6 (2.5 has two significant digits)

$3.6 \div 4.2 = 0.857142857$ or 0.86
(3.6 and 4.2 each have two significant digits)

Problems

Remember to observe the use of significant digits.

6. Add
   a. $16.5 + 8 + 4.37$
   b. $13.25 + 10.00 + 9.6$
   c. $2.36 + 3.38 + 0.355 + 1.06$
   d. $0.0853 + 0.0547 + 0.0370 + 0.00387$
   e. $25.37 + 6.850 + 15.07 + 8.056$

7. Subtract
   a. $23.27 - 12.058$ c. $350.0 - 200$
   b. $13.57 - 6.3$ d. $27.68 - 14.369$

8. Multiply
   a. 2.6×3.78 e. 3.08×5.2
   b. 6.54×0.37 f. 0.036×0.02
   c. $3.15 \times 2.5 \times 4.00$ g. $4.35 \times 2.74 \times 3.008$
   d. $0.085 \times 0.050 \times 0.655$ h. $35.7 \times 0.78 \times 2.3$

9. Divide
   a. $35 \div 0.62$ c. $0.58 \div 2.1$ e. $3.76 \div 1.62$
   b. $39 \div 24.2$ d. $40.8 \div 5.05$ f. $0.075 \div 0.030$

10. A clean empty crucible and cover have a mass of 12.57 grams. The mass of the crucible, cover, and unheated sample is 14.85 grams. If the crucible, cover, and sample, after heating, have a mass which is 0.92 gram less, what will be the mass of the residue in the crucible?

11. What is the mass (in grams) of 250 cm³ of mercury if mercury has a density of 13.34 grams per cm³?

12. What is the volume of a box (in cubic centimeters) which measures 200.00 mm by 150.0 mm by 10.0 cm?

13. Four students report the following results after performing the same experiment. What is the average of their results? 2.78 g, 2.695 g, 2.72 g, 2.75 g

1:8 Scientific Notation

The average distance between the earth and the sun is 150 000 000 kilometers. This large number can be written as 1.5×10^8 kilometers. The diameter of atoms is about 0.000 000 02 centimeters. This small number can be written as 2×10^{-8} centimeters.

Both large and small numbers can be manipulated with ease in multiplication and division problems by putting them in scientific notation. In scientific notation the number is expressed in the form $M \times 10^n$, where $1 \leq M < 10$ and n is an integer. To find n count the number of places from the original decimal point to the desired decimal point. For 150 000 000, this number is 8 and it becomes the power of 10 or the exponent of 10. Counting to the left of the decimal point indicates that the exponent should be positive.

Similarly, 0.000 000 02 can be written as 2×10^{-8} by counting from the original decimal point to 2. This number of places is 8, and counting to the right from the decimal point indicates that the power or exponent of 10 is a negative number. Any number can be expressed in powers of 10. For example:

0.0003	= 3.	$\times 10^{-4}$	0.00067	= 6.7	$\times 10^{-4}$
0.003	= 3.	$\times 10^{-3}$	0.0067	= 6.7	$\times 10^{-3}$
0.03	= 3.	$\times 10^{-2}$	0.067	= 6.7	$\times 10^{-2}$
0.3	= 3.	$\times 10^{-1}$	0.67	= 6.7	$\times 10^{-1}$
3.0	= 3.0	$\times 10^0$	6.7	= 6.7	$\times 10^0$
30.0	= 3.00	$\times 10^1$	67.0	= 6.70	$\times 10^1$
300.0	= 3.000	$\times 10^2$	670.0	= 6.700	$\times 10^2$
3000.0	= 3.0000	$\times 10^3$	6700.0	= 6.7000	$\times 10^3$
30 000.0	= 3.00000	$\times 10^4$	67 000.0	= 6.70000	$\times 10^4$

Numbers written as powers of 10 can be used to indicate the number of significant digits when zeros are both decimal point spaces and significant.

	Power of Ten	Number of Significant Digits
150 000	1.5×10^5	2
	1.50×10^5	3
	1.500×10^5	4
	1.5000×10^5	5

The total number of digits in the first portion of a value in scientific notation indicates the number of significant digits.

Scientific notation involves numbers in exponential form. Let us review the addition, subtraction, multiplication, and division of values expressed in scientific notation.

Addition and Subtraction

To add or subtract numbers with exponents ($M \times 10^n$), all exponents must be the same before you can add or subtract the values of M. Note that the following procedure gives the wrong answer.

$$10^3 + 10^2 = 10^5$$

In place notation

$$1000 + 100 \neq 100\,000$$

The correct way to add $10^3 + 10^2$ is

$$1 \times 10^3 = 10 \times 10^2$$
$$1 \times 10^2 = \underline{\ 1 \times 10^2}$$
$$11 \times 10^2 = 1100$$

Example 4

$$6.5 \times 10^2 + 2.0 \times 10^3 + 30.0 \times 10^3$$

Solving Process:

Change 6.5×10^2 to $M \times 10^3$: $6.5 \times 10^2 = 0.65 \times 10^3$

$$0.65 \times 10^3 + 2.0 \times 10^3 + 30.0 \times 10^3$$
$$= (0.65 + 2.0 + 30.0) \times 10^3 = 32.7 \times 10^3$$
$$= 3.27 \times 10^4$$

Example 5

$$7.8 \times 10^5 - 5.5 \times 10^4$$

Solving Process:

Change 5.5×10^4 to $M \times 10^5$: $.55 \times 10^5$

$$7.8 \times 10^5 - 0.55 \times 10^5 = (7.8 - 0.55) \times 10^5 = 7.3 \times 10^5$$

Multiplication

To multiply numbers with exponents ($M \times 10^n$), multiply the values of M and add the exponents. The exponents do not need to be alike as they do in addition and subtraction.

$$10^2 \times 10^3 = 10^{2+3} = 10^5$$
$$100 \times 1000 = 100\,000 = 10^5$$

To multiply 2×10^2 by 3×10^3 use the following procedure:

$$\overset{\text{add}}{(2 \times 10^2)(3 \times 10^3)} = (2 \times 3) \times 10^{2+3} = 6 \times 10^5$$
multiply

Example 6

Find the product of $(1 \times 10^3)(1 \times 10^4)(1 \times 10^{-2})$

Solving Process:
Add the exponents: $3 + 4 + (-2) = 5$
Multiply the values of M: $(1)(1)(1) = 1$
$$(1 \times 10^3)(1 \times 10^4)(1 \times 10^{-2}) = 1 \times 10^{3+4-2} = 1 \times 10^5$$

Example 7

Find the product of $(4.0 \times 10^{-2})(3.0 \times 10^{-4})(2.0 \times 10^1)$.

Solving Process:
Add the exponents: $-2 + (-4) + 1 = -5$
Multiply the values of M: $4.0 \times 3.0 \times 2.0 = 24$
$$(4.0 \times 10^{-2})(3.0 \times 10^{-4})(2.0 \times 10^1) = (4.0 \times 3.0 \times 2.0) \times 10^{-2-4+1}$$
$$= 24 \times 10^{-5} = 2.4 \times 10^{-4}$$

Division

Division is similar to multiplication except the exponents are subtracted instead of added. The exponents do not need to be the same. To divide exponential numbers ($M \times 10^n$), divide the values of M and subtract the exponent of the denominator from the exponent of the numerator. For example:

$$\frac{6 \times 10^3}{2 \times 10^2} = \overset{\text{subtract}}{6 \times 10^3 \div 2 \times 10^2} = \frac{6}{2} \times 10^{3-2} = 3 \times 10^1$$
divide

Be careful. Always subtract the exponent of the denominator from the exponent of the numerator and be sure to maintain the proper signs:

$$\frac{1 \times 10^2}{1 \times 10^6} = 1 \times 10^{2-6} = 1 \times 10^{-4}$$

and

$$\frac{1 \times 10^2}{1 \times 10^{-6}} = 1 \times 10^{2-(-6)} = 1 \times 10^8$$

Example 8

Divide (6×10^4) by (3×10^2).

Solving Process:

Subtract the exponents: $4 - 2 = 2$

Divide the values of M: $\frac{6}{3} = 2$

$$\frac{6 \times 10^4}{3 \times 10^2} = \frac{6}{3} \times 10^{4-2} = 2 \times 10^2$$

Example 9

Divide (12×10^{-6}) by (4×10^2).

Solving Process:

Subtract the exponents: $-6 - (2) = -8$

Divide the values of M: $\frac{12}{4} = 3$

$$\frac{12 \times 10^{-6}}{4 \times 10^2} = \frac{12}{4} \times 10^{-6-2} = 3 \times 10^{-8}$$

Multiplication and Division

Example 10

$$\frac{(4 \times 10^3)(6 \times 10^{-1})}{(8 \times 10^2)}$$

Solving Process:

$$\frac{(4 \times 10^3)(6 \times 10^{-1})}{(8 \times 10^2)} = \frac{(4 \times 6) \times 10^{3-1}}{8 \times 10^2} = \frac{24}{8} \times \frac{10^2}{10^2}$$

$$= 3 \times 10^{2-2} = 3 \times 10^0 = 3 \times 1 = 3$$

Example 11

$$\frac{(5 \times 10^{-6})(6 \times 10^{-4})}{(3 \times 10^{-5})}$$

Solving Process:

$$\frac{(5 \times 10^{-6})(6 \times 10^{-4})}{(3 \times 10^{-5})} = \frac{(5 \times 6) \times 10^{-6+(-4)}}{3 \times 10^{-5}} = \frac{30}{3} \times \frac{10^{-10}}{10^{-5}}$$

$$= 10 \times 10^{-10-(-5)} = 10 \times 10^{-10+5}$$

$$= 10 \times 10^{-5}$$

$$= 1 \times 10^{-4}$$

Example 12

$$\frac{(8.0 \times 10^{6})(4.0 \times 10^{3})(3.0 \times 10^{-2})}{(3.0 \times 10^{4})(2.0 \times 10^{-2})}$$

Solving Process:

$$\frac{(8.0 \times 10^{6})(4.0 \times 10^{3})(3.0 \times 10^{-2})}{(3.0 \times 10^{4})(2.0 \times 10^{-2})} = \frac{(8.0 \times 4.0 \times 3.0) \times 10^{6+3+(-2)}}{(3.0 \times 2.0) \times 10^{4+(-2)}}$$

$$= \frac{96}{6.0} \times \frac{10^{7}}{10^{2}} = 16 \times 10^{7+(-2)}$$

$$= 16 \times 10^{5} = 1.6 \times 10^{6}$$

Problems

14. Express the following in scientific notation.

a.	0.000 03	**c.**	55 000 000	**e.**	0.000 007
b.	8 000 000	**d.**	0.002	**f.**	65 000

15. Do the following calculations using scientific notation:

a. 0.0005×0.002

b. $500\,000 \times 6000$

c. $65\,000 \times 0.003$

d. $9\,000 \div 300$

e. $400 \div 20\,000$

f. $0.008 \div 0.00002$

g. $\dfrac{60\,000 \times 7000}{1000}$

h. $\dfrac{0.0006 \times 0.002}{0.0003}$

i. $\dfrac{0.0006 \times 8000}{120}$

j. $\dfrac{0.08 \times 200 \times 0.004}{800 \times 300}$

k. $0.007 \times 0.005 \times 0.002$

l. $750\,000 \times 20\,000 \times 3000$

m. $0.000\,08 \times 0.0002 \times 3000$

n. $75\,000 \div 250$

o. $0.0009 \div 0.003$

p. $0.006 \div 0.0003$

q. $\dfrac{5000 \times 800}{40\,000}$

r. $\dfrac{0.004 \times 0.0003}{0.002 \times 0.005}$

s. $\dfrac{400\,000 \times 0.0008 \times 3\,000}{0.0002 \times 0.0006}$

t. $\dfrac{0.006 \times 0.02 \times 300}{9000 \times 0.0001}$

16. A nuclide of hydrogen consists of one proton and one electron. A proton has a mass of 1.673×10^{-24} grams and an electron has a mass of 9.108×10^{-28} grams. Calculate the mass in grams of this hydrogen nuclide.

17. Another nuclide of hydrogen consists of one electron, one proton, and one neutron. The masses of the proton and electron are the same as in problem 16. A neutron has a mass of 1.675×10^{-24} grams. What is the mass in grams of this hydrogen isotope?

18. Instead of using the small numbers in problems 16 and 17, it is common practice to convert grams to atomic mass units (a.m.u.). One a.m.u. is equivalent to 1.660×10^{-24} grams. Calculate the a.m.u. for a proton, an electron, and a neutron. Use the masses given in problems 16 and 17.

19. The atomic mass unit is equal to 1.660×10^{-24} grams. Use the answers in problems 16 and 17 and calculate the atomic masses (in a.m.u.) of the two isotopes.

20. The wavelengths of certain lines in the spectrum of a sodium atom are: 330.2323 nm, 568.8224 nm, 588.9953 nm. Convert each wavelength from nanometers to meters. (nm represents nanometer, $1 \text{ nm} = 1 \times 10^{-9} \text{ m}$)

1:9 Problem Solving—Factor Label Method

The study of chemistry requires skill in handling units and solving problems. You can develop this skill in problem solving by practice. Essentially, successful problem solving requires that you look for a pattern.

Problems consist of three parts: a known beginning; a desired end; and a connecting path or conversion method. For any word problem, first select the information that will get you started. The connecting path comes from your general knowledge and the chemical knowledge you acquire on a regular basis through study. This connecting path involves the use of conversion factors.

What if you were asked how many quarters are in $3.75. Thinking through the problem you would say that there are 4 quarters in one dollar. Then $3 equals (4 × 3) or 12 quarters plus the 3 quarters in the 75¢. Thus, 12 + 3 quarters is 15 quarters. To do this problem you have used a conversion factor, $1 = 4 quarters. Conversion factors are ratios with a value equal to one.

This money problem could be set up as follows:

$$\text{number of quarters} = \frac{\$3.75 \mid 4 \text{ quarters}}{\$1} = 15 \text{ quarters}$$

The 4 quarters/$1 is the conversion factor or connecting path between the known ($3.75) and the desired answer of quarters. Note that the $ sign and the word quarters are units. The $ signs are divided out and the unit quarters remain. If the conversion factor had been written incorrectly (upside down) the units would multiply to give dollars squared/quarter, an incorrect result.

The money problem is an example of a Factor-Label problem. The numbers are multiplied and/or divided. The labels or units are regarded as factors and divided out until only the desired label(s) remain.

Consider the following problem. Ask yourself what is known, what is desired, and what is the connecting path.

Example 13

At a meeting, 28 people are each given 3 pens. If there are 8 pens in one package, priced at $1.88 per package, what is the total cost of giving away pens?

Solving Process:

To develop your skill in solving problems, it is a good practice to write down the conversion factors.

$$3 \text{ pens} = 1 \text{ person}$$
$$8 \text{ pens} = 1 \text{ package}$$
$$\$1.88 = 1 \text{ package}$$

Note that the statement (3 pens = 1 person) does not actually mean equals or that pens equal persons. The statement simply indicates there are 3 pens per 1 person.

The problem involves starting with the known quantity (28 people) and converting to the desired answer (dollars). To make the change, the conversion factors are arranged in such a way as to divide out the labels.

For example, 3 pens = 1 person could be written

$$\frac{1 \text{ person}}{3 \text{ pens}} \quad \text{or} \quad \frac{3 \text{ pens}}{1 \text{ person}}$$

Use the second factor in order to divide out persons. The problem would be set up as follows:

$$\text{Known} \longleftarrow \text{Conversion Factors} \longrightarrow \begin{array}{l} \text{Desired} \\ \text{Answer} \end{array}$$

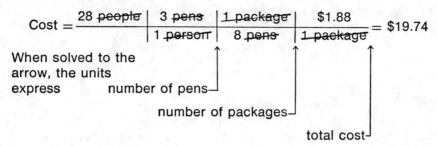

Cost = $\dfrac{28 \text{ people}}{}$ $\dfrac{3 \text{ pens}}{1 \text{ person}}$ $\dfrac{1 \text{ package}}{8 \text{ pens}}$ $\dfrac{\$1.88}{1 \text{ package}}$ = \$19.74

When solved to the arrow, the units express

number of pens⏋

number of packages⏋

total cost⏋

The factor label method of solving problems is used throughout the text.

Example 14

An object is traveling at a speed of 7500 centimeters per second. Convert the value to kilometers per minute.

Solving Process:

From the problem, the known value and the desired value can be written as ratios.

$$\frac{7500 \text{ centimeters}}{\text{second}} \quad \text{and} \quad \frac{? \text{ kilometers}}{\text{minute}}$$

What relationships are known between centimeters and kilometers? Between second and minute? Write them down.

$$100 \text{ cm} = 1 \text{ m}; \ 1000 \text{ m} = 1 \text{ km}; \ 60 \text{ s} = 1 \text{ min}$$

Use these relationships as ratios in such a way that seconds, centimeters, and meters divide out. If the units don't divide out, your answer will have unusual units such as seconds squared.

$$\frac{\text{km}}{\text{min}} = \frac{7500 \text{ cm}}{\text{s}} \left| \frac{60 \text{ s}}{1 \text{ min}} \right| \frac{1 \text{ m}}{100 \text{ cm}} \left| \frac{1 \text{ km}}{1000 \text{ m}} \right. = \frac{4.5 \text{ km}}{\text{min}}$$

Example 15

A solid rod of copper measured 12.00 mm × 2.00 cm × 1.00 m. If the density of copper is 8.92 g/cm³, what is the mass in kilograms of the copper rod?

Solving Process:

First change the measurements of the rod to centimeters since the density is in g/cm³. Then multiply to obtain the volume.

$$\frac{12.00 \text{ mm}}{} \left| \frac{1 \text{ cm}}{10 \text{ mm}} \right. = 1.200 \text{ cm} \qquad \frac{1.00 \text{ m}}{} \left| \frac{100 \text{ cm}}{1 \text{ m}} \right. = 100 \text{ cm}$$

The volume of the copper rod (1.200 × 2.00 × 100.) equals 240. cm³. Rewrite the density equation solving for mass, then substitute.

$$m = DV = \frac{8.92\ \cancel{g}}{\cancel{cm^3}} \cdot \frac{240.\ \cancel{cm^3}}{} \cdot \frac{1\ kg}{1000\ \cancel{g}} = 2.14\ kg$$

Example 16

Benzene is an organic liquid which has a density of 0.879 g/cm³ at 20°C. What is the mass in milligrams of 25.0 cm³ of benzene?

Solving Process:

The relationship between milligram and gram is 1000 mg = 1 g. The known value is 25.0 cm³ and the answer desired is in milligrams. The problem would be set up as:

$$mg = \frac{25.0\ \cancel{cm^3}}{} \cdot \frac{0.879\ \cancel{g}}{1\ \cancel{cm^3}} \cdot \frac{1000\ mg}{1\ \cancel{g}} = 22\ 000\ mg$$

$$= 2.20 \times 10^4\ mg$$

Chapter Review Problems

21. Convert
   a. 3.5 liters to cubic centimeters
   b. 0.75 kilograms to milligrams
   c. 1500 millimeters to kilometers
   d. 1.00 day to seconds
   e. 5000 cubic centimeters to milliliters
   f. 0.52 kilometers to meters
   g. 65 grams to kilograms
   h. 750 micrograms to grams
   i 0.25 megameters to centimeters

22. Calculate the number of minutes in the entire month of May.

23. A sign in a town gives the speed limit at 50 km/hr. What is this speed in centimeters per second?

24. A chemistry instructor provides each student with 8 test tubes at the beginning of the school year. If there are 28 students per class, how many test tubes are required for three chemistry classes?

25. Near a lake on an old building a sign reads, "Rowboats for rent, $1.75 per half hour." What will it cost to rent a rowboat for five hours?

26. In your favorite restaurant, a sandwich you like costs $1.25. If you order two sandwiches, how many quarters must you pay? How many dimes?

27. A young child is sent to a store with exactly $3.00 to buy donuts. If the donuts on a special sale cost 95 cents per dozen, how many donuts can be bought? Assume the baker will sell individual donuts.

28. What is the cost in dollars for the nails used to build a fence 125 meters long if it requires 30 nails per meter? Assume that 40 nails are sold per box at a cost of 75 cents per box.

29. Determine the volume that 35.2 grams of carbon tetrachloride will occupy if it has a density of 1.60 g/cm³.

30. The density of ethanol is 0.789 g/cm³ at 20°C. What is the mass of 150 cm³ of this alcohol?

31. A block of lead measures 20.00 mm × 30.00 mm × 45.00 mm. Calculate the mass of this block, if the density of lead is 11.34 g/cm³.

32. A light-year is the distance that light can travel in one year. If the sun is 150 000 000 kilometers away, how many light years is the sun from the earth? Assume that light travels at a speed of 3.0×10^{10} cm/s.

33. The angstrom (Å) is a unit of length used for measuring small dimensions such as the diameters of atoms. $1 \text{ Å} = 1 \times 10^{-10}$ m. If the diameter of an atom is 3 Å, calculate this value in millimeters. In kilometers.

Chemical Nomenclature__2

2:1 Chemical Language

Chemical nomenclature provides us with a unique word, or group of words, for each element or compound. An **element** is composed of only one kind of atom. Chemists now know that 88 naturally-occurring elements exist. A **compound** is made up of more than one kind of atom. Millions of compounds exist. The chemical name for a compound indicates the components and sometimes the structure of a compound. For convenience, a chemist uses symbols of elements much like you use abbreviations to represent names of states, months, or days. The chemical name for an element is abbreviated to form a chemical symbol, usually the first letter of the element's name. If two names begin with the same letter, another letter from one name is added. For instance: B is boron, Br is bromine. The first letter is always uppercase, the second letter is always lowercase: Na is sodium, O is oxygen, and He is helium.

The use of upper and lowercase letters is important. For instance, the following elements and compounds are both represented by the same letters.

Elements	Compounds
Co, cobalt	CO, carbon monoxide
No, nobelium	NO, nitrogen oxide

A **chemical formula** provides the clearest and simplest method of designating compounds. The representation could be termed a form of chemical shorthand. The chemical formula of water is H_2O. Thus, in one molecule of water there are 2 hydrogen atoms and 1 oxygen atom. The 2 is the subscript and the 1 is understood.

An atom or group of atoms which become positively or negatively charged are known as **ions.** For example, Mg represents the metallic element magnesium, while Mg^{2+} represents the magnesium ion. The nonmetallic element fluorine is represented by the symbol F, while F^-

represents the fluoride ion. Chemically, these elements combine to form magnesium fluoride, MgF_2.

Elements such as Na and Fe exist as single atoms and are known as **monatomic elements.** The gases H_2 and O_2 are composed of **diatomic molecules,** that is, molecules containing two similar atoms. Other elements at normal conditions which are diatomic gases are chlorine, Cl_2; nitrogen, N_2; and fluorine, F_2. At elevated temperatures bromine, Br_2, and iodine, I_2, are also diatomic gases.

2:2 Binary Compounds

Compounds which consist of two elements are called binary compounds (HCl, H_2O, H_2O_2, C_2H_6). The formula of a compound composed of a metal and a nonmetal is written with the symbol of the metal first, as in NaCl and $BaCl_2$. You can determine approximately whether an element is a metal or a nonmetal by its position in the periodic table. Metals are listed at the left and center in the standard periodic table and nonmetals are listed at the extreme right. Notice the diagonal line that divides the table into metallic and nonmetallic elements.

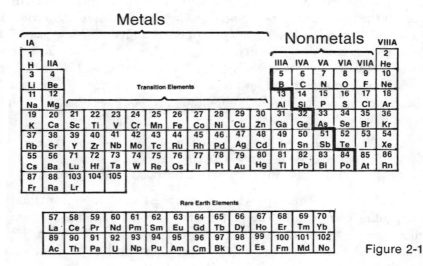

Figure 2-1

In general, a binary compound is named by adding the name of the first element in the formula to the name of the second element, which is modified to end in *-ide*. Thus, NaCl is sodium chloride. The *-ide* endings for the nonmetals are found in Table 2-1.

Table 2-1
Names for Nonmetals In Binary Compounds

B boride	C carbide	N nitride	O oxide	F fluoride
	Si silicide	P phosphide	S sulfide	Cl chloride
		As arsenide	Se selenide	Br bromide
		Sb antimonide	Te telluride	I iodide
				At astatide

The binary compounds containing hydrogen and a nonmetal, which would be called **hydrides,** often have common names, such as ammonia, NH_3; methane, CH_4; and so on. These compounds will be discussed later.

Some ions which contain more than one atom are considered as a unit because in combination with positive metallic ions they react as negative ions. They are named as indicated:

OH^-	hydroxide ion	N_3^-	azide ion
O_2^{2-}	peroxide ion	NH_2^-	amide ion
CN^-	cyanide ion		

Problems

1. Which symbol would be written first in the formula for the compound formed from each of the following pairs of elements? Use the periodic table.

   a. S and Cu   f. Al and As
   b. Bi and S   g. N and Ga
   c. N and Nb   h. Li and Se
   d. C and Mg   i. Zr and H
   e. Ta and Cl   j. Cr and O

2. Which symbol would be placed first in the formula for the compound formed from each of the following pairs of elements? Consult the periodic table on the inside back cover for symbols of elements you do not know.

   a. oxygen, copper   e. sodium, chlorine
   b. sulfur, potassium   f. magnesium, bromine
   c. lithium, fluorine   g. iodine, barium
   d. calcium, nitrogen   h. sulfur, aluminum

3. Name the following compounds:
   a. Na_2S f. H_2S
   b. Li_2O g. HCl
   c. $MgBr_2$ h. AlN
   d. Cl_2O i. CaF_2
   e. NO j. KI

4. Name the following compounds:
   a. $Mg(OH)_2$ e. CaO_2
   b. KCN f. NaN_3
   c. $NaOH$ g. $Ca(NH_2)_2$
   d. $Zn(CN)_2$ h. KOH

2:3   Ions and Polyatomic Ions

A large number of inorganic compounds are ionic compounds which consist of positive and negative ions arranged in one of several possible crystal structures. The positive ions are usually metallic.

Some examples are: Na^+, sodium ion, and Mg^{2+}, magnesium ion. Negative ions are derived from the nonmetals. Representative ions are Cl^-, chloride ion; Br^-, bromide ion; and O^{2-}, oxide ion.

Some metals have the same positive charge in all compounds. The elements of Group IA, which are called the **alkali metals,** lithium, sodium, potassium, etc., always have a charge of $1+$. Group IIA metals, the **alkaline earth elements,** magnesium, calcium, strontium, barium, etc., always have a charge of $2+$. Aluminum and the Group IIIA elements always have a charge of $3+$.

In ionic compounds, the total positive charge is equal to the total negative charge. One Mg^{2+} ion with a charge of $2+$ will combine with one O^{2-} ion or two Cl^- ions to form MgO and $MgCl_2$. For MgO the total positive charge is $2+$ and the total negative charge is $2-$. For $MgCl_2$ the total positive charge is $2+$ and the total negative charge is $(1- \times 2)$ or $2-$. In a correctly written formula, the sum of the total positive charge and total negative charge is zero.

The term **polyatomic ion** is used to designate a group of atoms that react and exist as a unit in a wide variety of chemical reactions and maintain a constant charge. The only common positive polyatomic ion is NH_4^+, the ammonium ion. Common names are often used for the oxyanions such as SO_4^{2-}, $HCOO^-$ and CO_3^{2-}. Prefixes and suffixes are used to indicate the oxygen content of the polyatomic ion in relation to other ions in a series of similar ions. A common negative polyatomic ion is hydroxide ion, OH^-.

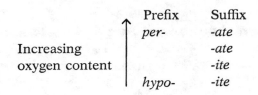

	Prefix	Suffix
	per-	*-ate*
Increasing		*-ate*
oxygen content		*-ite*
	hypo-	*-ite*

Table 2-2
Some Common Oxyanions

ClO_4^-	perchlorate ion		IO_6^{5-}	periodate ion
ClO_3^-	chlorate ion	BrO_3^- bromate ion	IO_3^-	iodate ion
ClO_2^-	chlorite ion			
ClO^-	hypochlorite ion	BrO^- hypobromite ion	IO^-	hypoiodite ion

SO_4^{2-} sulfate ion	NO_3^-	nitrate ion
SO_3^{2-} sulfite ion	NO_2^-	nitrite ion

In the formulas $Mg(OH)_2$ and $(NH_4)_2S$, the parentheses are used to indicate that more than one polyatomic ion is present. The subscript located to the right of the parenthesis indicates the number of polyatomic ions present. In $Mg(OH)_2$ there are two hydroxide ions. In $(NH_4)_2S$ there are two ammonium ions.

Parentheses are used only when two or more polyatomic ions are involved. *Note that these parentheses are absolutely necessary.* For example, $Ca(OH)_2$ is not the same thing as $CaOH_2$. Omission of parentheses is a common error you should be careful to avoid. There is no compound $CaOH_2$.

Compounds containing the ammonium ion are named by using the name "ammonium" followed by the appropriate name for the negative ion. In any compound containing a negative polyatomic ion, the appropriate positive ion name is followed by the name of the polyatomic ion.

ammonium bromide	ammonium sulfide	ammonium nitride
NH_4Br	$(NH_4)_2S$	$(NH_4)_3N$
sodium sulfate	magnesium sulfate	aluminum sulfate
Na_2SO_4	$MgSO_4$	$Al_2(SO_4)_3$
potassium hydroxide	calcium hydroxide	aluminum hydroxide
KOH	$Ca(OH)_2$	$Al(OH)_3$

Table 2-3
Oxidation Numbers of Some Monatomic Ions*

1+	2+	3+	4+
cesium, Cs^+	barium, Ba^{2+}	aluminum, Al^{3+}	germanium(IV), Ge^{4+}
hydrogen, H^+	beryllium, Be^{2+}	cerium(III), Ce^{3+}	silicon(IV), Si^{4+}
lithium, Li^+	cadmium, Cd^{2+}	chromium(III), Cr^{3+}	thorium(IV), Th^{4+}
potassium, K^+	calcium, Ca^{2+}	gallium(III), Ga^{3+}	
rubidium, Rb^+	cobalt(II), Co^{2+}	iron(III), Fe^{3+}	
silver, Ag^+	copper(II), Cu^{2+}		
sodium, Na^+	iron(II), Fe^{2+}		
thallium(I), Tl^+	lead(II), Pb^{2+}		
	magnesium, Mg^{2+}		
	manganese(II), Mn^{2+}		
	mercury(II), Hg^{2+}		
	nickel(II), Ni^{2+}		
	strontium, Sr^{2+}		
	zinc, Zn^{2+}		

1–	2–	3–
bromide, Br^-	oxide, O^{2-}	nitride, N^{3-}
chloride, Cl^-	selenide, Se^{2-}	phosphide, P^{3-}
fluoride, F^-	sulfide, S^{2-}	
hydride, H^-	telluride, Te^{2-}	
iodide, I^-		

Charges of Some Polyatomic Ions*

1+
ammonium, NH_4^+

1–	2–	3–	4–
acetate, $C_2H_3O_2^-$	carbonate, CO_3^{2-}	arsenate, AsO_4^{3-}	pyrophosphate, $P_2O_7^{4-}$
bromate, BrO_3^-	chromate, CrO_4^{2-}		
chlorate, ClO_3^-	dichromate, $Cr_2O_7^{2-}$	phosphate, PO_4^{3-}	
cyanide, CN^-	hexafluorosilicate,		
hydroxide, OH^-	SiF_6^{2-}		
iodate, IO_3^-	oxalate, $C_2O_4^{2-}$		
nitrate, NO_3^-	selenate, SeO_4^{2-}		
perchlorate, ClO_4^-	sulfate, SO_4^{2-}		
	sulfite, SO_3^{2-}		
	tartrate, $C_4H_4O_6^{2-}$		

*Appendix A lists additional ions and their charges.

In more complex compounds the metallic ions are still written first. If more than one metallic ion is present, the metallic ions with the lesser charge are written first. Negative ions are placed at the end of the formula. Hydrogen is indicated by adding the word "hydrogen" immediately in front of the name of the negative ion. For example, $NaHCO_3$ is called sodium hydrogen carbonate and K_2HPO_4 is called potassium monohydrogen phosphate.

Problems

5. Write formulas for the following compounds:
   a. lithium fluoride, lithium chloride, lithium bromide, lithium iodide, lithium oxide, lithium sulfide
   b. sodium fluoride, sodium chloride, sodium bromide, sodium iodide, sodium oxide, sodium sulfide
   c. potassium fluoride, potassium chloride, potassium bromide, potassium iodide, potassium oxide, potassium sulfide
   d. ammonium fluoride, ammonium chloride, ammonium bromide, ammonium iodide, ammonium sulfide

6. Write formulas for the following compounds:
   a. magnesium chloride, magnesium bromide, magnesium hydroxide, magnesium sulfide
   b. calcium chloride, calcium bromide, calcium hydroxide, calcium oxide, calcium cyanide, calcium sulfide

7. Write formulas for the following compounds:
   a. sodium hydroxide, sodium cyanide
   b. ammonium cyanide
   c. barium chloride, barium hydroxide, barium cyanide, barium oxide, barium sulfide

8. Name the following compounds:

   a. Na_2SO_4 l. KNO_2
   b. $NaNO_3$ m. $MgSO_4$
   c. $Mg(NO_3)_2$ n. $Ca(ClO)_2$
   d. $NH_4C_2H_3O_2$ o. $Ba(NO_2)_2$
   e. $KClO_4$ p. $Ba(ClO_3)_2$
   f. NH_4ClO_3 q. $CaSO_3$
   g. $NaClO_4$ r. $KBrO_3$
   h. $BaCO_3$ s. $Cd(IO_3)_2$
   i. NaH_2PO_4 t. $NaNH_4HPO_4$
   j. $KNaCO_3$ u. $NaHSO_4$
   k. NH_4MgPO_4

9. Write formulas for the following compounds:
   a. calcium sulfate   i. magnesium sulfite
   b. sodium nitrate   j. lithium nitrite
   c. potassium perchlorate   k. sodium chlorite
   d. aluminum sulfate   l. ammonium dichromate
   e. potassium chlorate   m. sodium nitrite
   f. sodium hypochlorite   n. sodium bromate
   g. barium phosphate   o. potassium phosphate
   h. ammonium carbonate   p. silver carbonate

2:4 Roman Numeral System

A number of metallic elements can form compounds in which the metal ions have different charges. For example, iron forms one series of compounds in which the iron is Fe^{2+}, and another series in which iron is Fe^{3+}. In naming these compounds, the charge (or oxidation number) of the metal is written in Roman numerals enclosed in parentheses following the metal. The Roman numeral system is thus used to differentiate between ions which have two or more possible charges.

The following rules will enable you to determine the positive charge on metal ions by using the formulas of compounds.

1. *In metallic halides and other binary metallic compounds, the halogen* (F, Cl, Br, and I) *always has an oxidation number of $1-$.* $AuCl_3$ is gold(III) chloride (read as "gold three chloride"). The three Cl atoms have a total charge of $3-$. Since the compound has no charge, the total charge of the gold atom must be $3+$.

2. *In compounds which contain oxygen combined with a metal, the oxygen can usually be assumed to have an oxidation number of $2-$.* FeO is iron(II) oxide. Compounds which appear to contain oxygen atoms which have a fractional oxidation state can be considered to be mixtures of two oxidation states. The compound Fe_3O_4 contains iron atoms in two different oxidation states: Fe(II) and Fe(III). It is named iron(II, III) oxide and can be written $FeO \cdot Fe_2O_3$.

3. *The sum of the charges of the atoms composing an ion is the charge on the ion.* This charge is indicated by a superscript. The perchlorate ion, ClO_4^-, has an ionic charge of $1-$ and the sum of the charges of one Cl atom and four O atoms is $1-$. Since the sum of all the oxidation numbers in a compound is zero, in $Fe(ClO_4)_2$ the Fe must have an oxidation number of $2+$. This compound is named iron(II) perchlorate. The sulfate ion, SO_4^{2-}, has an ionic charge of $2-$ because the sum of the oxidation numbers of one S and four O atoms is $2-$. $FeSO_4$ is named iron(II) sulfate.

Problems

10. Name the following using the Roman numeral system.
    a. $TiCl_2$ k. $TiCl_3$
    b. $TiBr_4$ l. $NiBr_2$
    c. $CuCl$ m. $CuBr_2$
    d. PbI_2 n. $PbCl_2$
    e. $SnCl_4$ o. CrF_3
    f. Cu_2O p. CuO
    g. CrO_3 q. SnO
    h. Mn_3O_4 r. TiO
    i. TiO_2 s. Fe_2O_3
    j. PbO t. Mn_2O_3

11. Write formulas for the following compounds:
    a. manganese(III) chloride   k. iron(II) chloride
    b. iron(III) bromide   l. copper(II) chloride
    c. chromium(III) bromide   m. tin(II) chloride
    d. tin(IV) chloride   n. titanium(IV) iodide
    e. manganese(II) bromide   o. nickel(II) fluoride
    f. tin(IV) oxide   p. manganese(IV) oxide
    g. chromium(III) oxide   q. lead(IV) oxide
    h. lead(II) oxide   r. nickel(II) oxide
    i. manganese(VII) oxide   s. mercury(II) oxide
    j. mercury(I) oxide   t. cobalt(III) oxide

12. Name the following compounds using the Roman numeral system:
    a. $Fe_2(SO_4)_3$ g. $Hg(IO_3)_2$
    b. $Cr(OH)_2$ h. $Pb(ClO_2)_2$
    c. $Hg_2(ClO_3)_2$*   i. $Cu(C_2H_3O_2)_2$
    d. $Fe(ClO_4)_2$ j. Cu_2SO_4
    e. $MnSO_4$ k. $CoSO_4$
    f. $Cr_2(SO_3)_3$ l. $Pb_3(PO_4)_2$

13. Write the formulas for the following compounds:
    a. copper(II) chlorate   g. chromium(III) sulfate
    b. cobalt(III) sulfate   h. iron(II) hydroxide
    c. manganese(III) sulfate   i. copper(II) phosphate
    d. iron(III) nitrate   j. mercury(I) nitrite
    e. tin(IV) nitrate   k. lead(II) nitrate
    f. cobalt(II) perchlorate   l. mercury(I) sulfate

*Mercury exists as Hg_2^{2+}, mercury (I), in which two mercury atoms are bound together. It also exists as Hg^{2+} mercury (II).

14. Name the following compounds:
    a. $FeSO_4$
    b. NH_4ClO_3
    c. $Fe(C_2H_3O_2)_2$
    d. $CuCrO_4$
    e. $Mg(NO_3)_2$
    f. $AlPO_4$
    g. Na_2SO_3
    h. $Ca(ClO_2)_2$
    i. $(NH_4)_2CO_3$
    j. Ag_2CrO_4
    k. $Ba_3(PO_4)_2$
    l. $KClO_4$

15. Write formulas for the following compounds:
    a. magnesium nitrate
    b. silver acetate
    c. barium perchlorate
    d. potassium nitrite
    e. ammonium sulfate
    f. ammonium dichromate
    g. sodium carbonate
    h. calcium phosphate

2:5 Greek Prefix System

Greek prefixes are typically used for binary compounds composed of nonmetals which form a series of two or more compounds. The formulas N_2O, NO, NO_2, N_2O_5, etc. would all be named nitrogen oxide. The prefix system indicates the number of atoms involved. The number of atoms of a given kind is indicated by the use of a Greek prefix preceding the name of the element to which it refers. The prefixes are *mono*-(1), *di*-(2), *tri*-(3), *tetra*-(4), *penta*-(5), *hexa*-(6), *hepta*-(7), *octa*-(8). The prefix *mono*- is usually omitted except where it is used for emphasis, as in carbon monoxide. Common usage omits the double vowel. That is, CO is named carbon monoxide, not mono-oxide.

Problems

16. Name the following by using Greek prefixes to denote composition:
    a. N_2O
    b. NO_2
    c. N_2O_5
    d. PCl_3
    e. NO
    f. N_2O_4
    g. P_2O_5(or P_4O_{10})
    h. PCl_5

17. Write formulas for the following compounds:
    a. dichlorine oxide
    b. chlorine dioxide
    c. carbon disulfide
    d. chlorine trifluoride
    e. chlorine heptoxide
    f. sulfur hexafluoride

2:6 Acids

Water solutions of binary hydrides form acids. The stem derived from the hydride is given a prefix *hydro-* and a suffix *-ic* and is followed by the word *acid*. The binary hydride HCl is called hydrogen chloride as a gas, but as an aqueous solution it is called hydrochloric acid.

Table 2-4
Binary Acids

Formula	Name	Anion
HF	hydrofluoric acid	F$^-$, fluoride ion
HCl	hydrochloric acid	Cl$^-$, chloride ion
HBr	hydrobromic acid	Br$^-$, bromide ion
H$_2$S	hydrosulfuric acid	S^{2-}, sulfide ion

Many common acids contain only oxygen, hydrogen, and a nonmetallic ion or a polyatomic ion. Such acids are called **oxyacids.** The long established common names of these acids do not indicate the presence of oxygen atoms. Instead, the suffixes *-ous* and *-ic* indicate the oxidation state of the atom bound to the oxygen and hydrogen. The *-ous* suffix indicates a lower oxidation state. Table 2-5 lists common acids and anions.

Table 2-5
Acids Containing Oxygen

Formula	Name	Anion	
HClO$_4$	perchloric acid	ClO$_4^-$	perchlorate
HClO$_3$	chloric acid	ClO$_3^-$	chlorate
HClO$_2$	chlorous acid	ClO$_2^-$	chlorite
HClO	hypochlorous acid	ClO$^-$	hypochlorite
HNO$_3$	nitric acid	NO$_3^-$	nitrate
HNO$_2$	nitrous acid	NO$_2^-$	nitrite
H$_2$SO$_4$	sulfuric acid	SO$_4^{2-}$	sulfate
H$_2$SO$_3$	sulfurous acid	SO$_3^{2-}$	sulfite
HC$_2$H$_3$O$_2$	acetic acid	C$_2$H$_3$O$_2^-$	acetate
H$_2$CO$_3$	carbonic acid	CO$_3^{2-}$	carbonate
H$_3$PO$_4$	phosphoric acid	PO$_4^{3-}$	phosphate
H$_2$C$_2$O$_4$	oxalic acid	C$_2$O$_4^{2-}$	oxalate
H$_4$SiO$_4$	silicic acid	SiO$_4^{4-}$	silicate

Problems

18. Name the following salts. Include the name of the acid from which the salt is obtained.

    a. $NaClO_3$
    b. $Fe(ClO_4)_2$
    c. NH_4BrO_3
    d. $Mg(IO_3)_2$
    e. MnI_2

    f. $Ba(NO_3)_2$
    g. $PbCl_2$
    h. $Hg(BrO_3)_2$
    i. $ZnSO_4$
    j. $Ca(ClO)_2$

19. Write formulas for each salt and name the acid from which the salt can be obtained.

    a. ammonium sulfate
    b. barium hypochlorite
    c. lithium chlorate
    d. cobalt(II) sulfite

    e. mercury(I) bromate
    f. chromium(III) nitrate
    g. magnesium chloride
    h. potassium perchlorate

2:7 Hydrates

A number of compounds called **hydrates** attract and hold water molecules. The water is called **water of hydration** and may be removed by heating. The solid residue remaining after the water is removed is called the anhydrous material. **Anhydrous** means "without water."

In the formula of a hydrated compound, the number of water molecules involved is indicated by placing a raised dot after the anhydrous formula and writing the water formula with a coefficient if necessary. For example, $CuSO_4 \cdot 5H_2O$ is copper(II) sulfate pentahydrate. "Hydrate" means water and the Greek prefix *penta* indicates the number of water molecules per molecule of compound. For example:

$$Na_2CO_3 \qquad \text{sodium carbonate}$$
$$Na_2CO_3 \cdot H_2O \qquad \text{sodium carbonate monohydrate}$$
$$Na_2CO_3 \cdot 7H_2O \qquad \text{sodium carbonate heptahydrate}$$
$$Na_2CO_3 \cdot 10H_2O \qquad \text{sodium carbonate decahydrate}$$

Problems

20. Write the formula or the name:

    a. $MgCO_3$
    b. magnesium carbonate trihydrate
    c. $Mg_3(PO_4)_2 \cdot 4H_2O$
    d. $CoCl_2 \cdot 2H_2O$
    e. calcium nitrate trihydrate

Chapter Review Problems

In Problems 21–23 write formulas for the following compounds:

21.
  a. sodium nitrite
  b. sodium carbonate
  c. sodium sulfate
  d. potassium hydroxide
  e. potassium nitrate
  f. potassium sulfite
  g. potassium phosphate

  h. cadmium hydroxide
  i. cadmium carbonate
  j. cadmium sulfate
  k. cadmium phosphate
  l. aluminum bromide
  m. aluminum nitrate
  n. aluminum sulfide

22.
  a. magnesium nitrate
  b. magnesium sulfate
  c. magnesium carbonate
  d. barium bromide
  e. barium nitrate
  f. barium sulfate

  g. iron(II) oxide
  h. iron(II) hydroxide
  i. iron(II) carbonate
  j. iron(II) sulfate
  k. iron(II) phosphate
  l. iron(III) bromide

23.
  a. strontium chloride
  b. strontium hydroxide
  c. strontium nitrate
  d. strontium sulfite
  e. strontium sulfide

  f. iron(III) sulfate
  g. iron(III) phosphate
  h. mercury(II) bromide
  i. mercury(II) carbonate
  j. mercury(II) sulfide

In Problems 24–26 write names for the following compounds:

24.
  a. $NaNO_3$
  b. Na_2SO_3
  c. Na_3PO_4
  d. KNO_2
  e. K_2CO_3
  f. K_2SO_4

  g. $CdBr_2$
  h. $Cd(NO_3)_2$
  i. $CdSO_3$
  j. CdS
  k. $AlCl_3$
  l. $Al(OH)_3$

25.
  a. $Mg(NO_2)_2$
  b. $MgSO_3$
  c. $Mg_3(PO_4)_2$
  d. $Ba(NO_2)_2$
  e. $BaSO_3$
  f. $BaCO_3$

  g. $Al_2(SO_4)_3$
  h. $AlPO_4$
  i. $FeBr_2$
  j. $Fe(NO_3)_2$
  k. $FeSO_3$
  l. FeS

26.
  a. $Ba_3(PO_4)_2$
  b. $SrBr_2$
  c. $Sr(NO_3)_2$
  d. $SrCO_3$
  e. $SrSO_4$
  f. $Sr_3(PO_4)_2$

  g. $FeCl_3$
  h. $Fe(NO_3)_3$
  i. Fe_2S_3
  j. $HgCl_2$
  k. $Hg(NO_3)_2$
  l. $HgSO_4$

27. Write formulas for the following compounds:

a.	sodium hydroxide	**i.**	lead(II) acetate
b.	mercury(II) sulfate	**j.**	manganese(IV) oxide
c.	calcium hypochlorite	**k.**	manganese(III) sulfate
d.	lead(II) phosphate	**l.**	silver oxide
e.	aluminum chlorate	**m.**	zinc nitrate
f.	ammonium sulfide	**n.**	chromium(III) sulfite
g.	copper(I) carbonate	**o.**	ammonium dichromate
h.	mercury(I) sulfide	**p.**	iron(III) oxide

28. Write the names of the following compounds:

a.	$NaC_2H_3O_2$	**g.**	$MgBr_2$	**l.**	$Sn(NO_3)_4$
b.	$Ni(NO_3)_2$	**h.**	CuN_3	**m.**	$(NH_4)_2SO_4$
c.	Hg_2Cl_2	**i.**	CaH_2	**n.**	PbO_2
d.	$Sn_3(PO_4)_2$	**j.**	$Ba(NO_2)_2$	**o.**	KCN
e.	$Cr(OH)_2$	**k.**	MnS	**p.**	$Co(ClO_4)_2$
f.	$Zn(ClO_3)_2$				

Atomic, Molecular, and Formula Mass_____3

3:1 Atomic Mass, Atomic Number, Mass Number

The actual mass of an atom is extremely small. One hydrogen atom has a mass of 1.67×10^{-24} gram and one oxygen atom has a mass of 2.67×10^{-23} gram. Such small masses are hard to deal with both in the laboratory and in mathematical calculations. In spite of the difficulties, certain basic patterns have been experimentally established and the following terms apply to all atoms.

Atoms are made of electrons, protons, and neutrons. Atoms of different elements contain a different number of protons in the nucleus. The number of protons in the nucleus is called the **atomic number** and is represented by the letter Z. The atomic number is placed as a subscript in front of the symbol of the element ($_8O$, $_1H$). All atoms of the same element have the same atomic number. If the number of protons in an atom is changed, the properties of the atom itself are changed, and the atom is changed (transmuted) to an atom of a different element (occurs in nuclear reactions).

The name **nucleon** is given to either a neutron or a proton in the nucleus. A **nuclide** is a particular nucleus. Nuclides of the same element of a specified Z but slightly different atomic masses are called isotopes. **Isotopes** of an element have the same number of protons but a different number of neutrons.

The total number of nucleons is called the **mass number** and is represented by a superscript in front of the symbol of an element (^1H, ^{16}O). An element which has more than one nuclide contains atoms which have the same atomic number but a different mass number. Nuclides of the same element contain a different number of neutrons.

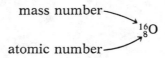

The actual mass of an atom is called its **atomic mass.** Atoms of different elements have different masses. Because the relative percentage of each nuclide occurring in nature is relatively constant, it is possible to assign an average atomic mass to each element. Because the actual mass in grams is so small that it is impractical to use, chemists have agreed upon a system which allows them to express atomic masses in terms of large numbers of atoms. For convenience, the carbon-12 nuclide has been arbitrarily assigned the atomic mass of 12. One carbon-12 atom is defined as having a mass of 12 atomic mass units (a.m.u.). An **atomic mass unit** is defined to be $\frac{1}{12}$ the mass of this carbon-12 nuclide.

Table 3-1
Approximate Atomic Mass Units of Common Atoms

hydrogen	H	1.01	sulfur	S	32.1
carbon	C	12.0	potassium	K	39.1
oxygen	O	16.0	bromine	Br	79.9
sodium	Na	23.0	silver	Ag	108

The figures in Table 3-1 have been rounded off to the numbers frequently used. In precise laboratory work, more significant digits are used when a more precise answer is required. The atomic mass unit indicates the mass relative to a standard. The carbon-12 nuclide (the standard) is defined as having a mass of 12 a.m.u. The hydrogen atom is approximately $\frac{1}{12}$ the mass of the carbon atom; the sulfur atom is twice the mass of the oxygen atom; the bromine atom is 80 times the mass of the hydrogen atom.

This relationship between the masses of different elements is of importance because it enables the chemist to predict the amount of one element that will react with a given amount of a second element to yield a certain amount of product.

The **atomic mass** of an element is the average mass of the naturally occurring isotopes of that element's nuclides compared to the nuclide carbon-12 which is defined to be exactly 12.0000. Look at a periodic table and note that the atomic mass of carbon is not exactly 12. Why? Does carbon have several isotopes?

3:2 Molecular Mass

Molecular mass is the sum of the atomic masses of the atoms in a molecule.

Example 1 _____

Ethanol, C_2H_5OH, is a product of sugar fermentation and is the intoxicating agent in wine, beer, and spirits. What is the molecular mass of ethanol?

Solving Process:

Number of Atoms		Atomic Mass	Molecular Mass
carbon	2	12.0	$2 \times 12.0 = 24.0$
hydrogen	6	1.01	$6 \times 1.01 = 6.06$
oxygen	1	16.0	$1 \times 16.0 = \underline{16.0}$
			46.1

Example 2 _____

Find the molecular mass of acetic acid, the active ingredient in vinegar, used for flavoring and preserving food. The formula for acetic acid is $HC_2H_3O_2$.

Solving Process:

Number of Atoms		Atomic Mass	Molecular Mass
hydrogen	4	1.01	$4 \times 1.01 = 4.04$
carbon	2	12.0	$2 \times 12.0 = 24.0$
oxygen	2	16.0	$2 \times 16.0 = \underline{32.0}$
			60.0

3:3 Formula Masses

The **formula mass** is used to express the mass of compounds which contain both positive and negative ions and are termed ionic compounds. Examples include sodium chloride, NaCl, and potassium sulfate, K_2SO_4.

Ionic compounds do not exist in the form of molecules. The **formula mass** is the sum of the atomic masses of the atoms present in a formula or simplest unit of an ionic compound. Both the molecular and formula masses are calculated in the same manner, and it is possible to calculate masses without first determining whether the substance is ionic or molecular.

Molecular mass should be used only to refer to molecular compounds. Formula mass may be used in referring to all compounds. Formula mass is a more general term than molecular mass.

Example 3 _____

Find the formula mass of potassium chlorate, $KClO_3$.

Solving Process:

Number of Atoms		Atomic Mass	Formula Mass
potassium	1	39.1	$1 \times 39.1 = 39.1$
chlorine	1	35.5	$1 \times 35.5 = 35.5$
oxygen	3	16.0	$3 \times 16.0 = \underline{48.0}$
			122.6

Example 4

Ammonium sulfate has the formula $(NH_4)_2SO_4$. What is the formula mass of ammonium sulfate? (Hint: the formula could be written NHHHH NHHHH SOOOO.)

Solving Process:

Number of Atoms		Atomic Mass	Formula Mass
nitrogen	2	14.0	$2 \times 14.0 = 28.0$
hydrogen	8	1.01	$8 \times 1.01 = 8.08$
sulfur	1	32.1	$1 \times 32.1 = 32.1$
oxygen	4	16.0	$4 \times 16.0 = \underline{64.0}$
			132.2

or

Number of Ions		Formula Mass	
ammonium	2	18.0	$2 \times 18.0 = 36.0$
sulfate	1	96.1	$1 \times 96.1 = \underline{96.1}$
			132.1

Example 5

Find the formula mass of calcium phosphate, $Ca_3(PO_4)_2$.

Solving Process:

Number of Atoms		Atomic Mass	Formula Mass
calcium	3	40.1	$3 \times 40.1 = 120.3$
phosphorus	2	31.0	$2 \times 31.0 = 62.0$
oxygen	8	16.0	$8 \times 16.0 = \underline{128.0}$
			310.3

or

calcium	3	40.1	$3 \times 40.1 = 120.3$
phosphate ion	2	95.0	$2 \times 95.0 = \underline{190.0}$
			310.3

Example 6

A hypothetical element, E, has an atomic mass of 18.40 and consists of two isotopes: ^{17}E of mass 16.95 and ^{20}E of mass 19.35. How much ^{20}E does the hypothetical element contain?

Solving Process:

Let x represent the percentage of ^{20}E. Then the percentage of ^{17}E will equal $100 - x$. The total masses of both will equal 100×18.40. Solve the equation for x.

$$19.35(x) + 16.95(100 - x) = 100 \times 18.40$$
$$2.40x = 145$$
$$x = 60.4$$

The element, E, contains 60.4% of ^{20}E. Also it contains $100\% - 60.4\% = 39.6\%$ of ^{17}E.

Chapter Review Problems

1. Calculate the formula (or molecular) mass of the following compounds:

   a. H_2SO_4
   b. $NaOH$
   c. NH_4NO_3
   d. $Fe(C_2H_3O_2)_3$
   e. $CuSO_4$
   f. $CaSO_4 \cdot 2H_2O$
   g. $MnCl_2 \cdot 4H_2O$

   h. $C_{12}H_{22}O_{11}$
   i. $Pb(OH)_2$
   j. K_2SO_4
   k. $CaSO_3$
   l. $CuSO_4 \cdot 5H_2O$
   m. N_2O_5
   n. $(NH_4)_3PO_4$

   o. $MgSO_4$
   p. $Al(NO_3)_3$
   q. Li_3PO_4
   r. SO_2
   s. $MgCO_3$
   t. Na_2CO_3
   u. $CHCl_2COOH$

2. Hydrocarbons and various oxides of nitrogen react photochemically (a chemical process that requires light) to form a variety of pollutants. The formula of one of the pollutants, peroxyacetylnitrate, is

$$CH_3C \overset{\displaystyle O}{\underset{\displaystyle OONO_2}{\big\langle}}$$

   What is the molecular mass of this compound?

3. An essential amino acid which cannot be made (synthesized) by the body and must be obtained in the diet is lysine. Determine the molecular mass of lysine which has the formula $H_2N-(CH_2)_3-\underset{\underset{\displaystyle NH_2}{|}}{C}HCOOH.$

4. Aspirin is used universally to decrease pain and fever. Calculate the molecular mass of acetylsalicylic acid (aspirin) which has the formula

$$
\begin{array}{c}
O \\
\| \\
O-C-CH_3 \\
| \\
C \\
\diagup \quad \diagdown \\
CH \quad\quad C-COOH \\
| \quad\quad\quad | \\
CH \quad\quad CH \\
\diagdown \quad \diagup \\
CH
\end{array}
$$

5. Hard water is caused by calcium and magnesium ions in the water. The hardness of water can be determined by titration using a complex organic chelating agent, ethylenediaminetetraacetic acid (EDTA). Calculate the molecular mass of EDTA which has the formula $(HOOCCH_2)_2NCH_2CH_2N(CH_2COOH)_2$.

6. Lead has an atomic number of 82 and an atomic mass of 207. Assuming the mass of an electron is 5.49×10^{-4} a.m.u., determine what percent of a lead atom's mass is due to the electrons.

7. The element chlorine has a normal atomic mass of 35.453 and consists of two isotopes: ^{35}Cl of mass 34.969 a.m.u. and ^{37}Cl of mass 36.966 a.m.u. How much ^{35}Cl does the element chlorine contain?

8. The four most numerous atoms in igneous rocks are oxygen, silicon, aluminum and sodium. The relative number of atoms of each are, respectively, 296, 100, 30.5 and 12.4. If you had a rock consisting only of these atoms in this ratio, what percent of the rock's mass is due to the aluminum atoms?

The Mole _____4

4:1 Avogadro's Number

The atomic mass of a single atom is so small that it cannot be measured in the laboratory. The atomic mass unit is only 1.66×10^{-24} grams. To make mass easier to use, the gram is substituted for the a.m.u. For purposes of mathematical calculations, it is appropriate to choose a number of atoms which have a mass in grams equivalent to the mass of one atom in a.m.u. This number applies to all elements since an equal number of different atoms always have the same mass ratio. Chemists have determined that 6.02×10^{23} atoms of an element have a mass in grams equivalent to the mass of one atom in a.m.u. This number of atoms is termed **Avogadro's number.** For example, one atom of oxygen is 15.9994 a.m.u. The mass of 6.02×10^{23} atoms of oxygen is 15.9994 grams. However, for the majority of calculations this number is rounded off to 16.0.

4:2 The Mole

The molecular mass or the formula mass of a compound can also be expressed in grams. The atomic mass refers to elements; the molecular mass refers to molecular compounds; the formula mass refers to any compound.

The word **mole** (mol) refers to a molecular mass in grams, a formula mass in grams, or an atomic mass in grams. *One mole of any element or compound contains Avogadro's number (6.02×10^{23}) of particles, whether these particles are atoms, ions, or molecules.* The mole is an important quantitative unit used in practically all chemical calculations. It is always understood to refer to one molecular mass in grams, one atomic mass in grams, or one formula mass of a substance in grams.

An element which is diatomic (such as nitrogen) can be measured as one mole of molecules or as one mole of atoms. Note the difference in Table 4-1.

Table 4-1
Mole Relationships

Substance	Mass	Number of particles	Moles
C	12.0 grams	6.02×10^{23} atoms	1 mole C
Na	23.0 grams	6.02×10^{23} atoms	1 mole Na
K^+	39.1 grams	6.02×10^{23} ions	1 mole K^+
CO_2	44.0 grams	6.02×10^{23} molecules	1 mole CO_2
H_2O	18.0 grams	6.02×10^{23} molecules	1 mole H_2O
NaCl	58.5 grams	6.02×10^{23} ion pairs	1 mole NaCl
N_2	28.0 grams	6.02×10^{23} molecules	1 mole N_2
N	14.0 grams	6.02×10^{23} atoms	1 mole N

These relationships are important in a number of different chemical calculations, not only in this chapter but also in subsequent chapters. Conversion ratios are used to convert from one unit (such as grams) to a different unit (such as moles).

Since the atomic mass in grams of an element = 1 mole of the element = 6.02×10^{23} atoms of an element, two useful relations may be written.

$$(1) \quad \frac{1 \text{ mol Na}}{23 \text{ g Na}} \quad \text{or} \quad \frac{23 \text{ g Na}}{1 \text{ mol Na}}$$

$$(2) \quad \frac{1 \text{ mol } K^+ \text{ ions}}{6.02 \times 10^{23} \, K^+ \text{ ions}} \quad \text{or} \quad \frac{6.02 \times 10^{23} \, K^+ \text{ ions}}{1 \text{ mol } K^+ \text{ ions}}$$

The actual form used depends upon the units desired in the answer.

Example 1

Calculate the mass in grams of 2.00 moles of sodium.

Solving Process:

Use the conversion ratio

$$\frac{23.0 \text{ g Na}}{1 \text{ mol Na}}$$

This ratio will give the final answer in grams and result in the dividing out of the unit mole.

$$\text{grams of Na} = \frac{2.00 \text{ mol Na}}{} \left| \frac{23.0 \text{ g Na}}{1 \text{ mol Na}} \right. = 46.0 \text{ g Na}$$

Example 2 _____

Calculate the number of moles in 64.0 grams of oxygen molecules.

Solving Process:

We are considering a diatomic molecule which has the formula, O_2. Thus, 32.0 grams O_2 equal 1 mole O_2.

$$\text{moles } O_2 = \frac{64.0 \text{ g } O_2}{} \left| \frac{1 \text{ mol } O_2}{32.0 \text{ g } O_2} \right. = 2.00 \text{ mol } O_2$$

Example 3 _____

Determine the number of atoms in 2.00 moles of sodium.

Solving Process:

A ratio involving Avogadro's number must be used.

$$\text{number of Na atoms} = \frac{2.00 \text{ mol Na}}{} \left| \frac{6.02 \times 10^{23} \text{ Na atoms}}{1 \text{ mol Na}} \right.$$
$$= 1.20 \times 10^{24} \text{ Na atoms}$$

Example 4 _____

Find the number of atoms in 16.0 grams of sulfur.

Solving Process:

Convert from grams to moles of sulfur, then from moles of sulfur to atoms of sulfur. This conversion will involve two ratios.

$$\text{atoms S} = \frac{16.0 \text{ g S}}{} \left| \frac{1 \text{ mol S}}{32.1 \text{ g S}} \right| \frac{6.02 \times 10^{23} \text{ atoms S}}{1 \text{ mol S}}$$
$$= 3.00 \times 10^{23} \text{ atoms}$$

Chapter Review Problems

Solve the following problems in the same manner as Example problems were worked. Remember to work so that units in the conversion ratios divide out.

1. Calculate the mass in grams for each of the following:

   a.   3.00 moles Na
   b.   2.50 moles Ca
   c.   5.00 moles Mg
   d.   0.500 mole Cl_2
   e.   3.50 moles $CaCO_3$
   f.   0.250 moles $MgCl_2$
   g.   3.00 moles Al_2O_3
   h.   6.00 moles O_2
   i.   4.00 moles Al
   j.   3.00 moles H
   k.   2.00 moles H_2SO_4
   l.   5.00 moles KI
   m.   1.500 moles $Ca(OH)_2$
   n.   0.500 mole $Ca(NO_3)_2 \cdot 3H_2O$

2. Calculate the number of moles for each of the following:
   a. 200.0 grams F_2 h. 150.0 grams Zn
   b. 25.0 grams Li   i. 160.0 grams Br
   c. 60.0 grams Ne   j. 250.0 grams Fe
   d. 180.0 grams Ca   k. 32.0 grams SO_2
   e. 200.0 grams NaOH   l. 10.0 grams Na_2S
   f. 100.0 grams $MgCO_3$ m. 60.0 grams K_2SO_4
   g. 50.0 grams ZnO   n. 80.0 grams H_2O_2

3. Calculate the number of atoms, molecules, or ions for each of the following:
   a. 2.00 moles Na atoms   f. 25.0 grams S atoms
   b. 1.00 mole N atoms   g. 20.0 grams Ca atoms
   c. 46.0 grams Na atoms   h. 2.00 moles CO_2 molecules
   d. 3.00 moles K^+ ions   i. 35.0 grams H_2O molecules
   e. 68.0 grams H_2S molecules   j. 0.500 mole Mg^{2+} ions

4. Calculate both the moles and grams in each of the following:
   a. 6.02×10^{23} atoms of Na
   b. 3.01×10^{23} formula units of NaOH
   c. 1.20×10^{24} molecules of CO_2
   d. 1.50×10^{23} ions of Na^+
   e. 3.01×10^{23} atoms of S
   f. 2.41×10^{24} molecules of H_2O

Percentage Composition___5

5:1 Percentage Composition Calculations

The **percentage composition** of a compound gives the relative amount of each element present. A similar process would be to state the percentage (relative number) of children, men, and women in a group which consists of 9 children, 10 men, and 8 women. To calculate the percentage of children the total number of children is compared to the total number of people as follows:

$$\% \text{ children} = \frac{\text{number of children}}{\text{total number of people}} \Bigg| 100 = \frac{9}{27} \Bigg| 100 = 33.3\%$$

$$\% \text{ men} = \frac{10}{27} \Bigg| 100 = 37.0\%$$

$$\% \text{ women} = \frac{8}{27} \Bigg| 100 = 29.7\%$$

If any two of these values are known, the third value can also be calculated by adding the other two percentages and subtracting from 100%:

$$\% \text{ women} = 100\% - (33.3\% + 37.0\%) = 29.7\%$$

The total percentage is not always 100%, because we are using rounded-off numbers.

Similarly, for problems involving the percentage composition of a chemical compound, the mass of each element is divided by the formula mass of the compound. The mass of an element in a compound equals the atomic mass of the element multiplied by the number of atoms. The % of an element in a compound is

$$\frac{\text{atomic mass of element} \times \text{number of atoms of element}}{\text{formula mass of the compound}} \Bigg| 100$$

Example 1

Find the percentage of each element in aluminum oxide, Al_2O_3.

Solving Process:

Find the formula mass.

$$\begin{array}{lll} 2 \text{ atoms Al} & 2 \times 27.0 = & 54.0 \\ 3 \text{ atoms O} & 3 \times 16.0 = & \underline{48.0} \\ & \text{formula mass} = & 102.0 \end{array}$$

There are 54.0 parts of aluminum and 48.0 parts of oxygen in 102 parts of compound. Since these are relative masses, we can use any desired mass unit, because the units cancel out leaving a unitless ratio.

$$\% \text{ Al} = \frac{\text{total mass Al}}{\text{formula mass } Al_2O_3} \bigg| \frac{100}{} = \frac{54.0 \cancel{g}}{102 \cancel{g}} \bigg| \frac{100}{} = 52.9\% \text{ Al}$$

Since there are only two elements in the compound, the percentage of oxygen can be obtained in two different ways:

(1) Subtraction: $100\% - 52.9\%$ aluminum $= 47.1\%$ oxygen

(2) $\% \text{ O} = \dfrac{\text{total mass O}}{\text{formula mass } Al_2O_3} \bigg| \dfrac{100}{} = \dfrac{48.0 \cancel{g}}{102 \cancel{g}} \bigg| \dfrac{100}{} = 47.1\% \text{ O}$

Example 2

Find the percentage of nitrogen in ammonium nitrate, NH_4NO_3, an important compound used in the manufacture of matches and as a source of nitrogen in fertilizers.

Solving Process:

Calculate the formula mass; then find the percentage.

$$\begin{array}{lll} 2 \text{ atoms N} & 2 \times 14.0 & = 28.0 \\ 4 \text{ atoms H} & 4 \times 1.01 & = 4.04 \\ 3 \text{ atoms O} & 3 \times 16.0 & = \underline{48.0} \\ & \text{formula mass} & = 80.0 \end{array}$$

$$\% \text{ N} = \frac{\text{total mass N}}{\text{formula mass } NH_4NO_3} \bigg| \frac{100}{} = \frac{28.0 \cancel{g}}{80.0 \cancel{g}} \bigg| \frac{100}{} = 35.0\% \text{ N}$$

Example 3

Copper(II) sulfate pentahydrate, $CuSO_4 \cdot 5H_2O$, is a blue compound used to make colored pigments, insecticides, and electric batteries. Calculate (a) the percentage of oxygen, and (b) the percentage of water in copper(II) sulfate pentahydrate.

Solving Process:

Determine the formula mass and then find the desired percentages.

$$
\begin{array}{ll}
\text{1 atom Cu} & 1 \times 63.5 = 63.5 \\
\text{1 atom S} & 1 \times 32.1 = 32.1 \\
\text{4 atoms O} & 4 \times 16.0 = 64.0 \\
\text{5 molecules } H_2O & 5 \times 18.0 = \underline{90.0} \\
& \text{formula mass} = 249.6 = 250
\end{array}
$$

(a) Percentage of oxygen. This question refers to both the oxygen in the $CuSO_4$ and the oxygen in the attached water molecules. Thus, there are a total of 9 oxygen atoms.

$$
\% \text{ O} = \frac{\text{total mass O}}{\text{total mass } CuSO_4 \cdot 5H_2O} \bigg| \frac{100}{} = \frac{9(16)\,g}{250\,g} \bigg| \frac{100}{} = 57.6\% \text{ O}
$$

$$
\% \text{ } H_2O = \frac{\text{total mass } H_2O}{\text{total mass } CuSO_4 \cdot 5H_2O} \bigg| \frac{100}{} = \frac{90.0\,g}{250\,g} \bigg| \frac{100}{} = 36.0\% \text{ } H_2O
$$

Example 4

An ore is a compound or mixture of elements or compounds that must be treated in some way to obtain the pure element desired. Ore = useful metal + waste material. Calculate in kilograms the amount of iron available from 50.0 kilograms of the iron ore, hematite, if the ore contains 60.0% Fe_2O_3.

Solving Process:
Determine the formula mass.

$$
\begin{array}{ll}
\text{2 atoms Fe} & 2 \times 55.8 = 111.6 \\
\text{3 atoms O} & 3 \times 16.0 = \underline{48.0} \\
& \text{formula mass} = 159.6 = 160
\end{array}
$$

Using the ratio of the mass of iron to the formula mass, the kilograms of iron in the impure sample equals

$$
\frac{50.0 \text{ kg iron ore}}{} \bigg| \frac{60.0 \text{ kg } Fe_2O_3}{100 \text{ kg iron ore}} \bigg| \frac{112 \text{ kg Fe}}{160 \text{ kg } Fe_2O_3} = 21.0 \text{ kg Fe}
$$

Example 5

The compound calcium carbonate, $CaCO_3$, can be broken down to form carbon dioxide, CO_2, and calcium oxide, CaO. Calculate the kilograms of CaO that can be produced from 80.0 kilograms of $CaCO_3$.

Solving Process:
Determine the formula masses.

$$
\begin{array}{ll}
 CaCO_3 & CaO \\
\text{1 atom Ca} \quad 1 \times 40.1 = 40.1 & \text{1 atom Ca} \quad 1 \times 40.1 = 40.1 \\
\text{1 atom C} \quad 1 \times 12.0 = 12.0 & \text{1 atom O} \quad 1 \times 16 = \underline{16.0} \\
\text{3 atoms O} \quad 3 \times 16.0 = \underline{48.0} & \text{formula mass} = 56.1 \\
 \text{formula mass} = 100.1 = 100 &
\end{array}
$$

This calculation gives a conversion factor: 56.1 kilograms of CaO/100 kilograms of $CaCO_3$.

$$kg \text{ of } CaO = \frac{80.0 \text{ kg } CaCO_3}{} \left| \frac{56.1 \text{ kg } CaO}{100 \text{ kg } CaCO_3} \right. = 44.9 \text{ kg } CaO$$

Example 6

In an experiment, a student gently heats a hydrated copper compound to remove the water of hydration. The following data is recorded:

1. mass of crucible, cover, and contents before
    heating   21.54 g
2. mass of empty crucible and cover   19.82 g
3. mass of crucible, cover, and contents after
    heating to constant mass   20.94 g

Calculate (a) the experimental percent of water in the compound and (b) the percent error assuming that the compound is copper (II) sulfate pentahydrate.

Solving Process:

The mass of the original compound is found by subtracting item 2 from item 1. Calculate the experimental percent of water by subtracting item 3 from item 1. Then calculate the percent of water.

$$\% \, H_2O = \frac{g \, H_2O \text{ removed}}{g \text{ original compound}} \left| \frac{100}{} = \frac{0.60 \, g}{1.72 \, g} \right| \frac{100}{} = 34.9\%$$

Calculate the percent error. From a previous calculation based on formula masses found on pg. 45, the percent of water in the original compound is 36.0%. Therefore, the error is

$$36.0\% - 34.9\% = 1.1\%$$

The percent error is

$$\frac{error}{actual \text{ value}} \left| \frac{100}{} = \frac{1.1\%}{36.0\%} \right| \frac{100}{} = 3.1\% \text{ error}$$

5:2 Summary of Percentage Composition

To calculate percentage composition:

(a) Calculate the formula mass for the entire compound.
(b) Calculate the total mass for each element or elements for which the percentage is desired.
(c) Divide the total mass of each element by the formula mass of the compound and multiply by 100.

Chapter Review Problems

1. Calculate the percentage composition of the following compounds:
   a. Fe_2O_3 **b.** Ag_2O **c.** HgO **d.** Na_2S

2. Determine the percentage of sodium in sodium sulfate, Na_2SO_4.

3. For the compound sodium sulfate decahydrate, $Na_2SO_4 \cdot 10H_2O$, calculate the following:
   a. % Na   **b.** % O   **c.** % H_2O

4. Calculate the percentage of nitrogen in each of the following compounds:
   a. NH_4NO_3 **b.** $(NH_4)_2SO_3$ **c.** HNO_2

5. Calculate the mass of the metal in each of the following:
   a. 50.0 grams MgS   **d.** 200.0 kilograms Al_2O_3
   b. 80.0 kilograms $FeCO_3$ **e.** 150.0 grams $SrCl_2 \cdot 2H_2O$
   c. 25.0 kilograms $PbCl_2 \cdot Pb(OH)_2$

6. Calcium chloride can exist as the anhydrous compound $CaCl_2$ or in three different hydrated forms which are mono-, di-, and hexa-hydrates. Calculate the following:
   a. the percent calcium in each compound
   b. the percent water in the three hydrates

7. The compound ammonium carbonate, $(NH_4)_2CO_3$, when heated, decomposes completely to give ammonia, water, and carbon dioxide. Calculate **(a)** how many grams of ammonia and **(b)** how many grams of carbon dioxide will result from the complete decomposition of 50.0 grams of ammonium carbonate.

8. Calculate the mass of the metal in each of the following compounds:
   a. 20.0 grams of chromium(II) chloride
   b. 20.0 grams of chromium(III) chloride
   c. 10.0 grams of copper(I) bromide
   d. 10.0 grams of copper(II) bromide

9. Calculate the mass in grams of the lead which could be obtained from the following samples of different lead oxides:
   a. 50.0 grams of lead(II) oxide which is 30.0% pure
   b. 40.0 grams of lead(III) oxide which is 60.0% pure
   c. 30.0 grams of lead(IV) oxide which is 70.0% pure

10. In a laboratory experiment, barium chloride dihydrate is heated to remove completely its water of hydration. Calculate (a) the experimental percent of water, (b) the percent of $BaCl_2$, and (c) the percent error. The data obtained in the experiment:

    1. empty crucible and cover   20.286 grams
    2. crucible, cover, and contents before
        heating   21.673 grams
    3. crucible, cover, and contents after
        heating   21.461 grams

11. A bituminous coal sample had a mass of 20.0 grams after complete drying. The coal's sulfur was chemically converted to the precipitate barium sulfate, $BaSO_4$. If the mass of the dry precipitate is 2.35 grams, what was the percent sulfur in the dry coal?

12. The active ingredient in common household liquid bleaches is the hypochlorite ion, ClO^-. Determine the percent of active ingredient in sodium hypochlorite, $NaClO$. If household bleach contains a 5.00% solution by mass of sodium hypochlorite, calculate the percent of hypochlorite ion in the bleach.

13. Copper phthalocyanine is a complex organic molecule possessing a brilliant greenish blue color. Millions of pounds are produced yearly to color products such as plastics, automobile finishes, rubber goods and printing inks. Determine the percent copper and the percent carbon in copper phthalocyanine which has the formula $Cu(C_8H_4N_2)_4$.

14. Calcium dihydrogen phosphate is an important fertilizer. What is the percent phosphorus in $Ca(H_2PO_4)_2$.

15. The sugar substitute sodium benzosulfimide (sodium saccharin) has a sweetness of about 500 times that of sucrose. Calculate the percentage of sodium and carbon in the sweetener whose formula is

16. In a hypothetical industrial process, it is necessary to react a base with another chemical. One of three bases could be used—XOH, $Y(OH)_2$, or $Z(OH)_3$. XOH has a formula mass of 70 and costs $1.25 per one mole of XOH. Comparable figures for $Y(OH)_2$ are 124 and $1.40 while $Z(OH)_3$ figures are 248 and $1.55. In the interest of economy, which base would a chemist suggest using? Assume that the hydroxide ion is the reactive part in the industrial process.

17. An essential amino acid which cannot be made (synthesized) by the body and must be obtained in the diet is methionine. What is the percentage of carbon, nitrogen and sulfur in this amino acid? The formula of methionine is $CH_3SCH_2CH_2CHCOOH$.

$\qquad\qquad\qquad\qquad\qquad\qquad NH_2$

18. Potassium chlorate can be decomposed by heating and gives products of potassium chloride and oxygen. If a 2.45 gram sample of $KClO_3$ shows a mass loss of 0.192 gram, what percent of original potassium chlorate has decomposed?

19. An underground mine and surface processing company needs to produce 40.0 metric tons of pure silver every month. If the ore averages 1.00% silver, how many metric tons of the silver ore must be processed to obtain the 40.0 metric tons? (1 metric ton = 1000 kilograms)

20. The mining industry often reports the concentration of metal in an ore in terms of the amount of oxide formed by the metal. Naturally, this figure does not represent the actual amount of metal present. If a rock ore sample is analyzed as containing 1.00% by mass of Fe_2O_3, what is the percent by mass of iron in the rock?

21. A sample of brass contains by mass 28.0% zinc and 72.0% copper. How many kilograms of brass could be produced from 6.00 kilograms of copper?

22. Sodium phosphate, Na_3PO_4; sodium hypophosphate, Na_2PO_3; and sodium pyrophosphate, $Na_4P_2O_7$ are salts. Upon analysis, one of these salts was found to contain 23.3% phosphorus. Determine which salt contains this percentage of phosphorus.

23. A household detergent contains 35.0% sodium tripolyphosphate, $Na_5P_3O_{10}$. This complex salt keeps the pH of the wash water slightly basic by buffering action. The tripolyphosphate can also form soluble complexes with hard water ions (such as Ca^{2+} and Mg^{2+}) that would otherwise form insoluble precipitates with detergent molecules. Determine the percent of phosphorus in the household detergent.

24. One common method for isolating barium in the laboratory is by precipitating all the barium from a sample with sulfate ion and determining the mass of the dried barium sulfate. A 5.000 gram sample of soluble material contains an unknown amount of barium chloride, $BaCl_2$. To determine the percent of $BaCl_2$ in the sample, you precipitate the barium as barium sulfate. What is the percentage of $BaCl_2$ in the original sample if 1.357 grams of $BaSO_4$ were precipitated?

Empirical and Molecular Formulas___6

In Chapter 5, the formula of a compound was given and we calculated the percentage composition of the compound. The reverse often happens in a laboratory where an unknown compound is being analyzed to determine its formula.

The **empirical formula** of a compound is the smallest whole number ratio of the number of atoms of each element in the substance. For instance, CH_2 is the empirical formula for the series of compounds: C_2H_4, C_3H_6, C_4H_8, and so on.

There is a definite relationship between the empirical and the molecular formula. Note that the molecular formula is always a whole number multiple of the empirical formula. As can be seen in Table 6-1 the empirical formula and the molecular formula are sometimes different and sometimes identical. Both water and methane have the same molecular and empirical formulas.

Table 6-1
Relationships Between Empirical and Molecular Formulas

Compound	Empirical Formula	Molecular Formula
sodium chloride	NaCl	—
water	H_2O	H_2O
hydrogen peroxide	HO	H_2O_2
dinitrogen tetroxide	NO_2	N_2O_4
mercury(I) bromide	HgBr	Hg_2Br_2
methane	CH_4	CH_4
ethane	CH_3	C_2H_6
benzene	CH	C_6H_6
acetylene	CH	C_2H_2
glucose	CH_2O	$C_6H_{12}O_6$

Why doesn't sodium chloride have a molecular formula? Because it is composed of ions. It is an ionic compound, and ionic compounds are composed of groups of regularly arranged ions, not of molecules.

6:1 Finding the Empirical Formula

You have worked with formulas in the preceding chapters and have manipulated them in several different ways, but you have always been given the formula. What would you do if you were given a sample of the material and no formula? How does a chemist determine the formula of a new compound? How does a chemist know that the formula for water is H_2O and not HO_2 or HO?

In Chapter 5, we used the formula of a compound to determine its percentage composition. Now we reverse the procedure and determine the empirical formula from the percentage composition. The elements in compounds combine in simple whole number ratios of atoms. Therefore, an empirical formula is the simplest ratio of the compound's atoms. To determine an empirical formula, masses of elements are converted to moles and then a ratio of moles is determined.

Example 1

Calcium bromide is a compound used in photography and in the manufacture of fire extinguishing materials. Analysis reveals that calcium bromide contains 20.0% calcium and 80.0% bromine. Calculate the empirical formula.

Solving Process:
Assume a 100 gram sample so that each percentage is numerically equal to the number of grams of the element. Thus, 20.0 grams Ca and 80.0 grams Br form 100 grams of compound. The atomic mass of calcium gives the relationship: 40.1 grams Ca = 1.00 mole Ca. For bromine the relationship is 79.9 grams Br = 1.00 mole Br.
(a) Calculate the number of moles.

$$Ca \quad \frac{20.0 \text{ g Ca}}{} \left| \frac{1 \text{ mol Ca}}{40.1 \text{ g Ca}} \right. = 0.499 \text{ mol Ca}$$

$$Br \quad \frac{80.0 \text{ g Br}}{} \left| \frac{1 \text{ mol Br}}{79.9 \text{ g Br}} \right. = 1.01 \text{ mol Br}$$

(b) Determine the ratio of moles.

$$Ca$$

$$\frac{0.499}{0.499} = 1.00$$

$$Br$$

$$\frac{1.01}{0.499} = 2.02$$

Since there is one Ca atom for every two Br atoms, the empirical formula is $CaBr_2$.

Example 2

Find the empirical formula for sodium sulfite. Sodium sulfite contains 36.5% sodium, 25.4% sulfur, and 38.1% oxygen.

Solving Process:

The percentage composition data indicates that there are 36.5 grams Na, 25.4 grams S, and 38.1 grams O in 100 grams of compound.

(a) Number of moles.

$$Na \qquad \frac{36.5 \text{ g Na}}{} \left| \frac{1 \text{ mol Na}}{23.0 \text{ g Na}} \right. = 1.59 \text{ mol Na}$$

$$S \qquad \frac{25.4 \text{ g S}}{} \left| \frac{1 \text{ mol S}}{32.1 \text{ g S}} \right. = 0.791 \text{ mol S}$$

$$O \qquad \frac{38.1 \text{ g O}}{} \left| \frac{1 \text{ mol O}}{16.0 \text{ g O}} \right. = 2.38 \text{ mol O}$$

(b) Ratio of moles.

$$Na \qquad\qquad S \qquad\qquad O$$

$$\frac{1.59}{0.791} = 2.01 \qquad \frac{0.791}{0.791} = 1.00 \qquad \frac{2.38}{0.791} = 3.01$$

The empirical formula is Na_2SO_3.

Example 3

What is the empirical formula of a compound which contains 53.73% Fe and 46.27% S?

Solving Process:

There are 53.73 grams Fe and 46.27 grams S in 100 grams of compound.

(a) Number of moles.

$$Fe \qquad \frac{53.73 \text{ g Fe}}{} \left| \frac{1 \text{ mol Fe}}{55.85 \text{ g Fe}} \right. = 0.9620 \text{ mol Fe}$$

$$S \qquad \frac{46.27 \text{ g S}}{} \left| \frac{1 \text{ mol S}}{32.06 \text{ g S}} \right. = 1.443 \text{ mol S}$$

(b) Ratio of moles.

$$\frac{0.9620}{0.9620}=1.0000 \qquad\qquad \frac{1.443}{0.9620}=1.500$$

In the previous sample problems, the relative numbers of atoms were small whole numbers and we could write the formula directly from them. The ratio 1 to 1.5 must be expressed in terms of whole numbers, since a fractional part of an atom does not exist. By multiplying both numbers in the ratio by two, we obtain two atoms Fe and three atoms S. The empirical formula is Fe_2S_3.

Example 4

Analysis of a compound gives 90.7% Pb and 9.33% O. What is the empirical formula of this compound?

Solving Process:

There are 90.7 grams Pb and 9.33 grams O in 100 grams of compound.

(a) Number of moles.

Pb $\qquad \dfrac{90.7 \text{ g Pb}}{} \Big| \dfrac{1 \text{ mol Pb}}{207 \text{ g Pb}} = 0.438 \text{ mol Pb}$

O $\qquad \dfrac{9.33 \text{ g O}}{} \Big| \dfrac{1 \text{ mol O}}{16.0 \text{ g O}} = 0.583 \text{ mol O}$

(b) Ratio of moles.

Pb	O	Pb	O
$\dfrac{0.438}{0.438}=1.00$	$\dfrac{0.583}{0.438}=1.33$	$1 \times 3 = 3$	$1.33 \times 3 = 4$

As in the previous problem, we multiply the ratio 1 to 1.33 by a small whole number so that the ratio is expressed by two whole numbers. Atoms exist only as whole units. We multiply by three to obtain a ratio of 3 to 4. The empirical formula is Pb_3O_4.

Example 5

What is the empirical formula of a compound if the percentage composition is aluminum 15.77%, sulfur 28.11%, and oxygen 56.12%?

Solving Process:

In 100 grams of compound there are 15.77 grams Al, 28.11 grams S, and 56.12 grams O.

(a) Number of moles.

Al $\qquad \dfrac{15.77 \text{ g Al}}{} \Big| \dfrac{1 \text{ mol Al}}{26.98 \text{ g Al}} = 0.5845 \text{ mol Al}$

$$\text{S} \qquad \frac{28.11 \, \cancel{g \, S} \; \big| \; 1 \text{ mol S}}{32.06 \, \cancel{g \, S}} = 0.8768 \text{ mol S}$$

$$\text{O} \qquad \frac{56.12 \, \cancel{g \, O} \; \big| \; 1 \text{ mol O}}{16.00 \, \cancel{g \, O}} = 3.508 \text{ mol O}$$

(b) Ratio of moles.

Al

$$\frac{0.5845}{0.5845} = 1.000 \qquad 1 \times 2 = 2$$

S

$$\frac{0.8768}{0.5845} = 1.500 \qquad 1.5 \times 2 = 3$$

O

$$\frac{3.508}{0.5845} = 6.002 \qquad 6 \times 2 = 12$$

Thus we obtain a ratio for Al:S:O of 1:1.5:6. Multiply by 2 to obtain a whole number ratio of 2:3:12. The empirical formula is $Al_2S_3O_{12}$ or, written in an alternate form, $Al_2(SO_4)_3$.

Example 6

If 8.87 grams of phosphorus react with 11.43 grams of oxygen, what is the empirical formula of the compound formed?

Solving Process:
(a) Number of moles.

$$\text{P} \qquad \frac{8.87 \, \cancel{g \, P} \; \big| \; 1 \text{ mol P}}{31.0 \, \cancel{g \, P}} = 0.286 \text{ mol P}$$

$$\text{O} \qquad \frac{11.43 \, \cancel{g \, O} \; \big| \; 1 \text{ mol O}}{16.00 \, \cancel{g \, O}} = 0.7144 \text{ mol O}$$

(b) Ratio of moles.

P

$$\frac{0.286}{0.286} = 1.00 \qquad 1 \times 2 = 2$$

O

$$\frac{0.7144}{0.286} = 2.50 \qquad 2.5 \times 2 = 5$$

The ratio 1:2.5 is multiplied by 2 to give 2:5. The empirical formula is P_2O_5.

Example 7

A small coil of magnesium ribbon is placed in a crucible. The crucible and cover have a mass of 21.35 grams. Remeasuring the mass, including the magnesium, gives 21.63 grams. The crucible, cover, and contents are heated and then cooled and treated with water. A second heating and measuring of the final product (magnesium combined with oxygen) gives a mass of 21.82 grams. Determine the empirical formula of this oxide of magnesium.

Solving Process:
Find the mass of magnesium and the mass of oxygen which are combined. Then determine the mole relationship and finally the relative number of moles of Mg and O.

Masses: Mg = 21.63 − 21.35 = 0.28 grams Mg
        O = 21.82 − 21.63 = 0.19 grams O

$$\text{Moles:} \quad Mg = \frac{0.28 \, \text{g Mg}}{} \cdot \frac{1 \, \text{mol}}{24.0 \, \text{g Mg}} \qquad O = \frac{0.19 \, \text{g O}}{} \cdot \frac{1 \, \text{mol}}{16.0 \, \text{g O}}$$

= 0.012 mol Mg   = 0.012 mol O

Ratio of moles:

$$Mg = \frac{0.012 \, \text{mol Mg}}{0.012} = 1.0 \qquad O = \frac{0.012 \, \text{mol O}}{0.012} = 1.0$$

1:1 ratio

The empirical formula is MgO.

Problems

1. Calculate the empirical formula for the compounds with the following percentages:
    a.   Fe 46.56%, S 53.44%
    b.   Fe 63.53%, S 36.47%
    c.   Mn 63.1%, S 36.9%
    d.   K 26.6%, Cr 35.4%, O 38.0%

2. Calculate the empirical formulas for the following three compounds containing sodium, sulfur, and oxygen:
    a.   Na 36.5%, S 25.4%, O 38.1%   c.   Na 29.1%, S 40.5%, O 30.4%
    b.   Na 32.4%, S 22.6%, O 45.0%

6:2 Molecular Formulas

The molecular formula indicates not only the ratio of the atoms of the elements in a compound but also the actual number of atoms of each element in one molecule of the compound.

The molecular formula calculation is the same as the empirical formula calculation, except that the formula mass is used in an additional step. To calculate a molecular formula, the formula mass must be known. The molecular formula is always a whole number multiple of the empirical formula.

Example 8

An organic compound is found to contain 92.25% carbon and 7.75% hydrogen. If the molecular mass is 78, what is the molecular formula?

Solving Process:

Determine the empirical formula.

(a) Number of moles.

$$C \qquad \frac{92.25 \, \cancel{gC} \mid 1 \text{ mol C}}{\mid 12.01 \, \cancel{gC}} = 7.681 \text{ mol C}$$

$$H \qquad \frac{7.75 \, \cancel{gH} \mid 1 \text{ mol H}}{\mid 1.01 \, \cancel{gH}} = 7.67 \text{ mol H}$$

(b) Ratio of moles.

$$H \qquad\qquad\qquad C$$
$$\frac{7.67}{7.67} = 1.00 \qquad\qquad \frac{7.681}{7.67} = 1.00$$

The empirical formula is CH. Since the CH unit has a molecular mass of 13:

$$13x = 78$$
$$x = 78/13 = 6.0$$

Six times the molecular formula is $(CH)_6$. Written in customary form, the formula is C_6H_6.

Alternate Method: It is possible to eliminate the last step of the first method by introducing the unit factor:

$$\frac{78 \text{ g}}{1 \text{ mol}}$$

The final answer then gives the moles of each element in one mole of compound and enables you to write the molecular formula immediately.

(a) Number of moles of element per mole of compound

$$C \qquad \frac{92.25 \, \cancel{gC} \mid 1 \text{ mol C} \mid 78 \, \cancel{g \, cmpd}}{100 \, \cancel{g \, cmpd} \mid 12.01 \, \cancel{gC} \mid 1 \text{ mol cmpd}} = \frac{6 \text{ mol C}}{\text{mol cmpd}}$$

$$H \qquad \frac{7.75 \, \cancel{gH} \mid 1 \text{ mol H} \mid 78 \, \cancel{g \, cmpd}}{100 \, \cancel{g \, cmpd} \mid 1.01 \, \cancel{gH} \mid 1 \text{ mol cmpd}} = \frac{6 \text{ mol H}}{\text{mol cmpd}}$$

Since the ratio of moles of carbon and hydrogen to 1 mole of compound is 6:6:1, the molecular formula must be C_6H_6.

Example 9

If the molecular mass of an oxide of nitrogen is 108 and 4.02 grams of N combine with 11.48 grams of O, what is the molecular formula of this compound?

Solving Process:
(a)   Number of moles.

$$\text{N} \qquad \frac{4.02 \text{ g N} \mid 1 \text{ mol N}}{14.01 \text{ g N}} = 0.287 \text{ mol N}$$

$$\text{O} \qquad \frac{11.48 \text{ g O} \mid 1 \text{ mol O}}{16.00 \text{ g O}} = 0.7175 \text{ mol O}$$

(b)   Ratio of moles.

N   O

$$\frac{0.287}{0.287} = 1.00 \quad 1 \times 2 = 2 \qquad \frac{0.7175}{0.287} = 2.50 \quad 2.5 \times 2 = 5$$

Multiply the ratio 1:2.5 by 2 to give 2:5. The empirical formula is N_2O_5. Since the molecular mass of N_2O_5 is 108, the empirical formula and the molecular formula are the same. The N_2O_5 unit has a molecular mass of 108.

$$108x = 108$$

$x = 1$, so the empirical and molecular formulas are the same.

Problems

3. The formula mass of a compound is 92. Analysis of the compound shows that there are 0.608 grams of nitrogen and 1.388 grams of oxygen. What is the molecular formula of this compound?

4. There are two oxides of phosphorus. Both oxides can exist in different forms depending on the temperature and the pressure. Calculate the empirical and molecular formulas from the data:
    a. P 56.4%, O 43.7%, molecular mass 220
    b. P 43.6%, O 56.4%, molecular mass 284

6:3 Empirical Formulas of Hydrates

A number of compounds, called **hydrates**, contain water attached to the molecules or ions. The method used to calculate the formulas of hydrates is basically the same except that it is necessary to determine the number of moles of water involved.

Example 10 _____

A hydrated compound has an analysis of 18.29% Ca, 32.37% Cl, and 49.34% H_2O. What is its formula?

Solving Process:
(a) Number of moles.

$$\text{Ca} \qquad \frac{18.29 \text{ g Ca}}{40.08 \text{ g Ca}} \Big| \frac{1 \text{ mol Ca}}{} = 0.4563 \text{ mol Ca}$$

$$\text{Cl} \qquad \frac{32.37 \text{ g Cl}}{35.45 \text{ g Cl}} \Big| \frac{1 \text{ mol Cl}}{} = 0.9131 \text{ mol Cl}$$

$$H_2O \qquad \frac{49.34 \text{ g } H_2O}{18.02 \text{ g } H_2O} \Big| \frac{1 \text{ mol } H_2O}{} = 2.738 \text{ mol } H_2O$$

(b) Ratio of moles.

Ca	Cl	H_2O
$\dfrac{0.4563}{0.4563} = 1.000$	$\dfrac{0.9131}{0.4563} = 2.001$	$\dfrac{2.738}{0.4563} = 6.000$

The empirical formula is $CaCl_2 \cdot 6H_2O$. The raised dot between the $CaCl_2$ and the $6H_2O$ means that this substance is a hydrated compound.

Example 11

A hydrated sodium salt containing 39.7% water is analyzed as follows: Na 16.9%, C 17.7%, H 6.67%, and O 58.8%. What is the empirical formula of this salt?

Solving Process:
In addition to the Na and C, note that the percentage of H and O is also given. The water of hydration is in addition to the 100%. In other words, H and O are given separately, and the water of hydration percentage is also given.
(a) Number of moles.

$$\text{Na} \qquad \frac{16.9 \text{ g Na}}{23.0 \text{ g Na}} \Big| \frac{1 \text{ mol Na}}{} = 0.735 \text{ mol Na}$$

$$\text{C} \qquad \frac{17.7 \text{ g C}}{12.0 \text{ g C}} \Big| \frac{1 \text{ mol C}}{} = 1.48 \text{ mol C}$$

$$\text{H} \qquad \frac{6.67 \text{ g H}}{1.01 \text{ g H}} \Big| \frac{1 \text{ mol H}}{} = 6.60 \text{ mol H}$$

$$\text{O} \qquad \frac{58.8 \text{ g O}}{16.0 \text{ g O}} \Big| \frac{1 \text{ mol O}}{} = 3.68 \text{ mol O}$$

$$H_2O \qquad \frac{39.7 \text{ g } H_2O}{18.0 \text{ g } H_2O} \Big| \frac{1 \text{ mol } H_2O}{} = 2.21 \text{ mol } H_2O$$

(b) Ratio of moles.

Na	C	H	O	H_2O
$\dfrac{0.735}{0.735} = 1.00$	$\dfrac{1.48}{0.735} = 2.01$	$\dfrac{6.60}{0.735} = 5.01$	$\dfrac{3.68}{0.735} = 5.01$	$\dfrac{2.21}{0.735} = 3.01$

Since there are three moles of water, six moles of hydrogen and three moles of oxygen are combined as water of hydration. This leaves three moles of hydrogen and two moles of oxygen in the salt molecule. The empirical formula is $NaC_2H_3O_2 \cdot 3H_2O$.

Problem

5. The masses of the hydrates listed below were measured, heated to drive off the water of hydration, and cooled. Then the masses of the residues were measured. Find the formulas of the hydrates:
    a. 1.62 grams of $CoCl_2 \cdot xH_2O$ gave a residue of 0.88 grams
    b. 1.21 grams of $Pb(C_2H_3O_2)_2 \cdot xH_2O$ gave a residue of 1.03 grams
    c. 1.04 grams $NiSO_4 \cdot xH_2O$ gave a residue of 0.61 grams
    d. 1.26 grams of $CaSO_4 \cdot xH_2O$ gave a residue of 0.99 grams

Chapter Review Problems

6. Calculate the simplest (empirical) formulas of the compounds which have the following percentages.
    a. K 40.2%, Cr 26.9%, O 32.9%
    b. Mg 21.8%, P 27.9%, O 50.3%
    c. Sr 65.7%, Si 10.4%, O 23.9%
    d. Na 34.58%, P 23.30%, O 42.12%

7. Calculate the empirical formulas for the following three iron ores:
    a. Fe 77.7%, O 22.3%   c. Fe 70.0%, O 30.0%
    b. Fe 72.4%, O 27.6%

8. A hydrated magnesium compound has a formula mass of about 174 and contains 31.0% water of hydration. From the following analysis, calculate the molecular formula: Mg 13.90%, P 17.74%, H 4.01%, O 64.30%.

9. What is the molecular formula of a hydrated sodium salt which has a formula mass of about 268 and contains 46.9% water of hydration? An analysis reveals the following composition: Na 17.18%, P 11.57%, H 5.60%, O 65.70%.

10. A hydrated salt contains 13.05% water of hydration and analysis reveals the following percentages: Na 16.66%, S 23.19%, H 2.19%, and O 57.96%. What is the empirical formula of this hydrated sodium salt?

11. Calcium nitrate, $Ca(NO_3)_2$, forms two different hydrated salts. One contains 24.7% water; the other 30.4% water. What are the formulas for these two hydrated salts?

12. One compound of chromium contains 57.9% chlorine and a second compound contains 67.3% chlorine. What are the empirical formulas of these two chromium chloride compounds?

13. A hydrated sodium salt has a formula mass of approximately 248 and contains 36.2% water of hydration. Determine the molecular formula from the data: Na 18.50%, S 25.80%, H 4.04%, O 51.50%

14. Chromium exists in four different oxide compounds. From the following data, calculate the empirical formula for each oxide:
    a. 0.765 grams Cr combines with 0.235 grams O
    b. 5.60 grams Cr combines with 2.62 grams O
    c. 1.24 grams Cr combines with 0.76 grams O
    d. 0.52 grams Cr combines with 0.48 grams O

15. Two compounds are analyzed and found to contain:
    a. 0.89 grams K, 1.18 grams Cr, 1.27 grams O
    b. 1.03 grams K, 0.69 grams Cr, 0.84 grams O
    Determine the empirical formulas for these two compounds.

16. To find the experimental empirical formula of a compound, a student heats a uniform coil of magnesium ribbon 35.00 centimeters long in a crucible. The resulting mixed product is treated with water, and subsequent heating gives an oxide of magnesium. The data is recorded as follows:

    1. mass of empty crucible and cover   20.74 grams
    2. mass of two meters of magnesium ribbon   1.44 grams
    3. mass of crucible, cover, and final product   21.17 grams

    Determine the empirical formula for the oxide of magnesium.

17. White lead contains 80.1% lead, 16.5% oxygen, 3.10% carbon, and 0.260% hydrogen. What is the formula of this compound?

18. A fat is composed, in part, of long chains of carbon and hydrogen atoms. In a reaction with a strong base, a fat forms a soap and glycerol. What is the empirical formula of a fat containing 76.7% C, 11.1% O and 12.2% H, if it has a molecular mass of 860?

19. Citric acid, an organic acid found in lemons and other fruits, contains 37.5% carbon, 58.3% oxygen and 4.20% hydrogen. What is the empirical formula of citric acid if it has a molecular mass of 192?

20. Antibiotics are complex organic chemicals which have the ability to destroy or inhibit the growth of microorganisms such as bacteria and viruses. Aureomycin is an antibiotic which contains 55.2% C, 26.7% O, 5.85% N, 7.40% Cl and 4.84% H. What is the empirical formula of aureomycin which has a molecular mass of 479?

21. A hypothetical compound which contains some water of hydration is shown to have the following elemental composition: Na 19.17%; C 10.00%; H 4.17%; and O 66.66%. After heating to 100°C to eliminate only the water of hydration, the composition is found to have changed as follows: Na 27.38%; C 14.28%, H 1.19%; and O 57.15%. From this information, deduce the probable molecular formula correctly depicting the water of hydration.

Equation $\mathcal{W}$riting _____ 7

A **chemical equation** is a concise shorthand expression which represents the relative amount of reactants and products involved in a chemical reaction.

$$\underbrace{CO_2 + H_2O}_{\text{reactants}} \longrightarrow \underbrace{H_2CO_3}_{\text{product}}$$

The first step in writing a chemical equation is the word equation. It is composed of the names of the materials that enter into chemical reaction, the **reactants,** and the names of the materials that result from the reaction, the **products.**

The second step in writing a chemical equation is a **skeleton equation.** This equation includes the chemical formulas and symbols for all the reactants and products.

The third step is a **balanced equation.** This equation is similar to a skeleton equation, but it also includes coefficients placed directly in front of the chemical formulas and symbols. The coefficients of a balanced equation indicate the number of units of each substance involved.

Hydrogen burns in oxygen to form water. The reactants are hydrogen and oxygen. The product is water. The word equation for this reaction is

$$\text{hydrogen} + \text{oxygen} \longrightarrow \text{water}$$

It is read, "hydrogen plus oxygen yield water."

Since hydrogen and oxygen are diatomic gases, the H_2 and O_2 represent one molecule of hydrogen and one molecule of oxygen. The compound, water, is represented by the formula H_2O. The skeleton equation is

$$H_2 + O_2 \longrightarrow H_2O$$

7:1   The Balanced Equation

The skeleton equation indicates that two hydrogen atoms react with two oxygen atoms on the reactant side of the equation. On the product side, two hydrogen atoms are bonded to one oxygen atom. The equation is deficient by one oxygen atom on the product side.

Balance the equation by putting coefficients directly in front of any of the reactants or products. A coefficient should be a whole number. *Never change the subscripts.* Changing the subscript changes the chemical formula of the compound. Place a 2 in front of the H_2O so that there are two oxygen atoms on each side of the equation.

$$H_2 + O_2 \longrightarrow 2H_2O$$

The 2 placed in front of the H_2O changes the balance of the hydrogen atoms. Correct this imbalance by placing another 2 in front of the H_2. The equation is now balanced.

$$2H_2 + O_2 \longrightarrow 2H_2O$$

Symbols are used in an equation to indicate the physical state of each substance. The symbols used (placed in parenthesis) are (g) for gas, (l) for liquid, (c) for solid, (aq) for aqueous (water) solution, and (amor) for amorphous substances.

$$2H_2(g) + O_2(g) \longrightarrow 2H_2O(l)$$

What can we infer from a balanced equation? An equation indicates:

(1)   two parts of hydrogen react with one part of oxygen to yield two parts of water.
(2)   two molecules of hydrogen react with one molecule of oxygen to give two molecules of water.
(3)   a quantitative relationship between the reactants and products. This relationship is the basis for working all quantitative problems.

Steps in Writing a Balanced Equation

Step 1.   In writing a chemical reaction, the reactants and the products are written down. If the products are not known, they can be predicted in many cases.

Step 2.   The formulas of each substance must be correct. The diatomic gases are hydrogen, H_2; nitrogen, N_2; oxygen, O_2; fluorine, F_2; chlorine, Cl_2; bromine, Br_2; and iodine, I_2.

Step 3.   The equation is then balanced. The balancing is done by putting a coefficient before compounds until the atoms of each element on one side of the equation equal the number of atoms of that element on the other side of the equation.

Example 1

Sodium reacts with water to produce a metallic hydroxide and hydrogen gas. Write a balanced equation for the reaction.

Solving Process:

Step 1. Write the word equation:

$$sodium + water \longrightarrow sodium\ hydroxide + hydrogen$$

Step 2. Write a skeleton equation. Since hydrogen is a diatomic gas, its formula is H_2. The formula for water may be written as HOH if this makes it easier to balance the equation.

$$Na + HOH \longrightarrow NaOH + H_2$$

Step 3. Balance the equation. The metallic element sodium is balanced. One atom of sodium is on each side of the equation. There is one hydrogen atom on the reactant side (the H in OH has been accounted for) and 2 hydrogen atoms on the product side. Place a 2 in front of the HOH to balance the hydrogen atoms.

$$Na + 2HOH \longrightarrow NaOH + H_2$$

There are now 2OH on the left and 1 on the right. Place a 2 in front of the NaOH to give the same number of OH on each side.

$$Na + 2HOH \longrightarrow 2NaOH + H_2$$

Put a 2 in front of the sodium metal. The balanced equation reads

$$2Na(c) + 2HOH(l) \longrightarrow 2NaOH(aq) + H_2(g)$$

Check visually to see if the equation is balanced, or list all the atoms (the hydroxide can be listed as OH or can be separated into H and O).

	Reactants	Products
Na	2	2
H	4	4
O	2	2

Example 2

Iron(III) oxide reacts with carbon monoxide to give iron and carbon dioxide. What is the balanced equation?

Solving Process:

Step 1. Write the word equation.

$$iron(III)\ oxide + carbon\ monoxide \longrightarrow iron + carbon\ dioxide$$

Step 2. Write the formulas and symbols of all reactants and products.

$$Fe_2O_3 + CO \longrightarrow Fe + CO_2$$

Step 3. Balance the iron atoms.

$$Fe_2O_3 + CO \longrightarrow 2Fe + CO_2$$

The carbon atoms are already balanced. Visual inspection indicates that a 2 in front of the CO_2 to balance the oxygen atoms changes the carbon atom balance.

A 2 in front of carbon monoxide results in an odd number of oxygen atoms on the reactant side. This change will not work because any number placed in front of carbon dioxide will always give an even number of oxygen atoms on the product side.

A 3 in front of CO will give an even number of oxygen atoms on the reactant side. A 3 as a coefficient for CO_2 will balance the oxygen atoms and the carbon atoms.

The balanced equation is

$$Fe_2O_3(c) + 3CO(g) \longrightarrow 2Fe(c) + 3CO_2(g)$$

Check the equation.

	Reactants	Products
Fe	2	2
C	3	3
O	6	6

Example 3

Calcium hydroxide reacts with phosphoric acid to yield calcium phosphate and water. Determine the balanced equation.

Solving Process:

Step 1.

calcium hydroxide + phosphoric acid $\longrightarrow$ calcium phosphate + water

Step 2.

$$Ca(OH)_2 + H_3PO_4 \longrightarrow Ca_3(PO_4)_2 + HOH$$

Step 3. Balance the calcium atoms by placing a 3 in front of the $Ca(OH)_2$.

$$3Ca(OH)_2 + H_3PO_4 \longrightarrow Ca_3(PO_4)_2 + HOH$$

Since the phosphate and hydroxide ions are on both sides of the equation they can be balanced as units. Place a 2 in front of the phosphoric acid to balance the PO_4 group. Note that $2PO_4 = (PO_4)(PO_4)$. Place a 6 in front of the HOH to balance the OH group.

$$3Ca(OH)_2(c) + 2H_3PO_4(l) \longrightarrow Ca_3(PO_4)_2(c) + 6HOH(l)$$

Visual inspection shows that the hydrogen in H_3PO_4 and HOH is balanced. The hydrogen in the OH ion was balanced in Step 3.
Check the balanced equation.

	Reactants	Products
Ca	3	3
PO_4	2	2
OH	6	6
H	6	6

We have used only the smallest whole number coefficients. In balancing equations, you may sometimes obtain multiples of the smallest coefficients. If so, reduce the coefficients to the smallest whole numbers possible.

Problems

Write formulas for and balance the following:

1. magnesium bromide(aq) + chlorine(g) ⟶ magnesium chloride(aq) + bromine(g)

2. sodium(c) + water(l) ⟶ sodium hydroxide(aq) + hydrogen(g)

3. potassium nitrate(c) ⟶ potassium nitrite(c) + oxygen(g)

4. zinc(c) + hydrochloric acid(aq) ⟶ zinc chloride(aq) + hydrogen(g)

5. calcium oxide(c) + hydrochloric acid(aq) ⟶ calcium chloride(aq) + water(l)

Write balanced equations for each of the following chemical reactions.

6. $Mg(c) + O_2(g) \longrightarrow MgO(c)$

7. $Fe(c) + O_2(g) \longrightarrow Fe_2O_3(c)$

8. $H_2O(l) + N_2O_3(g) \longrightarrow HNO_2(aq)$

9. $Na_2O(c) + H_2O(l) \longrightarrow NaOH(aq)$

10. $Fe(c) + H_2O(l) \longrightarrow Fe_3O_4(c) + H_2(g)$

7:2 Prediction of Products

The products of a chemical reaction may often be predicted by applying known facts about common reaction types.

While there are hundreds of different "kinds" of chemical reactions, only four general types of reactions will be considered: single displacement, double displacement, decomposition, and synthesis. The following sections give examples of these general types.

7:3 Single Displacement

One metallic element displaces another metallic element in a compound, or a nonmetallic element displaces another nonmetallic element in a compound. A single displacement has the general form

$$\text{element} + \text{compound} \longrightarrow \text{element} + \text{compound}$$
$$A + BX \longrightarrow AX + B$$
$$X + BY \longrightarrow BX + Y$$

The following are some general types of single displacement reactions.

1. An active metal will displace the metallic ion in a compound of a less active metal.

$$Fe(c) + Cu(NO_3)_2(aq) \longrightarrow Fe(NO_3)_2(aq) + Cu(c)$$
$$Pb(c) + 2AgC_2H_3O_2(aq) \longrightarrow Pb(C_2H_3O_2)_2(aq) + 2Ag(c)$$

2. Some active metals such as sodium and calcium will react with water to give a metallic hydroxide and hydrogen gas.

$$2Na(c) + 2H_2O(l) \longrightarrow 2NaOH(aq) + H_2(g)$$
$$Ca(c) + 2H_2O(l) \longrightarrow Ca(OH)_2(aq) + H_2(g)$$

3. Active metals such as zinc, iron, and aluminum will displace the hydrogen in acids to give a salt and hydrogen gas.

$$Zn(c) + 2HCl(aq) \longrightarrow ZnCl_2(aq) + H_2(g)$$
$$Fe(c) + H_2SO_4(aq) \longrightarrow FeSO_4(aq) + H_2(g)$$

4. Halogens (which are active nonmetals) will displace less active halogens.

$$Cl_2(g) + 2NaBr(aq) \longrightarrow 2NaCl(aq) + Br_2(aq)$$
$$Br_2(g) + 2KI(aq) \longrightarrow 2KBr(aq) + I_2(g)$$

7:4 Double Displacement

The positive and negative ions of two compounds are interchanged. The form of these reactions is easy to recognize,

$$\text{compound} + \text{compound} \longrightarrow \text{compound} + \text{compound}$$
$$AX \quad + \quad BY \quad \longrightarrow \quad AY \quad + \quad BX$$

The following are some general types of double displacement reactions.

1. A reaction between an acid and a base yields a salt and water. Such a reaction is a **neutralization** reaction.

$$2KOH(aq) + H_2SO_4(aq) \longrightarrow K_2SO_4(aq) + 2H_2O(l)$$
$$Ca(OH)_2(aq) + 2HNO_3(aq) \longrightarrow Ca(NO_3)_2(aq) + 2H_2O(l)$$

2. Reaction of a salt with an acid forms a salt of the acid and a second acid which is volatile.

$$2KNO_3(aq) + H_2SO_4(aq) \longrightarrow K_2SO_4(aq) + 2HNO_3(g)$$
$$FeS(c) + 2HCl(aq) \longrightarrow FeCl_2(aq) + H_2S(g)$$
$$2NaCl(aq) + H_2SO_4(aq) \longrightarrow Na_2SO_4(aq) + 2HCl(g)$$

This same reaction of a salt with an acid or base may yield a compound which can be decomposed.

$$CaCO_3(aq) + 2HCl(aq) \longrightarrow CaCl_2(aq) + H_2CO_3(aq)$$
$$H_2CO_3(aq) \longrightarrow CO_2(g) + H_2O(l)$$

or

$$CaCO_3(c) + 2HCl(aq) \longrightarrow CaCl_2(aq) + CO_2(g) + H_2O(l)$$
$$K_2SO_3(aq) + 2HNO_3(aq) \longrightarrow 2KNO_3(aq) + SO_2(g) + H_2O(l)$$
$$NH_4Cl(aq) + NaOH(aq) \longrightarrow NaCl(aq) + NH_3(g) + H_2O(l)$$

3. Reaction of some soluble salts produces an insoluble salt and a soluble salt.

$$AgNO_3(aq) + NaCl(aq) \longrightarrow AgCl(c) + NaNO_3(aq)$$
$$Na_2SO_4(aq) + Ba(NO_3)_2(aq) \longrightarrow BaSO_4(c) + 2NaNO_3(aq)$$
$$CuSO_4(aq) + Na_2S(aq) \longrightarrow CuS(c) + Na_2SO_4(aq)$$
$$Ca(C_2H_3O_2)_2(aq) + (NH_4)_2CO_3(aq) \longrightarrow CaCO_3(c) + 2NH_4C_2H_3O_2(aq)$$

7:5 Decomposition

When energy in the form of heat, electricity, light, or mechanical shock is supplied, a compound may decompose to form simpler compounds and/or elements. The general form for this type of reaction is

$$\text{compound} \longrightarrow \text{two or more substances}$$
$$AX \longrightarrow A + X$$

The following are some general types of decomposition reactions.

1. If some acids are heated, they decompose to form water and an acidic oxide.

$$H_2SO_3(aq) \longrightarrow SO_2(g) + H_2O(l)$$
$$H_2CO_3(aq) \longrightarrow CO_2(g) + H_2O(l)$$

2. When some metallic hydroxides are heated, they decompose to form a metallic oxide and water.

$$Ca(OH)_2(c) \longrightarrow CaO(c) + H_2O(g)$$
$$2Fe(OH)_3(c) \longrightarrow Fe_2O_3(c) + 3H_2O(g)$$

3. Some metallic carbonates decompose to form a metallic oxide and carbon dioxide when heated.

$$Li_2CO_3(c) \longrightarrow Li_2O(c) + CO_2(g)$$
$$CaCO_3(c) \longrightarrow CaO(c) + CO_2(g)$$

4. Metallic chlorates decompose to form metallic chlorides and oxygen when heated.

$$2KClO_3(c) \longrightarrow 2KCl(c) + 3O_2(g)$$
$$Ni(ClO_3)_2(c) \longrightarrow NiCl_2(c) + 3O_2(g)$$

5. Most metallic oxides are stable, but a few decompose when heated.

$$2HgO(c) \longrightarrow 2Hg(l) + O_2(g)$$
$$2Ag_2O(c) \longrightarrow 4Ag(c) + O_2(g)$$

6. Some compounds cannot be decomposed by heat, but can be decomposed into their elements by electricity.

$$2H_2O(l) \longrightarrow 2H_2(g) + O_2(g)$$
$$2NaCl(l) \longrightarrow 2Na(l) + Cl_2(g)$$
$$MgCl_2(l) \longrightarrow Mg(l) + Cl_2(g)$$

7:6 Synthesis

In a synthesis reaction two or more simple substances (compounds and/or elements) are combined to form one new and more complex substance. Here the general form is

$$\begin{matrix} \text{element} & & \text{element} & \\ & + & & \longrightarrow \text{compound} \\ \text{or compound} & & \text{or compound} & \end{matrix}$$

$$A \quad + \quad X \quad \longrightarrow \quad AX$$

The following are some general types of synthesis reactions.

1. Combination of elements.

$$Fe(c) + S(l) \longrightarrow FeS(c)$$
$$2Na(c) + Cl_2(g) \longrightarrow 2NaCl(c)$$

2. Combination of an acid anhydride with water to give an acid.

$$SO_2(g) + H_2O(l) \longrightarrow H_2SO_3(aq)$$
$$N_2O_3(g) + H_2O(l) \longrightarrow 2HNO_2(aq)$$
$$CO_2(g) + H_2O(l) \longrightarrow H_2CO_3(aq)$$
$$P_2O_5(c) + 3H_2O(l) \longrightarrow 2H_3PO_4(aq)$$

3. Combination of a basic anhydride or a metallic oxide with water to form a base.

$$Na_2O(c) + H_2O(l) \longrightarrow 2NaOH(aq)$$
$$CaO(c) + H_2O(l) \longrightarrow Ca(OH)_2(aq)$$
$$BaO(c) + H_2O(l) \longrightarrow Ba(OH)_2(aq)$$

4. Combination of the metal of a basic oxide with the nonmetal of an acidic oxide to form a salt.

$$CO_2(g) + Na_2O(c) \longrightarrow Na_2CO_3(c)$$
$$P_2O_5(c) + 3BaO(c) \longrightarrow Ba_3(PO_4)_2(c)$$
$$SO_2(g) + MgO(c) \longrightarrow MgSO_3(c)$$

Chapter Review Problems

Balance the following equations.

11. $KClO_3(c) \longrightarrow KCl(c) + O_2(g)$

12. $PbO_2(c) \longrightarrow PbO(c) + O_2(g)$

13. $HgO(c) \longrightarrow Hg(l) + O_2(g)$

14. $H_2O(l) \longrightarrow H_2(g) + O_2(g)$

15. $Al(c) + Pb(NO_3)_2(aq) \longrightarrow Al(NO_3)_3(aq) + Pb(c)$

16. $Cu(c) + AgNO_3(aq) \longrightarrow Cu(NO_3)_2(aq) + Ag(c)$

17. $K(c) + H_2O(l) \longrightarrow KOH(aq) + H_2(g)$

18. $MnO_2(c) + HCl(aq) \longrightarrow MnCl_2(aq) + Cl_2(g) + H_2O(l)$

19. $Cl_2(g) + LiI(aq) \longrightarrow LiCl(aq) + I_2(g)$

20. $Ca(OH)_2(aq) + HCl(aq) \longrightarrow CaCl_2(aq) + H_2O(l)$

21. $KOH(aq) + H_3PO_4(aq) \longrightarrow K_3PO_4(aq) + H_2O(l)$

22. $Al(NO_3)_3(aq) + H_2SO_4(aq) \longrightarrow Al_2(SO_4)_3(aq) + HNO_3(aq)$

23. $Na_2SO_3(aq) + HCl(aq) \longrightarrow NaCl(aq) + H_2O(l) + SO_2(g)$

24. $(NH_4)_2SO_4(aq) + KOH(aq) \longrightarrow K_2SO_4(aq) + NH_3(g) + H_2O(l)$

25. $Pb(NO_3)_2(aq) + K_2S(aq) \longrightarrow PbS(c) + KNO_3(aq)$

Write a balanced equation and indicate the reaction type (single or double displacement, decomposition, or synthesis) for each of the following:

26. aluminum nitrate(aq) + sodium hydroxide(aq) ⟶ aluminum hydroxide(c) + sodium nitrate(aq)

27. potassium chlorate(c) ⟶ potassium chloride(c) + oxygen(g)

28. phosphoric acid(aq) + magnesium hydroxide(aq) ⟶ magnesium phosphate(c) + water(l)

29. ammonium nitrite(c) ⟶ nitrogen(g) + water(l)

30. ammonia(g) + oxygen(g) ⟶ nitrogen(II)oxide(g) + water(g)

31. barium chloride(aq) + sodium sulfate(aq) ⟶ sodium chloride(aq) + barium sulfate(c)

32. iron(III) oxide(c) + carbon monoxide(g) ⟶ iron(c) + carbon dioxide(g)

33. magnesium hydroxide(aq) + ammonium phosphate(aq) ⟶ magnesium phosphate(c) + ammonia(g) + water(l)

34. iron(III) bromide(aq) + ammonium sulfide(aq) ⟶ iron(III) sulfide(c) + ammonium bromide(aq)

35. calcium oxide(c) + disphosphorus pentoxide(c) ⟶ calcium phosphate(c)

36. magnesium chloride(aq) + silver nitrate(aq) ⟶ magnesium nitrate(aq) + silver chloride(c)

37. sodium carbonate(aq) + sulfuric acid(aq) ⟶ sodium sulfate(aq) + carbon dioxide(g) + water(l)

38. aluminum hydroxide(c) + acetic acid(aq) ⟶ aluminum acetate(g) + water(l)

39. lead(II) nitrate(aq) + copper(II) sulfate(aq) ⟶ lead(II) sulfate(c) + copper(II) nitrate(aq)

40. aluminum(c) + copper(II) chloride(aq) ⟶ aluminum chloride(aq) + copper(c)

41. iron(c) + silver acetate(aq) ⟶ iron(II) acetate(aq) + silver(c)

42. aluminum acetate(aq) + sodium hydroxide(aq) ⟶ aluminum hydroxide(c) + sodium acetate(aq)

43. bromine(l) + calcium iodide(aq) ⟶ calcium bromide(aq) + iodine(c)

44. copper(c) + sulfuric acid(aq) ⟶ copper(II) sulfate(aq) + sulfur dioxide(g) + water(l)

45. calcium   hydroxide(aq) + phosphoric   acid(aq) ⟶ calcium phosphate(c) + water(l)

46. magnesium nitrate(aq) + sulfuric acid(aq) ⟶ magnesium sulfate(aq) + nitric acid(aq)

47. potassium carbonate(aq) + barium chloride(aq) ⟶ potassium chloride(aq) + barium carbonate(c)

48. aluminum chloride(aq) + sulfuric acid(aq) ⟶ aluminum sulfate(aq) + hydrogen chloride(g)

49. cadmium phosphate(c) + ammonium sulfide(aq) ⟶ cadmium sulfide(c) + ammonium phosphate(aq)

50. sodium hydroxide(aq) + sulfuric acid(aq) ⟶ sodium sulfate(aq) + water(l)

51. magnesium(c) + oxygen(c) ⟶

52. aluminum(c) + hydrochloric acid(aq) ⟶

53. sodium oxide(c) + sulfur dioxide(g) ⟶

54. phosphoric acid(l) ⟶

55. sodium chlorate(c) ⟶

56. zinc chloride(aq) + ammonium sulfide(aq) ⟶

57. zinc sulfide(c) + oxygen(g) ⟶

58. calcium carbonate(c) ⟶

59. mercury(II) sulfate(aq) + ammonium nitrate(aq) ⟶

60. iron(c) + copper(II) sulfate(aq) ⟶

61. zinc(c) + sulfuric acid(aq) ⟶

62. dinitrogen pentoxide(c) + water(l) ⟶

63. chlorine(g) + magnesium iodide(aq) ⟶

64. potassium(c) + water(l) ⟶

65. iron(c) + hydrochloric acid(aq) ⟶

66. cobalt(III) hydroxide(aq) + nitric acid(aq) ⟶

67. bromine(l) + sodium iodide(aq) ⟶

68. sodium hydroxide(aq) + phosphoric acid(aq) ⟶

69. ammonium sulfate(aq) + calcium hydroxide(aq) ⟶

70. silver nitrate(aq) + potassium chloride(aq) ⟶

71. magnesium hydroxide(aq) + phosphoric acid(aq) ⟶

72. iron(II) sulfide(c) + hydrochloric acid(aq) ⟶

73. ammonium sulfide(aq) + iron(II) nitrate(aq) ⟶

74. sulfuric acid(aq) + potassium hydroxide(aq) $\longrightarrow$

75. aluminum sulfate(aq) + calcium phosphate(c) $\longrightarrow$

76. barium carbonate(c) + hydrochloric acid(aq) $\longrightarrow$

77. silver acetate(aq) + potassium chromate(aq) $\longrightarrow$

78. ammonium phosphate(aq) + barium hydroxide(aq) $\longrightarrow$

79. chromium(III) sulfite(aq) + sulfuric acid(aq) $\longrightarrow$

80. calcium hydroxide(aq) + nitric acid(aq) $\longrightarrow$

81. In a series of steps in an experiment, copper metal is converted into different compounds and then back to copper metal by treating the original copper step-wise with nitric acid, sodium hydroxide, heat, sulfuric acid, and zinc metal. Write the five equations representing these chemical changes if the overall experiment can be represented as:

$$Cu \longrightarrow Cu(NO_3)_2 \longrightarrow Cu(OH)_2 \longrightarrow CuO \longrightarrow CuSO_4 \longrightarrow Cu$$

82. One type of fire extinguisher contains concentrated sulfuric acid which reacts with a solution to produce carbon dioxide. What solution, sodium hydrogen carbonate or sodium carbonate, would give the greater amount of carbon dioxide in a reaction with the same amount of acid?

83. If iron pyrite, FeS_2, is not removed from coal, oxygen from the air will combine with both the iron and the sulfur as the coal burns. Write a balanced chemical equation illustrating the formation of iron(III) oxide and sulfur dioxide.

84. Sodium sulfite, Na_2SO_3, can be used for the removal of SO_2 produced as a by-product in manufacturing operations. The SO_2 reacts with a sodium sulfite solution to form sodium hydrogen sulfite. The $NaHSO_3$ solution is heated to regenerate the original sodium sulfite for reuse. Write the equation for this reaction.

Mass-Mass Problems ____8

8:1 Quantitative Relationships

Stoichiometry is the study of quantitative relationships in chemical reactions. A basic idea used in solving stoichiometric problems is the mole concept. A balanced chemical equation indicates the relative number of moles involved in a chemical reaction. There is a general procedure which applies in most stoichiometric problems. It involves the following steps.

1. Write a balanced equation.
2. Convert from mass of given material to moles.
3. Determine the mole ratio from the coefficients of the balanced equation and convert from moles of given material to moles of required material.
4. Express the moles of required material in grams.

If you are given the mass of one substance and know the balanced equation, you can calculate the reactants needed or the products produced because the equation shows relative number of moles of reactants and products.

The setup for a mass-mass calculation follows the format given below. Given the following equation:

$$2H_2S + 3O_2 \longrightarrow 2H_2O + 2SO_2$$

A typical calculation starting with the mass of H_2S in grams and finding the mass of H_2O in grams would be as follows:

$$\text{grams H}_2\text{O} = \frac{\text{grams H}_2\text{S}}{} \left| \frac{1 \text{ mole H}_2\text{S}}{\text{grams H}_2\text{S}} \right| \frac{2 \text{ mole H}_2\text{O}}{2 \text{ mole H}_2\text{S}} \left| \frac{\text{grams H}_2\text{O}}{1 \text{ mole H}_2\text{O}} \right|$$

Desired mass	Starting mass	Definition of mole H$_2$S	Coefficients from balanced equation	Definition of mole of H$_2$O
	a	b	c	d

At position b, there are moles H$_2$S; grams of H$_2$S were factored out.

At position c, there are moles H$_2$O; grams of H$_2$S and moles H$_2$S were factored out.

At position d, there are grams H$_2$O; grams of H$_2$S, moles H$_2$S, and moles H$_2$O were factored out.

Notice that as you work through a problem of this kind, first convert grams of given substance to moles, and then convert moles of required substance back to grams.

To calculate the grams of SO$_2$ in the above problem given the reactant mass in grams of H$_2$S factors a and b would be repeated. Then use these factors: 1 mole H$_2$S = 2 mole SO$_2$ and 1 mole SO$_2$ = grams SO$_2$.

$$\text{grams SO}_2 = \frac{\text{grams H}_2\text{S}}{} \left| \frac{1 \text{ mole H}_2\text{S}}{\text{grams H}_2\text{S}} \right| \frac{2 \text{ mole SO}_2}{2 \text{ mole H}_2\text{S}} \left| \frac{\text{grams SO}_2}{1 \text{ mole SO}_2} \right|$$

Desired mass	Starting mass	Definition of mole of H$_2$S	Coefficients from balanced equation	Definition of mole of SO$_2$

In the previous examples, if we wanted to calculate only the moles of reactant, we would stop at moles of H$_2$O or moles of SO$_2$.

Mole relationships can be further illustrated with the following balanced equation:

$$\text{Zn(c) + 2HCl(aq)} \longrightarrow \text{ZnCl}_2\text{(aq) + H}_2\text{(g)}$$

From the coefficients of the balanced equation we know that:

1 atom Zn + 2 molecules HCl $\longrightarrow$ 1 formula unit ZnCl$_2$
+ 1 molecule H$_2$

or

1 mole Zn + 2 moles HCl $\longrightarrow$ 1 mole ZnCl$_2$ + 1 mole H$_2$

One mole of any substance is one formula mass of the substance. Therefore

1 mole Zn = 65.4 grams Zn   1 mole HCl = 36.5 grams HCl
1 mole ZnCl$_2$ = 136 grams ZnCl$_2$ 1 mole H$_2$ = 2.02 grams H$_2$

Example 1

Calculate the number of grams of HCl needed to react with 10.0 grams of Zn.

Solving Process:

(a) Begin with the balanced equation.

$$Zn(c) + 2HCl(aq) \longrightarrow ZnCl_2(aq) + H_2(g)$$

(b) Convert grams of zinc to moles.

$$\dfrac{10.0 \text{ g Zn}}{} \; \bigg| \; \dfrac{1 \text{ mol Zn}}{65.4 \text{ g Zn}} \cdots$$

(c) Determine the mole ratio that exists between Zn and HCl.

1 mole Zn reacts with 2 moles HCl

$$\dfrac{10.0 \text{ g Zn}}{} \; \bigg| \; \dfrac{1 \text{ mol Zn}}{65.4 \text{ g Zn}} \; \bigg| \; \dfrac{2 \text{ mol HCl}}{1 \text{ mol Zn}} \cdots$$

(d) Convert moles of HCl to grams HCl.

$$\dfrac{10.0 \text{ g Zn}}{} \; \bigg| \; \dfrac{1 \text{ mol Zn}}{65.4 \text{ g Zn}} \; \bigg| \; \dfrac{2 \text{ mol HCl}}{1 \text{ mol Zn}} \; \bigg| \; \dfrac{36.5 \text{ g HCl}}{1 \text{ mol HCl}} = 11.2 \text{ g HCl}$$

Note that the conversion ratios are chosen and arranged so all the units divide out except the desired unit (in this case, grams of HCl). Note that since all the ratios are equal to 1, multiplying by one of them, or by all of them, only changes the units in which the answer is stated.

Steps in Mass-Mass Problems

(a) Write a balanced equation from the known facts about the reaction.
(b) Convert the mass of known substance to moles.
(c) Use the mole ratio to convert moles of known substance to moles of required substance.
(d) Convert the moles of desired substance to grams.

Example 2

How many grams of calcium metal will react completely with 10.0 grams of water to yield calcium hydroxide and hydrogen gas?

Solving Process:

(a) Begin with the balanced equation for the reaction.

$$Ca(c) + 2H_2O(l) \longrightarrow Ca(OH)_2(c) + H_2(g)$$

(b) Convert mass of water to moles of water.

$$\dfrac{10.0 \text{ g H}_2\text{O}}{} \; \bigg| \; \dfrac{1 \text{ mol H}_2\text{O}}{18.0 \text{ g H}_2\text{O}} \cdots$$

(c) Determine the mole ratio that exists between water and calcium metal.

$$1 \text{ mole Ca reacts with 2 moles } H_2O$$

$$\frac{10.0 \text{ g } H_2O}{} \left| \frac{1 \text{ mol } H_2O}{18.0 \text{ g } H_2O} \right| \frac{1 \text{ mol Ca}}{2 \text{ mol } H_2O} \cdots$$

(d) Convert the moles of Ca to grams.

$$\frac{10.0 \text{ g } H_2O}{} \left| \frac{1 \text{ mol } H_2O}{18.0 \text{ g } H_2O} \right| \frac{1 \text{ mol Ca}}{2 \text{ mol } H_2O} \left| \frac{40.1 \text{ g Ca}}{1 \text{ mol Ca}} \right. = 11.1 \text{ g Ca}$$

Hence, 10.0 grams of H_2O will react completely with 11.1 grams Ca.

Example 3

Calculate the grams of O_2 produced if 2.50 grams of $KClO_3$ are decomposed completely by heating.

Solving Process:

(a) Write the balanced equation for the reaction.

$$2KClO_3(c) \longrightarrow 2KCl(c) + 3O_2(g)$$

(b) Convert mass of $KClO_3$ to moles.

$$\frac{2.50 \text{ g } KClO_3}{} \left| \frac{1 \text{ mol } KClO_3}{123 \text{ g } KClO_3} \right. \cdots$$

(c) Determine the mole ratio that exists between $KClO_3$ and O_2.

$$2 \text{ moles } KClO_3 \text{ yield 3 moles } O_2$$

$$\frac{2.50 \text{ g } KClO_3}{} \left| \frac{1 \text{ mol } KClO_3}{123 \text{ g } KClO_3} \right| \frac{3 \text{ mol } O_2}{2 \text{ mol } KClO_3} \cdots$$

(d) Convert moles O_2 to grams.

$$\frac{2.50 \text{ g } KClO_3}{} \left| \frac{1 \text{ mol } KClO_3}{123 \text{ g } KClO_3} \right| \frac{3 \text{ mol } O_2}{2 \text{ mol } KClO_3} \left| \frac{32.0 \text{ g } O_2}{1 \text{ mol } O_2} \right. = 0.976 \text{ g } O_2$$

Hence, 2.50 grams $KClO_3$ decompose to yield 0.976 g O_2.

Example 4

Calculate the grams of NaOH required to produce 15.0 grams of Na_2SO_4 by the neutralization of NaOH with excess H_2SO_4.

Solving Process:

(a) Write the balanced equation for the reaction.

$$2NaOH(aq) + H_2SO_4(aq) \longrightarrow Na_2SO_4(aq) + 2H_2O(l)$$

(b) Convert mass of Na_2SO_4 to moles.

$$\frac{15.0 \text{ g } Na_2SO_4}{} \left| \frac{1 \text{ mol } Na_2SO_4}{142 \text{ g } Na_2SO_4} \right. \cdots$$

(c) Determine the mole ratio that exists between Na_2SO_4 and NaOH.

2 moles NaOH yield 1 mole Na_2SO_4

$$\frac{15.0 \text{ g } Na_2SO_4}{} \left|\frac{1 \text{ mol } Na_2SO_4}{142 \text{ g } Na_2SO_4}\right|\frac{2 \text{ mol NaOH}}{1 \text{ mol } Na_2SO_4} \cdots$$

(d) Convert moles NaOH to grams.

$$\frac{15.0 \text{ g } Na_2SO_4}{}\left|\frac{1 \text{ mol } Na_2SO_4}{142 \text{ g } Na_2SO_4}\right|\frac{2 \text{ mol NaOH}}{1 \text{ mol } Na_2SO_4}\left|\frac{40.0 \text{ g NaOH}}{1 \text{ mol NaOH}}\right.$$

$$= 8.45 \text{ g NaOH}$$

Each problem was solved by following the same approach and by using the same steps.

Problems

Solve the following problems. Note the equations given are not balanced.

1. If 20.0 grams of zinc react with excess hydrochloric acid, how many grams of zinc chloride are produced?

$$Zn(c) + HCl(aq) \longrightarrow ZnCl_2(aq) + H_2(g)$$

2. How many grams of chlorine gas must be reacted with excess sodium iodide if 10.0 grams of sodium chloride are needed?

$$NaI(aq) + Cl_2(g) \longrightarrow NaCl(aq) + I_2(c)$$

3. How many grams of oxygen are produced in the decomposition of 5.00 grams of potassium chlorate?

$$KClO_3(c) \longrightarrow KCl(c) + O_2(g)$$

4. How many grams of copper are required to replace 4.00 grams of silver nitrate which are dissolved in water?

$$Cu(c) + AgNO_3(aq) \longrightarrow Cu(NO_3)_2(aq) + Ag(c)$$

5. If excess ammonium sulfate reacts with 20.0 grams of calcium hydroxide, how many grams of ammonia are produced?

$$(NH_4)_2SO_4(aq) + Ca(OH)_2(c) \longrightarrow CaSO_4(c) + NH_3(g) + H_2O(l)$$

6. If excess sulfuric acid reacts with 30.0 grams of sodium chloride, how many grams of hydrogen chloride are produced?

$$NaCl(aq) + H_2SO_4(aq) \longrightarrow HCl(g) + Na_2SO_4(aq)$$

7. How much silver phosphate is produced if 10.0 grams of silver acetate are reacted with excess sodium phosphate?

$$AgC_2H_3O_2(aq) + Na_3PO_4(aq) \longrightarrow Ag_3PO_4(c) + NaC_2H_3O_2(aq)$$

8. How many grams of sodium hydroxide are needed to completely neutralize 25.0 grams of sulfuric acid?

$$NaOH(aq) + H_2SO_4(aq) \longrightarrow Na_2SO_4(c) + H_2O(g)$$

8:2   Calculations Involving Impure Substances

Raw chemicals sometimes are not pure. They contain the starting substance plus other inert material. In any problem involving such raw chemicals either the percentage of pure substance must be known or the actual amount of impure material must be known so that the actual mass of the pure substance can be calculated.

Example 5

A sample of Fe_2O_3 has a mass of 50.0 grams but contains by mass only 80.0% pure Fe_2O_3. What is the mass of pure Fe_2O_3 in the 50.0 gram sample?

Solving Process:

Convert the percentage (80.0%) to a decimal (0.800) and multiply this decimal by the mass of the sample.

grams pure Fe_2O_3 = (50.0 × 0.800) = 40.0 grams pure Fe_2O_3

Example 6

A sample of PbS has a mass of 30.0 grams and contains 10.0% inert material. What is the mass of the pure PbS?

Solving Process:

There are two ways of working this problem.

1. Subtract the 10.0% inert material from 100.0% to obtain 90.0%, which is the percentage of pure PbS. Then multiply as before.

    grams pure PbS = (30.0 × 0.900) = 27.0 grams pure PbS

    or

2. Multiply by the percentage of inert material and obtain the grams of inert material. Subtract the mass of the inert material from the mass of the sample to obtain the mass of pure material.

    grams inert material = (30.0 × 0.100)
                         = 3.00 grams inert material
    grams pure PbS = (30.0 − 3.00) = 27.0 grams pure PbS

Example 7

Washing soda (sodium carbonate decahydrate) is a hydrated compound used for washing, water softening, and bleaching. If a sample of sodium carbonate decahydrate has a mass of 20.0 grams and 10.0% of this 20.0 gram sample is inert, what mass of sodium carbonate will be left when the material is heated to drive off the water of hydration?

Solving Process:
(a) Write a balanced equation.

$$Na_2CO_3 \cdot 10H_2O(c) \longrightarrow Na_2CO_3(c) + 10H_2O(g)$$

Since the sample contains 10.0% inert material, 90.0% of the sample is pure $Na_2CO_3 \cdot 10H_2O$.

(b) Convert from grams of impure washing soda to grams of pure washing soda and then to grams of sodium carbonate.

$$\frac{20.0(0.900) \text{ g } Na_2CO_3 \cdot 10H_2O}{} \left| \frac{1 \text{ mol } Na_2CO_3 \cdot 10H_2O}{286 \text{ g } Na_2CO_3 \cdot 10H_2O} \right|$$

$$\frac{1 \text{ mol } Na_2CO_3}{1 \text{ mol } Na_2CO_3 \cdot 10H_2O} \left| \frac{106 \text{ g } Na_2CO_3}{1 \text{ mol } Na_2CO_3} \right| = 6.67 \text{ g } Na_2CO_3$$

Hence, 20.0 grams of $Na_2CO_3 \cdot 10H_2O$ which is 10.0% pure gives 6.68 grams of pure Na_2CO_3 when heated.

Example 8

A nitric acid-water solution has a mass of 60.0 grams and contains 20.0% by mass of nitric acid. What is the mass in grams of HNO_3 in the solution?

Solving Process:

Convert the percentage (20.0%) to a decimal (0.200) and multiply.

grams pure $HNO_3 = (60.0 \times 0.200) = 12.0$ g pure HNO_3

Example 9

Which solution contains more salt?
a. a 70.0 gram NaCl solution which contains 30.0% NaCl;
b. a 55.0 gram NaCl solution which contains 60.0% water.

Solving Process:
a. grams pure NaCl = 70.0(0.300) = 21.0 g pure NaCl
b. grams pure NaCl = 55.0(1.00 − 0.60) = 22.0 g pure NaCl
Solution b contains more NaCl.

Example 10

Zinc chloride is produced by the reaction of HCl with Zn. If 40.0 grams of a HCl solution containing 65.0% water reacts with an excess of Zn, how much $ZnCl_2$ will be produced?
(a) Write a balanced equation.

$$Zn(c) + 2HCl(aq) \longrightarrow ZnCl_2(aq) + H_2(g)$$

(b) Convert the 35.0% HCl solution to pure solution.

$$\frac{40.0(0.350) \text{ g HCl}}{} \left| \frac{1 \text{ mol HCl}}{36.5 \text{ g HCl}} \right| \frac{1 \text{ mol ZnCl}_2}{2 \text{ mol HCl}} \left| \frac{136 \text{ g ZnCl}_2}{1 \text{ mol ZnCl}_2} \right.$$

= 26.1 g ZnCl$_2$

Hence, 40.0 grams of 35.0% pure HCl solution will react with excess Zn to give 26.1 grams ZnCl$_2$.

Problems

9.   Iron(II) sulfide reacts with hydrochloric acid to produce an iron(II) salt and hydrogen sulfide gas; iron(II) sulfide reacts with sulfuric acid to produce another iron(II) salt and hydrogen sulfide gas. How many grams of each acid are needed to react with 20.0 gram samples of iron(II) sulfide ore which contains 10.0% inert material?

10. Iron(III) oxide can be converted to iron metal in a reaction with carbon monoxide. One sample of the original iron(III) oxide has mass 70.0 grams and contains 20.0% inert material. A second sample has mass 65.0 grams and contains only 10.0% inert material. Which ore sample will yield the larger amount of iron and what is the mass of the iron produced from this sample?

11. In one method for the production of zinc, the compound zinc sulfide is heated with oxygen to form zinc oxide and sulfur dioxide. In the second step the zinc oxide is heated with carbon to form zinc metal and carbon monoxide. If a sample of zinc sulfide has a mass of 150.0 grams and contains 30.0% inert material, how much zinc metal can be produced?

Chapter Review Problems

12. Copper(II) sulfate pentahydrate may be heated to drive off the water of hydration. If 5.00 grams of water are produced, what was the mass of the original compound?

$$CuSO_4 \cdot 5H_2O(c) \longrightarrow CuSO_4(c) + 5H_2O(g)$$

Solve problems 13–16 using the skeleton equation given below:

$$H_3PO_4(aq) + MgCO_3(c) \longrightarrow Mg_3(PO_4)_2(c) + CO_2(g) + H_2O(l)$$

13. How many moles and how many grams of magnesium phosphate are produced by starting with 100.0 grams of phosphoric acid and an excess of magnesium carbonate?

14. If 20.0 grams of carbon dioxide are produced, how many moles of magnesium carbonate were used initially?

15. Starting with 50.0 grams of magnesium carbonate and excess phosphoric acid, calculate the number of grams of each product produced.

16. How many grams of magnesium carbonate will react with 100.0 grams of a phosphoric acid solution which contains 70.0% water?

17. Phosphorus will burn in oxygen to give two different compounds: diphosphorus trioxide and diphosphorus pentoxide. How many grams of oxygen are required to produce the trioxide if 15.0 grams of phosphorus are used? How many grams of oxygen are required to produce the pentoxide if 15.0 grams of phosphorus are used?

18. Either aluminum or zinc will replace silver ion in silver nitrate to give silver metal and aluminum nitrate or silver metal and zinc nitrate. If 20.0 grams of silver nitrate are dissolved in water and the resulting solution is divided into two equal portions and poured into two beakers, how many moles of aluminum and how many moles of zinc are required to replace all of the silver in the separate reactions?

19. Hydrogen sulfide will burn in three different ways, depending upon the amount of oxygen present. In one reaction, sulfur dioxide and water are produced. In the second reaction, water, sulfur dioxide, and sulfur are produced. The third reaction produces water and sulfur. Using 50.0 grams of hydrogen sulfide gas, what is
   a. the maximum amount of sulfur dioxide that can be produced?
   b. the maximum amount of water?
   c. the maximum amount of sulfur?

20. If a plant needs to make 30.0 grams of glucose, $C_6H_{12}O_6$, through the process of photosynthesis from CO_2 and H_2O, how many grams of water are required? Photosynthesis is a complex process composed of many steps. The initial reactants are carbon dioxide and water and the final products are glucose and oxygen gas.

21. Four beakers each contain 5.00 grams of one of the following compounds dissolved in water: $Hg(ClO_3)_2$, $Cu(NO_3)_2$, $Bi(C_2H_3O_2)_3$, and $Sn(NO_3)_4$. All four metallic ions will react with sodium sulfide to form an insoluble metallic sulfide: HgS, CuS, Bi_2S_3, and SnS_2. Calculate the amount of sodium sulfide needed to completely precipitate the metallic ion in each reaction.

22. Magnesium will react with oxygen to form magnesium oxide and with nitrogen to form magnesium nitride. If 10.0 grams of magnesium are burned in an atmosphere containing excess oxygen, what is the mass of the product? What is the mass of the product if magnesium is burned in an atmosphere containing excess nitrogen?

23. A soda-acid fire extinguisher contains sodium hydrogen carbonate, which reacts with sulfuric acid to produce sodium sulfate, water, and carbon dioxide. Water, which is the principal extinguishing agent, is forced through a small nozzle by the pressure of the carbon dioxide gas. How many grams of water would the two following fire extinguishers produce? Which would be the better?
    a. One containing 400.0 grams of sulfuric acid and excess sodium hydrogen carbonate;
    b. One containing 650.0 grams of sodium hydrogen carbonate and excess sulfuric acid.

24. A copper solution such as a copper(II) nitrate will react with a base such as sodium hydroxide to form the copper(II) hydroxide, which settles to the bottom as a precipitate. How many grams of sodium hydroxide will react completely with 60.0 grams of a copper(II) nitrate solution which is 80.0% water by mass?

25. If 5.00 grams of the precipitate, silver chloride, are produced by the reaction of silver nitrate and calcium chloride, determine the following:
    a. grams of calcium chloride
    b. moles of silver nitrate
    c. grams of calcium nitrate produced

26. Calculate the grams of air required for the complete combustion of 50.0 mL of ethanol (C_2H_5OH, density 0.789 g/mL). The products are water and carbon dioxide. Assume that air contains 20.0% oxygen by mass.

27. How many grams of a zinc chloride solution are required to react with 15.0 grams of aluminum metal? The products are aluminum chloride and zinc metal. Assume that the zinc chloride solution contains 8.00% pure zinc chloride by mass.

28. From the overall reaction, determine the milliliters of sulfuric acid (density 1.83 g/mL) consumed if 5.00 grams of lead(II) sulfate are formed during the discharging of an automobile lead cell storage battery.

$$Pb(c) + PbO_2(c) + H_2SO_4(aq) \longrightarrow PbSO_4(c) + H_2O(l)$$

29. A detergent, sodium dodecanesulfonate, $C_{12}H_{25}OSO_3Na$, is made by the successive reactions of sulfuric acid and sodium hydroxide on dodecanol, $C_{12}H_{25}OH$. If a manufacturer needs to produce 30.0 metric tons of detergent daily, how many metric tons of dodecanol are needed? Assume the reaction is complete and there is no waste. (1 metric ton = 1000 kg)

30. Nitric acid is used to dissolve completely a 10.0 gram silver coin. Upon the addition of a sodium chloride solution, all the silver is precipitated as silver chloride. If 12.0 grams of AgCl are obtained, what is the percentage of silver in the coin?

31. Molten iron and carbon monoxide are produced in a blast furnace by the reaction of iron(III) oxide and coke (carbon). If 25.0 kilograms of pure Fe_2O_3 are used, how many moles of iron can be produced?

32. How much limestone must be decomposed by heating to produce 250.0 grams of lime, CaO? Assume that the limestone contains 95.0% pure $CaCO_3$.

33. Ammonia gas produced as a by-product in an industrial reaction can react with sulfuric acid in order that the gas does not escape into the atmosphere. The product, ammonium sulfate, can be used as a fertilizer. Determine how many kilograms of acid are required to produce 1000.0 kilograms of $(NH_4)_2SO_4$.

34. Coal gasification is a process which is carried out industrially in a series of steps. However, the net reaction involves coal, C, reacting with water to form methane, CH_4, and carbon dioxide. How many kilograms of methane can be produced from 1000 kilograms of coal?

35. A source of "acid rain" is automobile exhaust. Nitric oxide, formed in an internal combustion engine, reacts with oxygen in the air to produce nitrogen dioxide. The NO_2 reacts with water to form nitric acid. It is determined that the average car produces 10.0 cubic meters of exhaust gas per mile driven. Assume that the average concentration of NO in auto exhaust is 100.0 $\mu g/m^3$ and that traffic surveys have shown an average of 2.00×10^6 vehicle miles driven per day. From this data, determine the kilograms of nitric acid which could be produced annually.

$$2NO_2 + H_2O \longrightarrow HNO_2 + HNO_3$$

Gas Laws _____ 9

Air in a tire exerts pressure. A partially filled balloon will expand if it is placed over a hot radiator. In marked contrast to solids and liquids, gas volumes change noticeably with small changes in pressure and temperature. These changes were studied by experimenting with actual gases and the relations obtained were reduced to equations which defined the behavior of gases. These gas laws are valid only for an **ideal gas*** which does not actually exist. However, they give good approximations in most situations for real gases.

9:1 Gas Pressure

What is gas pressure? As gas molecules hit the walls of a container, the particles exert a force on the container. It is the number of collisions and the force of the collisions that cause gas pressure. Air pressure at sea level has been used as a scientific standard of pressure. However, this pressure changes with changing weather conditions. The standard is now defined in pascals which represent force per unit area. One pascal (Pa) is the pressure of 1 newton per square meter (N/m^2). Normal air pressure at sea level is 101 325 Pa or 101.325 kilopascals (kPa).

A barometer is used to measure atmospheric pressure. Most barometers are calibrated in millimeters of mercury (mm Hg). For converting units, 101.325 kPa equal 760 mm or 1 kPa = 7.50 mm Hg.

9:2 Boyle's Law

If the pressure on an ideal gas in a confined container is increased, the volume decreases. When the pressure is doubled, the new gas

*An ideal gas is one composed of particles with no attractive forces and no volume.

volume is half the original gas volume. If the pressure is decreased to half the original pressure, the new volume is double the old volume. Boyle's law is *the volume of an enclosed gas varies inversely as the pressure, if the temperature remains constant.* Boyle's law states that volume and pressure vary inversely. As one becomes larger, the other becomes smaller.

The preferred volume unit is cubic meters (m³). However cubic decimeters (dm³), cubic centimeters (cm³), and liters (L), are also used.

The following graph illustrates the relationship of pressure and volume as expressed by Boyle's Law. Pressure increases to the right along the horizontal axis. Volume increases upward on the vertical axis.

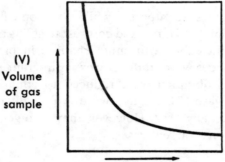

(V)
Volume
of gas
sample

Figure 9-1   Pressure (P) (at constant T)

Our primary interest in solving Boyle's law problems is to find a new volume when the original volume and the change in pressure are known. The change in pressure can be represented by a pressure ratio. The calculation of a new volume of a gas after a change in pressure at a constant temperature is

$$V_2 = V_1 \frac{P_1}{P_2}$$

where V_1 is the initial volume and P_1 is the initial pressure. The given values can be substituted into the equation or the changes in the gas volume can be visualized using Boyle's law.

Mentally determine whether the new volume will be larger or smaller and arrange the pressure ratio accordingly. If the new volume will be larger, multiply by a ratio that is greater than 1; if smaller, multiply by a ratio less than 1.

In summary:

A pressure increase decreases the volume, which means the pressure ratio should be less than 1.

A pressure decrease increases the volume, which means the pressure ratio should be greater than 1.

To calculate a new pressure when the old pressure and the volume change are known, use the relationship:

new pressure = old pressure × volume ratio

The volume and pressure vary inversely.

Example 1

If 400 cm³ of oxygen are collected at a pressure of 9.80 kPa what volume will the gas occupy if the pressure is changed to 9.40 kPa?

Solving Process:

The pressure decreases from 9.80 to 9.40 kPa. The volume should increase according to Boyle's law. To have a volume increase, the pressure ratio must be greater than 1. The pressure ratio is

$$\frac{9.80 \text{ kPa}}{9.40 \text{ kPa}}$$

In calculations, use the relationship:

new volume = old volume × pressure ratio

$$400 \text{ cm}^3 \left| \frac{9.80 \text{ kPa}}{9.40 \text{ kPa}} \right. = 417 \text{ cm}^3$$

Example 2

What is the volume of hydrogen at a pressure of 106 kPa if 200 cm³ of the hydrogen were collected at a pressure of 100 kPa?

Solving Process:

The pressure is increased from 100 to 106 kPa. Hence, the volume must decrease. The pressure ratio will be less than 1.

$$\frac{100 \text{ kPa}}{106 \text{ kPa}}$$

Therefore $$200 \text{ cm}^3 \left| \frac{100 \text{ kPa}}{106 \text{ kPa}} \right. = 189 \text{ cm}^3$$

Example 3

Calculate the pressure of a gas which occupies a volume of 100 cm³, if at a pressure of 95 kPa, it occupies a volume of 200 cm³.

Solving Process:

The volume decreases from 200 cm³ to 100 cm³. The pressure must increase, so the volume ratio must be greater than 1, or

$$\frac{200 \text{ cm}^3}{100 \text{ cm}^3}$$

$$95 \text{ kPa} \left| \frac{200 \text{ cm}^3}{100 \text{ cm}^3} \right. = 190 \text{ kPa}$$

Problems

1. The unit millimeter of mercury is used to measure blood pressure. As the blood is forced from the heart, the pressure is about 120.0 mm Hg. Before the next contraction, the pressure drops to about 80.0 mm Hg. Convert these pressures to pascals.

2. Correct the following gas volumes from the initial conditions to the new conditions (assume the temperature remains constant):
   a. 100.0 cm^3 oxygen at 10.50 kPa to 9.91 kPa
   b. 50.0 cm^3 hydrogen at 97.3 kPa to 101 000 Pa
   c. 500.0 cm^3 sulfur dioxide at 95.6 kPa to 101.3 kPa
   d. 150.0 cm^3 nitrogen at 101.30 kPa to 120.0 kPa
   e. 2.00 m^3 nitrogen at 158.0 kPa to 109.0 kPa
   f. 1.50 dm^3 neon at 98.2 kPa to 150 kPa

3. A flask containing 90.0 cm^3 of hydrogen was collected under a pressure of 97.5 kilopascals. At what pressure would the volume be 70.0 cm^3, assuming the temperature is kept constant?

4. A gas has a volume of 275 cm^3 when measured at a pressure of 9.80×10^4 Pa. If the temperature is not changed, what would be the volume of gas at standard pressure?

5. A gas has a volume of 50.0 m^3 at standard pressure. Assuming no temperature change, what volume will the gas occupy
   a. if the pressure is doubled?
   b. if the pressure is tripled?
   c. if the original pressure is cut in half?

6. What is the volume occupied by 10.0 dm^3 of gas at standard pressure after it has been compressed at constant temperature to 500.0 kPa?

7. A gas is confined in a cylinder with a movable piston at one end. When the volume of the cylinder is 760 cm^3 the pressure of the gas is 125.0 pascals. When the cylinder volume is reduced to 450 cm^3, what is the pressure?

9:3 Dalton's Law of Partial Pressure

If a gas is a mixture of two or more gases, each gas exerts a partial pressure independently of the other gases present. The partial pressure of a gas in a mixture is the pressure that the gas would exert if it were the only gas in the container. The total pressure is equal to the sum of the individual gas pressures. *Dalton's law of partial pressures can be stated as the sum of the partial pressures of a mixture of gases is the total pressure exerted by the enclosed gases.*

This statement means that each gas exerts the same pressure it would exert if it alone were present at the same temperature. In the chemistry laboratory, gases (such as oxygen, nitrogen, and hydrogen) are collected by water displacement. These gases bubble through water as they are collected. As a result, water vapor molecules become part of the total volume of the wet gas. Water vapor molecules exert a pressure along with the collected gas. Any temperature increase causes the water molecules to move faster and hit the sides of the container with more force. Water vapor pressure increases, as temperature increases.

Since gas pressure is caused by the collision of gas particles with the walls of the container, the total pressure in a container is due to the total number of particles. The pressure of the dry gas can be found only by deducting the pressure due to water molecules.

Look at Table 9-1 and note that the vapor pressure depends upon the temperature. The warmer the gas, the greater the pressure of the water vapor.

Table 9-1
Vapor Pressure of Water

Temperature (°C)	Pressure (kPa)	Temperature (°C)	Pressure (kPa)
0	0.6	26	3.4
5	0.9	27	3.6
8	1.1	28	3.8
10	1.2	29	4.0
12	1.4	30	4.2
14	1.6	35	5.6
16	1.8	40	7.4
18	2.1	50	12.3
20	2.3	60	19.9
21	2.5	70	31.2
22	2.6	80	47.3
23	2.8	90	70.1
24	3.0	100	101.3
25	3.2	200	1554.4

Assume that the atmospheric pressure is 98.0 kPa and the enclosed gas has been adjusted to atmospheric pressure. The pressure is a combination of the dry gas pressure and the water vapor pressure.

atmospheric pressure = pressure of dry gas + pressure of water vapor

pressure of dry gas = atmospheric pressure − pressure of water vapor

At 10°C: pressure of dry gas = 98.0 − 1.2 = 96.8 kPa
At 20°C: pressure of dry gas = 98.0 − 2.3 = 95.7 kPa

Problems

8. In a series of laboratory experiments, different gases were collected over water at the indicated water temperature and pressure. Correct each volume to the volume the dry gas would occupy at standard pressure. The temperature is constant.
   a. 52.0 cm³ gas at 18°C and 94.5 kPa
   b. 75.0 cm³ gas at 23°C and 97.2 kPa
   c. 135 cm³ gas at 21°C and 98.4 kPa
   d. 225 cm³ gas at 27°C and 102.5 kPa

9. A 79.9 cm³ sample of oxygen is collected by water displacement at 24°C. What volume would the gas occupy at standard pressure if the gas is collected originally at a pressure of 98.5 kPa?

10. The partial pressure of helium is 13.5 kPa in a mixture of helium, oxygen, and methane gases. If the total pressure is 96.4 kPa and the partial pressure of oxygen is 29.3 kPa, what is the partial pressure of the methane gas?

11. Determine the partial pressure of oxygen collected over water if the temperature is 28°C and the total gas pressure is 98.74 kPa.

9:4   Kelvin Temperature

All gases (in contrast to solids and liquids) expand and contract at approximately the same rate. When a gas is heated, it expands by 1/273 of its volume at 0° Celsius for each temperature increase of one Celsius degree. When a gas is cooled, it contracts 1/273 of its volume at 0° Celsius for each Celsius degree the temperature is lowered.

If a gas is heated to 200°C, it expands 1/273 of its original volume for each Celsius degree it is heated until its new volume is 200/273 greater than its volume at 0°C. If a gas is cooled to −200°C it contracts so its new volume is 200/273 less than its volume at 0°C.

No gas has ever been cooled to −273°C. All gases liquefy or solidify at temperatures higher than −273°C. The temperature −273°C is called absolute zero. It is written zero kelvin or 0 K.

To convert from °C to K, add 273 to the Celsius temperature.

$$\text{kelvin temperature equivalent} = 273 + °C$$

Scientists have chosen 273 K (0°C) as a standard temperature for working with gases.

9:5 Charles' Law

If the temperature of an ideal gas increases, the volume increases, if the pressure is to remain constant. If the temperature of a gas decreases, the volume decreases. Charles' law can be stated as *the volume of a quantity of gas varies directly as the kelvin temperature, if the pressure remains constant.* Note that temperature must be expressed in terms of the kelvin scale.

The graph illustrates the relationship defined by Charles' law.

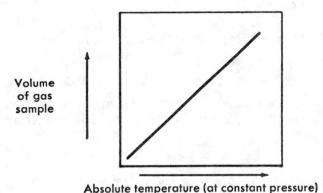

Absolute temperature (at constant pressure)   Figure 9-2

It is possible to predict the new volume of a gas when the old volume and the temperature change are known. The temperature change is expressed as an absolute temperature ratio. The equation used to calculate the new volume is

new volume = old volume × kelvin temperature ratio

$$V_2 = V_1 \frac{T_2}{T_1}$$

The subscripts represent the initial and final conditions as in the Boyle's law relationship. However, T refers to the temperature in kelvins. Volume and absolute temperature vary directly. If one increases, the other increases; if one decreases, the other decreases.

In summary:

An absolute temperature increase gives a volume increase, which means an absolute temperature ratio greater than 1.

An absolute temperature decrease gives a volume decrease, which means an absolute temperature ratio less than 1.

The new temperature in kelvins can be calculated when the initial kelvin temperature and new and old volumes are known:

new temperature (kelvins) = old temperature (kelvins) × volume ratio

The kelvin temperature varies directly as the volume varies.

Example 4

What volume will a sample of nitrogen occupy at 27°C if the gas occupies a volume of 400 cm³ at a temperature of 0°C? Assume the pressure remains constant.

Solving Process:
Convert the temperatures from Celsius to kelvin.

$$K = 273 + °C$$

$$K = 273 + 27°C = 300 \text{ K} \quad \text{and} \quad K = 273 + 0°C = 273 \text{ K}$$

A kelvin temperature increase (from 273 K to 300 K) will cause a volume increase. The kelvin temperature ratio must be greater than 1.

$$\frac{300 \text{ K}}{273 \text{ K}}$$

new volume = old volume × kelvin temperature ratio

$$\frac{400 \text{ cm}^3}{} \left| \frac{300 \text{ K}}{273 \text{ K}} \right. = 440 \text{ cm}^3$$

Example 5

What is the volume of a gas at −20°C if the gas occupied 50.0 cm³ at a temperature of 0°C?

Solving Process:
Convert the Celsius temperatures to kelvin temperatures.

$$K = 273 + -20°C = 253 \text{ K} \quad \text{and} \quad K = 273 + 0°C = 273 \text{ K}$$

A kelvin temperature decrease (from 273 K to 253 K) will cause a volume decrease, and the temperature ratio must be less than 1, or

$$\frac{253 \text{ K}}{273 \text{ K}}$$

$$\frac{50.0 \text{ cm}^3}{} \left| \frac{253 \text{ K}}{273 \text{ K}} \right. = 46.3 \text{ cm}^3$$

Example 6

If a gas occupies a volume of 700 cm³ at 10°C, at what temperature will it occupy a volume of 1000 cm³ if the pressure remains constant?

Solving Process:
An increase in volume (from 700 cm³ to 1000 cm³) indicates a temperature increase. The volume ratio must be greater than 1.

$$\frac{1000 \text{ cm}^3}{700 \text{ cm}^3}$$

$$\frac{283 \text{ K} \mid 1000 \text{ cm}^3}{700 \text{ cm}^3} = 404 \text{ K}$$

Convert 404 K to °C

$$°C = 404 \text{ K} - 273 = 131°C$$

Problems

12. Correct the following gas volumes from the initial conditions to the new conditions (assume that the pressure remains constant):
    a. 250.0 cm³ chlorine at 10°C to 60°C
    b. 75.0 cm³ hydrogen at 20°C to −10°C
    c. 100.0 cm³ oxygen at 27°C to standard temperature
    d. 300.0 cm³ nitrogen at 15°C to 38°C
    e. 2.30 dm³ nitrogen dioxide at standard temperature to 40°C
    f. 35.0 cm³ helium at 285 K to −50°C

13. A gas occupies a volume of 560 cm³ at a temperature of 100°C. To what temperature must the gas be lowered, if it is to occupy 400 cm³? Assume a constant pressure.

14. A gas has a volume of 10.0 m³ at standard temperature. Assuming no pressure change, what volume will the gas occupy
    a. if the kelvin temperature is doubled?
    b. if the original kelvin temperature is cut in half?

9:6 Combined Gas Law

Boyle's and Charles' laws can be used together to form a combined gas law. This law can be used in a situation where a pressure and a temperature change occur. A pressure ratio and a kelvin temperature ratio are needed to calculate the new volume.

new volume = old volume × pressure ratio × kelvin temperature ratio

Each ratio is considered independently in setting up the expression. If you have trouble juggling the figures, you may want to construct a pressure-volume-temperature table.

	Old conditions	New conditions	What happens to the gas volume?
Pressure			
Volume			
Temperature			

"What happens to the gas volume?" is answered with the word "decrease" or "increase," depending upon whether the pressure or temperature ratio is larger or smaller than 1.

The initials STP are often used in gas law problems. **STP** means standard temperature and pressure. The **standard pressure** for measuring gases is 101 325 Pa (101.325 kPa). For convenience in solving problems 101 300 Pa (101.3 kPa) is often used.

Standard temperature is 0°C or 273 K. All temperature ratios must be expressed in kelvins.

Example 7

Calculate the volume of a gas at STP if 500 cm^3 of the gas are collected at 27°C and 96.0 kPa.

Solving Process:

Organize the data given as shown and convert the Celsius temperatures to kelvins.

	Old conditions	New conditions	What happens to the gas volume?
P	96.0 kPa	101.3 kPa	decreases
V	500 cm^3	?	* * *
T	300 K	273 K	decreases

new volume = old volume × pressure ratio × kelvin temperature ratio

$$\frac{500 \text{ cm}^3}{} \left| \frac{96.0 \text{ kPa}}{101.3 \text{ kPa}} \right| \frac{273 \text{ K}}{300 \text{ K}} = 431 \text{ cm}^3$$

Example 8

If a gas occupies a volume of 100 cm^3 at a pressure of 101.3 kPa and 27°C, what volume will the gas occupy at 120.0 kPa and 50°C?

Solving Process:

Organize the data. Convert the Celsius temperatures to kelvins.

	Old conditions	New conditions	What happens to the gas volume?
P	101.3 kPa	120.0 kPa	decreases
V	100 cm³	?	* * *
T	300 K	323 K	increases

$$\frac{100 \text{ cm}^3 \mid 101.3 \text{ kPa} \mid 323 \text{ K}}{\mid 120.0 \text{ kPa} \mid 300 \text{ K}} = 90.9 \text{ cm}^3$$

Example 9

If 400 cm³ of oxygen are collected over water at 20°C, and the atmospheric pressure is 97 000 Pa, what is the volume of the dry oxygen at STP?

Solving Process:

Organize the data. Convert °C to K and correct the total pressure for water vapor pressure.

	Old conditions	New conditions	What happens to the gas volume?
P	97 000 − 2 300 = 94 700 Pa	101 300 Pa	decreases
V	400 cm³	?	* * *
T	293 K	273 K	decreases

$$\frac{400 \text{ cm}^3 \mid 94 700 \text{ Pa} \mid 273 \text{ K}}{\mid 101 300 \text{ Pa} \mid 293 \text{ K}} = 348 \text{ cm}^3$$

Note that the gas is not actually wet when it is collected over water. When a gas is collected over water, some of the water molecules inevitably escape from the liquid surface and form water vapor. The collected gas, therefore, contains both gas and water molecules. To find the pressure due to gas molecules, you must account for and deduct the pressure due to water vapor molecules.

Problems

15. Convert the following gas volumes to the new conditions using the combined gas law:
    a. 500 cm³ hydrogen at 20°C and 120 kPa to STP
    b. 250 cm³ oxygen at 27°C and 95 000 Pa to STP
    c. 100 cm³ chlorine at STP to 20°C and 98 000 Pa

   d. 80.0 cm³ carbon dioxide at 30°C and 9.25×10^4 Pa to 10°C and 9.90×10^4 Pa

   e. 140 cm³ hydrogen at 15°C and 110.0 kPa to 40°C and 94.5 kPa

16. The following gases are collected over water at the given conditions. Calculate the volume occupied by the dry gas at standard conditions.

   a. 200 cm³ oxygen at 15°C and 94 000 Pa

   b. 125 cm³ hydrogen at 20°C and 97 500 Pa

   c. 50.0 cm³ nitrogen at 28°C and 99 500 Pa

   d. 325 cm³ oxygen at 25°C and 98.6 kPa

17. A gas occupied 550 cm³ at a pressure of 9.95×10^4 Pa and a temperature of 21°C. Several days later it was measured at a pressure of 9.78×10^4 Pa and temperature of 15°C. What volume did the gas occupy under these new conditions?

18. The volume of nitrogen gas collected at a water temperature of 18°C and a pressure of 98.5 kPa measures 47.0 cm³. What volume will the gas occupy at standard conditions?

19. An automobile tire has a pressure of 300.0 kPa at 20°C. What will be the tire pressure after driving, if the tire temperature rises to 50°C?

20. The respiratory rate for a person is about 20 breaths per minute. Assume that each average breath is about 300 cm³ of air at 20°C and 9.95×10^4 Pa. What volume of air in cubic meters, corrected to standard conditions, does the individual breathe in one day?

9:7   Gas Density

   The volume of a gas changes with change in temperature, or change in pressure, or with a change in both T and P.

   Specifically, if we increase the pressure on a gas we decrease the volume; thus, we would have a greater density. If we increase the temperature of a gas, the volume increases, and the density is lower.

   For convenience, gas density is usually expressed in grams per cubic decimeter. Using g/cm³ would give very small numbers for gas densities. Remember that 1000 cm³ equal 1 dm³.

Table 9-2
Densities of Some Common Gases at STP

ammonia	0.760 g/dm³	hydrogen	0.0899 g/dm³
chlorine	3.163 g/dm³	oxygen	1.429 g/dm³
helium	0.179 g/dm³	sulfur dioxide	2.86 g/dm³

The density of a gas varies directly with the pressure and inversely with the temperature. For example if the original volume of a gas is 10 dm³ and the pressure is doubled, the new volume will be 5 dm³. If the mass of the gas is 25 grams the densities are

$$\frac{25\ g}{10\ dm^3} = 2.5\ g/dm^3 \quad \text{and} \quad \frac{25\ g}{5\ dm^3} = 5\ g/dm^3$$

Example 10

What is the density of a gas which has a mass of 2.50 g and occupies 1.50 dm³?

Solving Process:

$$\frac{2.50\ g}{1.50\ dm^3} = 1.67\ g/dm^3$$

Example 11

If the density of oxygen is 1.43 g/dm³ at standard pressure and temperature, what is the density of oxygen at 99.0 kPa and 27°C?

Solving Process:

The original density must be adjusted by a pressure ratio and a kelvin temperature ratio to the new conditions.

	Old conditions	New conditions	What happens to the density?
P	101.3 Pa	99.0 kPa	decreases
T	273 K	300 K	decreases
D	1.43 g/dm³	?	* * *

The pressure decreases and the temperature increases. A temperature increase gives a density decrease. The pressure and temperature ratios are

$$\frac{99.0\ kPa}{101.3\ kPa} \qquad \frac{273\ K}{300\ K}$$

new density = old density × pressure ratio × temperature ratio

$$\frac{1.43\ g}{dm^3} \left| \frac{99.0\ kPa}{101.3\ kPa} \right| \frac{273\ K}{300\ K} = 1.27\ g/dm^3$$

Chapter Review Problems

21. Sulfur dioxide has a density of $2.927\,g/dm^3$ at STP. What is its density at a pressure of $120.0\,kPa$ and a temperature of $50°C$?

22. A gas has a density of $3.472\,g/dm^3$ at STP. Determine its density at a pressure of $95.0\,kPa$ and a temperature of $27°C$.

23. A gas has a density of $2.851\,g/dm^3$ at STP. The pressure is dropped by $20.0\,kPa$ in order to attempt to change the density to $2.000\,g/dm^3$. What must be the new temperature to achieve this lower density?

24. Correct the following gas volumes from the initial conditions to the new conditions. Assume that the pressure or temperature is constant, if not given.
  a. $45.0\,cm^3$ at $40°C$ to $-20°C$
  b. $270\,cm^3$ at standard temperature to $25°C$
  c. $75.0\,cm^3$ at standard pressure to $90.8\,kPa$
  d. $165\,cm^3$ at $75\,000\,Pa$ to $84\,000\,Pa$
  e. $95.0\,cm^3$ at STP to $24°C$ and $91.5\,kPa$
  f. $1.50\,dm^3$ at STP to $-15°C$ and $110.0\,kPa$
  g. $325\,cm^3$ at $30°C$ and $95.0\,kPa$ to STP
  h. $240\,cm^3$ at $5°C$ and $92.0\,kPa$ to $40°C$ and $105.0\,kPa$

25. Oxygen has a density of $1.429\,g/dm^3$ at STP. Which change will result in a greater change in density? What is the new density?
  a. decreasing the temperature from $0°C$ to $-40°C$
  b. increasing the pressure from $100.0\,kPa$ to $114.5\,kPa$

26. What is the density of a gas at STP if its density is $1.75\,g/dm^3$ at $110.0\,kPa$ and $45°C$?

27. At STP, the density of a gas is $3.24\,mg/cm^3$. What is its density in g/dm^3 at $30°C$ and $95.0\,kPa$?

28. If the pressure on $100\,cm^3$ of a gas is doubled, what volume will the gas occupy, assuming no other changes?

29. The volume of a gas at a pressure of $90.0\,kPa$ is doubled and the temperature remains constant. What is the final pressure exerted by the gas?

30. If the temperature of a gas is $0°C$ and the temperature is changed so that the gas volume doubles, what is the new temperature of the gas?

31. An unbreakable meteorological balloon is released from the ground. Ground level pressure is 98.5 kPa and the temperature is 18°C. The balloon contains 74.0 dm³ of hydrogen gas. As the balloon ascends, the pressure drops to 7.0 kPa.

    a. What is the new volume of the balloon, assuming no temperature change?

    b. If a temperature drop of 80° occurs, what is the new volume of the balloon?

    c. Of the two factors, pressure and temperature, which had the greatest effect in changing the volume of the balloon?

32. A balloon will burst at a volume of 2.0 dm³. If it is partially filled at a temperature of 20°C and a pressure of 9.90×10^4 Pa to occupy 0.75 dm³, what is the temperature at which it will burst if the pressure is 1.01×10^5 Pa at the time it breaks?

33. Approximately 160 kilometers above the earth the pressure of the atmosphere is about 3.00×10^{-4} Pa and the temperature is about -180°C. If 100 cm of a gas at STP is released at this distance from the earth, what volume would it occupy?

The *Molar Volume* _____ 10

10:1 Avogadro's Principle and Molar Volume

What is the relationship between the mass of a gas and its volume? Avogadro's principle states that *equal volumes of all gases, measured under the same conditions of pressure and temperature, contain the same number of particles*. It has been found experimentally that 1 mole of any gas at STP contains 6.02×10^{23} particles. This number is called Avogadro's number of particles. One mole of any gas has a mass equal to its molecular mass. For example:

$$1 \text{ mole } N_2 = 28.0 \text{ g } N_2 = 6.02 \times 10^{23} \text{ molecules of } N_2$$
$$1 \text{ mole } CO_2 = 44.0 \text{ g } CO_2 = 6.02 \times 10^{23} \text{ molecules of } CO_2$$

Equal volumes of gases measured at the same temperature and pressure contain the same number of particles.

A volume of gas which contains one mole of the gas at STP is the molar volume of the gas. One mole of a gas at STP occupies 22.4 cubic decimeters (dm^3). This volume is the same for all gases at STP. The mass and volume of any gas are related as follows:

$$1 \text{ mole of any gas} = \text{molecular mass} = 22.4 \text{ } dm^3 \text{ of the gas}$$

Although the molar volume does vary slightly with different gases we shall assume we are dealing with ideal gases in which the volume at STP is always $22.4 \text{ } dm^3$.

The relationships among mole, molecular mass, and volume make it possible to calculate molecular mass, volume, and density under the following conditions.

1. the molecular mass of a gas if the volume and mass of the gas are known.
2. the volume of a specific mass of gas or the mass of a specific volume of gas.
3. the density of the gas from its molecular mass or its molecular formula.

Example 1

A sample of gas has a mass of 1.248 grams and occupies 300.0 cm³ at STP. What is the molecular mass of this gas?

Solving Process:

The molecular mass of the gas is equal to one mole of the gas. Start with the relationship between volume and mass of the gas given in the problem and calculate the mass of one mole of the gas. All units must be divided out except grams per mole.

The conversion ratios are

$$1.248 \text{ grams of gas} = 300.0 \text{ cm}^3$$

$$22.4 \text{ dm}^3 \text{ (STP)} = 1 \text{ mole gas}$$

$$\text{molecular mass} = \frac{1.248 \text{ g}}{300.0 \text{ cm}^3} \left| \frac{22.4 \text{ dm}^3 \text{ (STP)}}{1 \text{ mol gas}} \right| \frac{1000 \text{ cm}^3}{1 \text{ dm}^3} = 93.2 \text{ g/mol}$$

Example 2

How many grams of carbon dioxide, CO_2, will occupy a volume of 500 cm³ at STP?

Solving Process:

The conversion ratios are

$$1 \text{ mol } CO_2 = 22.4 \text{ dm}^3 CO_2 \text{ (STP)}$$

$$1 \text{ mol } CO_2 = 44.0 \text{ g } CO_2$$

$$\frac{500 \text{ cm}^3}{} \left| \frac{1 \text{ mol } CO_2}{22.4 \text{ dm}^3} \right| \frac{44.0 \text{ g } CO_2}{1 \text{ mol } CO_2} \left| \frac{1 \text{ dm}^3}{1000 \text{ cm}^3} \right| = 0.982 \text{ g } CO_2$$

Example 3

What is the density of nitrogen dioxide, NO_2, at STP in grams per cubic decimeter?

Solving Process:

Calculate the molecular mass of nitrogen dioxide and then convert to grams per cubic decimeter.

$$\frac{46.0 \text{ g } NO_2}{1 \text{ mol } NO_2} \left| \frac{1 \text{ mol } NO_2}{22.4 \text{ dm}^3 NO_2} \right| = 2.05 \text{ g/dm}^3$$

Example 4

A flask has a volume of 258 cm³. A gas with mass 1.475 grams is introduced into the flask at a temperature of 300 K and a pressure of 9.86×10^4 Pa. Calculate the molecular mass of the gas.

Solving Process:

Since 1 mole of a gas occupies 22.4 dm³ when the gas is at STP, the volume must be adjusted to STP by the kelvin temperature ratio and a pressure ratio. These ratios convert the original temperature and pressure to the equivalent standard temperature and pressure.

A decrease in temperature causes a volume decrease. An increase in pressure causes a volume decrease. The ratios are

temperature ratio	*pressure ratio*
$\dfrac{273 \text{ K}}{300 \text{ K}}$	$\dfrac{9.86 \times 10^4 \text{ Pa}}{10.13 \times 10^4 \text{ Pa}}$

Correct the volume to STP.

$$258 \text{ cm}^3 \left| \frac{273 \cancel{K}}{300 \cancel{K}} \right| \frac{9.86 \times 10^4 \cancel{Pa}}{10.13 \times 10^4 \cancel{Pa}} = 228 \text{ cm}^3$$

Calculate the molecular mass using the volume of gas at STP.

$$\frac{1.475 \text{ g}}{228 \cancel{cm^3}} \left| \frac{22.4 \cancel{dm^3} \text{ (STP)}}{1 \text{ mol}} \right| \frac{1000 \cancel{cm^3}}{1 \cancel{dm^3}} = 145 \text{ g/mol}$$

Problems

Assume the volumes given are at STP unless other conditions are specified.

1. Calculate the number of moles contained in each of the following gas volumes.

   a. 50 000 cm³ H_2
   b. 1000 cm³ N_2
   c. 6500 cm³ SO_2

   d. 15 000 cm³ NH_3
   e. 2500 cm³ O_2
   f. 2000 cm³ CO_2

2. Calculate the mass of each of the following volumes of gas.

   a. 20.0 m³ CH_4
   b. 1500.0 cm³ Cl_2
   c. 70.0 cm³ SO_3

   d. 0.300 m³ N_2O
   e. 3.0 m³ N_2
   f. 3500.0 cm³ H_2S

3. Calculate the volume in dm³ of each of the following:

   a. 4.0 moles Br_2
   b. 200.0 grams H_2S
   c. 25.5 grams SO_2
   d. 600.0 grams Cl_2

   e. 2.50 moles NH_3
   f. 50.0 grams NO_2
   g. 7.00 moles O_2
   h. 10.0 grams HCl

4. Calculate the density in g/dm^3 for each of the following:
   a. hydrogen sulfide, H_2S c. ammonia, NH_3
   b. methane, CH_4 d. chlorine, Cl_2

5. A carbon dioxide sample has a mass of 5.148 grams and occupies 2600.0 cm^3 at STP. What is the density (in grams per liter) of the carbon dioxide?

6. A sample of hydrogen chloride has a mass of 2.459 grams and occupies 1500.0 cm^3. What is its density?

10:2   Molar Volume and Gases Collected Over Water

We can apply what we know about molar volume to laboratory situations involving gases collected over water.

Example 5

A reaction produces 200 cm^3 of oxygen which is collected over water and measured at 22°C and 9.90 × 10^4 Pa. How many grams of the gas are produced? Assume a water vapor pressure of 2.6 kPa at 22°C.

Solving Process:

Convert the volume of oxygen produced to the volume of dry oxygen at STP, because 1 mole of gas occupies 22.4 dm^3 only when dry and at STP. Once the number of moles of oxygen has been calculated, the grams of oxygen can be determined using the conversion ratio, 1 mole O_2 = 32.0 grams O_2.

The numbers will be easier to work with if the pressures are all in kilopascals. Since the pressure increases, a decrease in gas volume will occur and the pressure ratio (allowing for water vapor pressure correction) is

$$\frac{99.0 - 2.6 \text{ kPa}}{101.3 \text{ kPa}} \quad \text{or} \quad \frac{96.4 \text{ kPa}}{101.3 \text{ kPa}}$$

The temperature decrease causes a decrease in gas volume. The kelvin temperature ratio is

$$\frac{273 \text{ K}}{295 \text{ K}}$$

Correct the volume to STP.

$$\frac{200 \text{ cm}^3}{} \left| \frac{96.4 \text{ kPa}}{101.3 \text{ kPa}} \right| \frac{273 \text{ K}}{295 \text{ K}} = 176 \text{ cm}^3 \text{ O}_2$$

Calculate the grams of O_2 produced.

$$\frac{176 \text{ cm}^3}{} \left| \frac{1 \text{ mol}}{22.4 \text{ dm}^3} \right| \frac{32.0 \text{ g O}_2}{1 \text{ mol O}_2} \left| \frac{1 \text{ dm}^3}{1000 \text{ cm}^3} \right. = 0.251 \text{ grams O}_2$$

10:3 Ideal Gas Equation

The ideal gas equation combines the four physical variables (pressure, volume, temperature, and number of particles) for gases into one equation. Remember that an ideal gas is composed of point masses with no mutual attraction. All real gases deviate somewhat from the gas laws since the molecules of real gases occupy volume and attract one another.

The ideal gas equation is $PV = nRT$, where P is the pressure in kilopascals. V is the volume in cubic decimeters and T is the temperature in kelvin. The n represents the number of moles of a gas. With these units, the value of the constant R is 8.31 dm^3 · kPa/mol · K. There are other values of R depending upon the units used to derive R.

We can use the ideal gas equation to determine the molecular mass (M) of a gas. The number of moles (n) of any species is equal to its mass (m) divided by the molecular mass (M). Thus, the ideal gas equation can also be written as

$$PV = nRT \quad \text{or} \quad PV = \frac{m}{M}RT \quad \text{or} \quad M = \frac{mRT}{PV}$$

Example 6_____

Use the data from Example 4 to calculate the molecular mass of the gas using the ideal gas equation.

Solving Process:
$$M = \frac{mRT}{PV}$$

1.475 g	8.31 dm³ · kPa	300 K	1000 Pa	1000 cm³
9.86 × 10⁴ Pa	mol · K	258 cm³	1 kPa	1 dm³

$$= 145 \text{ g/mol}$$

Remember that the units of volume, pressure, temperature, and quantity of gas must be consistent with the value of R.

Example 7_____

In an experiment, an oxygen generator is heated gently and the oxygen formed displaces water in a flask. The displaced water is collected and its temperature and volume are determined and assumed to be that of the oxygen gas produced. Calculate the molar volume of the oxygen gas from the data given.

1. mass of generator before heating   23.784 g
2. pressure   100.0 kPa
3. mass of generator after heating   23.505 g
4. temperature of oxygen   21.0°C
5. vapor pressure of water   2.5 kPa
6. pressure of dry oxygen (100.0 − 2.5 = 97.5) 97.5 kPa
7. volume of oxygen collected   225 cm³

Solving Process:
Determine the volume of dry oxygen gas at STP.

$$\frac{225 \text{ cm}^3 \text{ O}_2 \mid 97.5 \text{ kPa} \mid 273 \text{ K}}{\mid 101.3 \text{ kPa} \mid 294 \text{ K}} = 201 \text{ cm}^3 \text{ O}_2$$

Find the experimental molar volume.

$$\text{molar volume} = \frac{\text{molecular mass O}_2 \mid \text{volume O}_2}{\mid \text{mass O}_2}$$

$$\frac{32.0 \text{ g O}_2 \mid 201 \text{ cm}^3 \text{ O}_2 \mid 1 \text{ dm}^3}{\mid (23.784 - 23.505) \text{ g O}_2 \mid 1000 \text{ cm}^3} = 23.1 \text{ dm}^3 \text{ O}_2$$

Problems

7. What is the molecular mass of sulfur dioxide if 300.0 cm³ of the gas has a mass of 0.855 grams?

8. A sample of hydrogen iodide has a mass of 2.28 grams and occupies 400.0 cm³ at STP. What is the molecular mass of this compound?

9. If 0.179 grams of methane occupy 0.250 cm³, what is the molecular mass of methane if the volume is given at standard conditions?

10. The density of a sample of phosphorus trifluoride, PF_3 is 3.90 g/dm³. What is the molecular mass of this gas?

11. What is the molecular mass of nitrous oxide, N_2O, if the density of the gas is 1.978 g/dm³.

12. From the volume, temperature, and pressure, calculate the number of moles and the mass in grams for each gas listed:
    a. 750.0 cm³ O_2 at 27°C and 99.0 kPa
    b. 3.00 dm³ CO_2 at −10°C and 103.0 kPa
    c. 2000.0 cm³ NH_3 at 10°C and 105.0 kPa
    d. 5.00 dm³ SO_2 at 21°C and 100.0 kPa

13. Calculate the volume each gas will occupy under the conditions listed:
    a. 3.00 moles H_2 at 24°C and 100.5 kPa
    b. 150.0 grams Cl_2 at −10°C and 98.5 kPa
    c. 5.00 moles CH_4 at 27°C and 97.2 kPa
    d. 200.0 grams NH_3 at 12°C and 104.5 kPa

10:4 Gas Concentration

The concentration of a gas can be expressed in many ways—percent by volume, parts per million, and milligrams per cubic meter. Percent by volume is the volume of the given compound contained in 100 volumes of air. For example, air contains about 20% oxygen on a volume basis.

Parts per million (ppm) has been useful for very low concentrations commonly encountered in pollution work. Parts per million (ppm) expresses how many parts of a very small component are in a million parts of the whole. On a mass basis, ppm is the number of milligrams of component per one kilogram of the whole, since 1000 milligrams = 1 gram and 1000 grams = 1 kilogram. For example, if 1 kilogram of fish contains 4 milligrams of mercury, the concentration of mercury could be expressed as 4 parts per million.

Extremely small components of the whole can be expressed as parts per billion (ppb). A microgram (μg) is one billionth of a kilogram, thus ppb is the number of micrograms per kilogram or micrograms per cubic decimeter of solution.

Some comparisons of ppm and ppb are

1 ppm is one penny in $10 000

and

1 ppb is one penny in $10 000 000

1 ppm is 1 mm in 1 km

and

1 ppb is 1 mm in 1000 km

Chapter Review Problems

14. What volume will be occupied by 5.70 grams of oxygen which is collected over water at 98.0 kPa and 27°C? The vapor pressure of water at this temperature is 3.6 kPa.

15. If 0.850 grams of hydrogen are produced by a reaction, what volume in cubic decimeters will the gas occupy at the following conditions?
     a. standard temperature and pressure
     b. 20°C and 1.0×10^5 Pa
     c. collected over water at 20°C and 1.0×10^5 Pa, dry

16. How many moles and grams of nitrogen are produced if 250.0 cm^3 is collected over water at 20°C and 9.87×10^4 Pa?

17. A gas sample occupies a volume of 300.0 cm^3 when measured over water at 20°C and 1.00×10^5 Pa. What is the molecular mass of this gas if the sample has a mass of 0.700 gram?

18. A gas sample has a mass of 1.25 grams and occupies 125 cm^3 when collected over water at 27°C and 96.4 kPa. What is the molecular mass of this gas sample?

19. Calculate the density of oxygen under the following conditions:
    a. standard temperature and pressure
    b. 27°C and 98.6 kPa

20. A sample of gas has a density of $1.25 \, g/dm^3$ at 30°C and 1.02×10^5 Pa. What is the molecular mass of this gas?

21. What is the molecular mass of a gas if 5.75 grams of the gas occupy a volume of $3.50 \, dm^3$? The pressure was recorded as 9.525×10^4 Pa and the temperature is 50°C.

22. Determine the molecular mass of a gas if its density is $2.70 \, g/dm^3$ at a pressure of 132.0 kPa and temperature of 30°C.

23. At a pressure of 98.0 kPa and temperature of 31°C, ammonia gas occupies $18.9 \, dm^3$. Calculate the grams of ammonia in this volume.

24. Air is a mixture of gases but it can be assumed that the approximate composition of air is 21% O_2 and 79% N_2 by volume. Determine the mass of the molar volume of air at STP. Note that the answer is the *apparent* molecular mass of air.

Mass-Volume Problems — 11

Many chemical reactions involve gases. It is often necessary to know the volume of gas involved with a known mass of material in a reaction. Problems of this type are similar to mass-mass problems, however one additional piece of information is needed.

1 mole of any gas = molecular mass of that gas = $22.4 \, dm^3$ (STP)

In mass-volume problems, mass is changed to moles of the desired substance and then converted to volume using the relationship:

1 mole of any gas = $22.4 \, dm^3$ of that gas at STP

If conditions other than STP are desired, the volume of the gas must be converted to the conditions stated in the problem.

The reverse calculation may also be done. Volume is changed to moles and moles are changed to mass. The entire calculation must be carried out at STP. Thus, if the volume is not given at STP, it must be changed to STP.

Example 1

Calculate the volume of oxygen produced at STP by the decomposition of 10.0 grams of potassium chlorate, $KClO_3$.

Solving Process:

Write the balanced equation.

$$2KClO_3(c) \longrightarrow 2KCl(c) + 3O_2(g)$$

Start with the known mass of $KClO_3$ given in the problem and convert to volume of oxygen at STP.

$$\frac{10.0 \text{ g } KClO_3}{} \left| \frac{1 \text{ mol } KClO_3}{123 \text{ g } KClO_3} \right| \frac{3 \text{ mol } O_2}{2 \text{ mol } KClO_3} \left| \frac{22.4 \text{ dm}^3 O_2}{1 \text{ mol } O_2} \right| = 2.73 \text{ dm}^3$$

Thus, 10.0 grams $KClO_3$ will decompose to give 2.73 cubic decimeters of O_2 at STP.

Example 2

How many cubic centimeters of hydrogen are produced by the reaction of 0.750 grams of sodium metal with excess water?

Solving Process:
Write the balanced equation.

$$2Na(c) + 2H_2O(l) \longrightarrow 2NaOH(aq) + H_2(g)$$

Convert from grams of Na to cm^3 of H_2 at STP.

$$\frac{0.750 \text{ g } Na}{} \left| \frac{1 \text{ mol } Na}{23.0 \text{ g } Na} \right| \frac{1 \text{ mol } H_2}{2 \text{ mol } Na} \left| \frac{22.4 \text{ dm}^3 H_2}{1 \text{ mol } H_2} \right| \frac{1000 \text{ cm}^3}{1 \text{ dm}^3} = 365 \text{ cm}^3$$

Hence, 0.750 grams Na will react with water to give 365 cm^3 of H_2 at STP.

Example 3

Aluminum reacts with HCl to produce aluminum chloride and hydrogen gas. How many dm^3 of hydrogen at STP are produced if Al reacts with an HCl solution which has a mass of 80.0 grams and contains 70.0% water?

Solving Process:
Write the balanced equation.

$$2Al(c) + 6HCl(aq) \longrightarrow 2AlCl_3(aq) + 3H_2(g)$$

Convert from grams of HCl to liters of H_2 at STP.

$$\frac{80.0 \text{ g acid}}{} \left| \frac{30.0 \text{ g } HCl}{100 \text{ g acid}} \right| \frac{1 \text{ mol } HCl}{36.5 \text{ g } HCl} \left| \frac{3 \text{ mol } H_2}{6 \text{ mol } HCl} \right| \frac{22.4 \text{ dm}^3 H_2}{1 \text{ mol } H_2} = 7.36 \text{ dm}^3$$

Hence, an 80.0 gram solution of HCl which is 70.0% water will react with aluminum to give 7.36 dm^3 H_2 at STP.

Example 4

What mass of magnesium will react with excess hydrochloric acid to produce 500 cm^3 of H_2 at STP?

Solving Process:
This problem is just the reverse of the previous problems. The mass of one of the reactants is calculated from the volume of the gas which is to be produced.
Write the balanced equation.

$$Mg(c) + 2HCl(aq) \longrightarrow MgCl_2(aq) + H_2(g)$$

Calculate the mass of Mg required to produce 500 cm³ H_2.

$$\frac{500 \text{ cm}^3 \text{ H}_2}{} \left| \frac{1 \text{ mol H}_2}{22.4 \text{ dm}^3 \text{ H}_2} \right| \frac{1 \text{ mol Mg}}{1 \text{ mol H}_2} \left| \frac{24.3 \text{ g Mg}}{1 \text{ mol Mg}} \right| \frac{1 \text{ dm}^3}{1000 \text{ cm}^3} = 0.542 \text{ g}$$

Hence, to produce 500 cm³ H_2 at STP, it is necessary that 0.542 g Mg react with excess HCl.

Example 5

How many grams of ammonium sulfate must react with excess sodium hydroxide to produce 400 cm³ of ammonia measured at 27°C and 98.0 kPa?

Solving Process:
Write the balanced equation.

$$(NH_4)_2SO_4(c) + 2NaOH(aq) \longrightarrow Na_2SO_4(aq) + 2NH_3(g) + 2H_2O(l)$$

Convert 400 cm³ NH_3 at 27°C and 98.0 kPa to STP and then convert to grams of $(NH_4)_2SO_4$. Since the temperature decreases, the volume decreases and the absolute temperature ratio is

$$\frac{273 \text{ K}}{300 \text{ K}}$$

Since the pressure increases, the volume decreases and the pressure ratio is

$$\frac{98.0 \text{ kPa}}{101.3 \text{ kPa}}$$

$$\frac{400 \text{ cm}^3 \text{ NH}_3}{} \left| \frac{273 \text{ K}}{300 \text{ K}} \right| \frac{98.0 \text{ kPa}}{101.3 \text{ kPa}} \left| \frac{1 \text{ mol NH}_3}{22.4 \text{ dm}^3} \right| \frac{1 \text{ mol (NH}_4)_2\text{SO}_4}{2 \text{ mol NH}_3}$$
$$\left| \frac{132 \text{ g (NH}_4)_2\text{SO}_4}{1 \text{ mol (NH}_4)_2\text{SO}_4} \right| \frac{1 \text{ dm}^3}{1000 \text{ cm}^3} = 1.04 \text{ g (NH}_4)_2\text{SO}_4$$

To produce 400 cm³ NH_3 at 27°C and 9.80 × 10⁴ Pa, it is necessary to react 1.04 grams $(NH_4)_2SO_4$ with excess sodium hydroxide.

Example 6

What volume of hydrogen collected over water at 27°C and 97.5 kPa is produced by the reaction of 3.00 grams of zinc metal with an excess of sulfuric acid? The vapor pressure of water at 27°C is 3.6 kPa. (Your answer should be the volume of dry gas.)

Solving Process:
Write the balanced equation.

$$Zn(c) + H_2SO_4(aq) \longrightarrow ZnSO_4(aq) + H_2(g)$$

The cubic decimeters of H_2 at STP must be converted to the conditions given in the problem. As the temperature is increased, the volume will increase, so the absolute temperature ratio is

$$\frac{300 \text{ K}}{273 \text{ K}}$$

As the pressure is decreased the volume will increase, so that pressure ratio is

$$\frac{101.3 \text{ kPa}}{97.5 \text{ kPa}}$$

This ratio must be corrected for the vapor pressure of water, which is 3.6 kPa at this temperature. The corrected ratio is

$$\frac{101.3 \text{ kPa}}{97.5 - 3.6 \text{ kPa}} \quad \text{or} \quad \frac{101.3 \text{ kPa}}{93.9 \text{ kPa}}$$

Convert from grams of Zn to cubic decimeters of dry H_2 at 27°C. Then convert to cubic decimeters of H_2 at STP by using the absolute temperature and pressure ratios.

$$\frac{3.00 \text{ g Zn}}{} \left| \frac{1 \text{ mol Zn}}{65.4 \text{ g Zn}} \right| \frac{1 \text{ mol H}_2}{1 \text{ mol Zn}} \left| \frac{22.4 \text{ dm}^3 \text{ H}_2}{1 \text{ mol H}_2} \right| \frac{300 \text{ K}}{273 \text{ K}} \left| \frac{101.3 \text{ kPa}}{93.9 \text{ kPa}} \right.$$

$$= 1.22 \text{ dm}^3 \text{ H}_2$$

Hence, 3.00 grams Zn will react with excess sulfuric acid to give 1.22 cubic decimeters of dry H_2 measured at 27°C and 97.5 kPa.

Example 7

A student performs an experiment involving the reaction of magnesium metal with hydrochloric acid to form hydrogen gas. From the given data, calculate the mass of magnesium.

1. volume of hydrogen gas formed   42.0 cm
2. temperature of hydrogen   20.0°C
3. pressure   99.3 kPa
4. vapor pressure of water   2.3 kPa
5. pressure of dry hydrogen (99.3 − 2.3)   97.0 kPa

Solving Process:
Determine the volume of dry hydrogen at STP. Use the combined gas law.

$$\frac{42.0 \text{ cm}^3 \text{ H}_2}{} \left| \frac{97.0 \text{ kPa}}{101.3 \text{ kPa}} \right| \frac{273 \text{ K}}{293 \text{ K}} = 37.5 \text{ cm}^3 \text{ dry } H_2$$

Use the volume of dry H_2 (37.5 cm³) and the molar volume to find the moles of hydrogen gas formed at STP.

$$\frac{37.5 \text{ cm}^3 \text{ H}_2}{} \left| \frac{1 \text{ mol H}_2}{22.4 \text{ dm}^3 \text{ H}_2} \right| \frac{1 \text{ dm}^3}{1000 \text{ cm}^3} = 1.67 \times 10^{-3} \text{ mol H}_2$$

Write a balanced equation and use it to find the mass of magnesium.

$$Mg(c) + 2HCl(aq) \longrightarrow MgCl_2(aq) + H_2(g)$$

$$\frac{1.67 \times 10^{-3} \text{ mol H}_2}{} \left| \frac{1 \text{ mol Mg}}{1 \text{ mol H}_2} \right| \frac{24.3 \text{ g Mg}}{1 \text{ mol Mg}} = 0.0406 \text{ g Mg}$$

Chapter Review Problems

Assume that all volumes are at STP unless otherwise stated. Skeleton equations are included for some of the reactions.

1. How many cm³ of hydrogen are produced if 4.00 grams zinc react with excess hydrochloric acid?
$$Zn(c) + HCl(aq) \longrightarrow ZnCl_2(aq) + H_2(g)$$

2. How many cm³ of carbon dioxide will react with a sodium hydroxide solution that has a mass of 60.0 grams and contains 20.0% NaOH?
$$NaOH(aq) + CO_2(g) \longrightarrow Na_2CO_3(aq) + H_2O(l)$$

3. If excess chlorine gas reacts with a solution containing 20.0 grams of potassium bromide, how many cubic centimeters of bromine gas can be produced?
$$KBr(aq) + Cl_2(g) \longrightarrow KCl(aq) + Br_2(g)$$

4. How many grams of copper(II) oxide can be reduced to copper metal with 10.0 dm³ of H_2?
$$CuO(c) + H_2(g) \longrightarrow Cu(c) + H_2O(g)$$

5. Calculate the cm³ of oxygen that can be produced by the electrolysis of 5.00 grams of water.
$$H_2O(l) \longrightarrow H_2(g) + O_2(g)$$

6. In the reaction between aluminum and oxygen, how many grams of aluminum are required to react with 5.00 dm³ of oxygen?
$$Al(c) + O_2(g) \longrightarrow Al_2O_3(c)$$

7. If 10.0 grams of sodium peroxide (Na_2O_2) react with water to produce sodium hydroxide and oxygen gas, how many cm³ of oxygen are produced at 20°C and 1.0×10^5 Pa?

8. How many cm³ of chlorine gas measured at 15°C and 98.0 kPa can be produced by the electrolysis of 15.0 grams of sodium chloride to give sodium metal and chlorine gas?

9. How many grams of iron metal must react with excess steam to produce 10.0 dm³ of hydrogen collected over water at 20°C and 9.9×10^4 Pa? The other product is iron(II,III) oxide, Fe_3O_4 (Fe_3O_4 is actually $FeO \cdot Fe_2O_3$).

10. How many dm³ of nitrogen measured at 20°C and 9.55×10^4 Pa are required to react with excess calcium carbide (CaC_2) to produce 100.0 grams of calcium cyanamid ($CaCN_2$) and carbon?

11. How many cm³ of sulfur dioxide at 15°C and 9.6×10^4 Pa can be produced by the reaction of oxygen with a 20.0 gram sample of zinc sulfide which contains 15.0% inert material?

12. How many dm³ of carbon dioxide are produced when 10.0 cm³ of ethanol, C_2H_5OH, are burned completely in oxygen? The density of ethanol is 0.789 g/cm³.

13. How many grams of sodium hydrogen carbonate, $NaHCO_3$, must be heated to produce 2.50 dm³ of carbon dioxide measured at 20°C and 97.5 kPa? The other products are sodium carbonate and water.

14. If 3.20 grams of aluminum react with excess hydrochloric acid, how many cm³ of hydrogen collected over water at 20°C and 99.5 kPa are produced?

15. If 5.00 dm³ of hydrogen collected over water at 15°C and 98.5 kPa are needed, how many grams of aluminum metal must react with excess sodium hydroxide? The other product is sodium aluminate, Na_3AlO_3.

16. One reaction which may be used as a step in the production of sulfuric acid is the reaction of iron pyrite, FeS_2, with oxygen from air to produce sulfur dioxide and iron(III) oxide. On a small scale, if 454 grams of FeS_2 are used, how many dm³ of air at STP are required for a complete reaction? Assume that air contains 21.0% oxygen by volume and 23.0% oxygen by mass. Air has a density of 1.29 g/dm³ at STP.

17. Using the values from Problem 16, calculate the volume of air, in dm³, which is required at 20°C and 1.00×10^5 Pa.

18. Using the values given in Problem 16, calculate the volume of sulfur dioxide produced at 25°C and 99.3 kPa.

19. Nitric acid can be made by the Ostwald process. This industrial process consists of the oxidation of ammonia to nitric oxide; the oxidation of NO to nitrogen dioxide; and the conversion of NO_2 to nitric acid. The process occurs under pressure and temperature in the presence of a catalyst. What quantity of acid could be made from the process using $18\,000\ dm^3$ of ammonia gas measured at $275°C$ and $5.00 \times 10^2\ kPa$? Assume a yield of 92.5% is obtained considering the original quantity of ammonia gas. The equation for the reaction is

$$12NH_3 + 21O_2 \longrightarrow 8HNO_3 + 4NO + 14H_2O$$

Volume-Volume Problems_12

It is possible to calculate the volume of a gas in a reaction when the volume of another gas in the reaction is known. Two methods can be used in solving these volume-volume problems. The first method is the same as the mass-mass or mass-volume method.

The steps are
1. Convert the given volume to moles.
2. From the balanced equation, convert the moles of given substance to moles of required substance.
3. Convert the moles of required substance back to its volume.

In each case, the temperature and pressure must be taken into consideration. The second method usually involves only an inspection and simple mental calculation. It can be used easily when the temperature and pressure remain constant but this is a special case.

Example 1

If 6.00 dm³ of oxygen are available to burn carbon disulfide, CS_2, how many liters of carbon dioxide are produced? The products of the combustion of carbon disulfide are carbon dioxide and sulfur dioxide.

Solving Process:
Balance the equation for this reaction.

$$CS_2(l) + 3O_2(g) \longrightarrow CO_2(g) + 2SO_2(g)$$

Convert 6.00 dm³ O_2 to dm³ of CO_2.

$$\frac{6.00 \text{ dm}^3 \text{ O}_2}{} \left| \frac{1 \text{ mol O}_2}{22.4 \text{ dm}^3 \text{ O}_2} \right| \frac{1 \text{ mol CO}_2}{3 \text{ mol O}_2} \left| \frac{22.4 \text{ dm}^3 \text{ CO}_2}{1 \text{ mol CO}_2} \right. = 2.00 \text{ dm}^3 \text{ CO}_2$$

Therefore, $6.00 \text{ dm}^3 \text{ O}_2$ will produce $2.00 \text{ dm}^3 \text{ CO}_2$. Note that the changes to and from moles divide out.

Alternate method:

The balanced equation indicates the relative number of moles of reactant and product. The coefficients also indicate the relative volumes of the gases at constant temperature and pressure. The relationship is a result of the principle stated in Avogadro's hypothesis: *Equal volumes of gases at the same temperature and pressure contain the same number of particles.*

If the gases are measured under the same conditions of temperature and pressure then 3 volumes $O_2 = 1$ volume CO_2 or $3 \text{ dm}^3 \text{ O}_2 = 1 \text{ dm}^3 \text{ CO}_2$. The volume of CO_2 will be one-third the volume of O_2. Since the O_2 volume is 6.00 dm^3, the CO_2 volume is 2.00 dm^3. Conversion ratios could be used as follows:

$$\frac{6.00 \text{ dm}^3 \text{ O}_2}{} \left| \frac{1 \text{ dm}^3 \text{ CO}_2}{3 \text{ dm}^3 \text{ O}_2} \right. = 2.00 \text{ dm}^3 \text{ CO}_2$$

Example 2

When lead(II) sulfide is burned in air, lead(II) oxide and sulfur dioxide are produced. If $20\,000 \text{ cm}^3$ of sulfur dioxide were produced, how many cubic centimeters of oxygen gas were required to react with the lead(II) sulfide?

Solving Process:

Write the balanced equation for the reaction.

$$2\text{PbS(c)} + 3\text{O}_2\text{(g)} \longrightarrow 2\text{PbO(c)} + 2\text{SO}_2\text{(g)}$$

Determine the volume ratio from the balanced equation.

3 volumes of O_2 produce 2 volumes of SO_2

$$3 \text{ cm}^3 \text{ O}_2 = 2 \text{ cm}^3 \text{ SO}_2$$

$$\frac{20\,000 \text{ cm}^3 \text{ SO}_2}{} \left| \frac{3 \text{ cm}^3 \text{ O}_2}{2 \text{ cm}^3 \text{ SO}_2} \right. = 30\,000 \text{ cm}^3 \text{ O}_2$$

Example 3

When a hydrocarbon such as ethylene burns completely in oxygen, the products are carbon dioxide and water. Calculate the liters of air required to burn completely 15.0 dm^3 of ethylene gas, C_2H_4, measured at STP. Assume that air contains 21.0% oxygen by volume.

Solving Process:

The answer is to be stated as cubic decimeters of air. However, only the oxygen in the air reacts with ethylene gas. The conversion ratio between oxygen and air is

$$21.0 \text{ dm}^3 \text{ O}_2 = 100.0 \text{ dm}^3 \text{ air}$$

Write the balanced equation.

$$C_2H_4(g) + 3O_2(g) \longrightarrow 2CO_2(g) + 2H_2O(g)$$

The conversion ratio obtained from the balanced equation is

1 dm³ C_2H_4 reacts with 3 dm³ O_2

Convert from liters of ethylene gas to dm³ of air:

$$\frac{15.0 \text{ dm}^3 C_2H_4}{} \left| \frac{3 \text{ dm}^3 O_2}{1 \text{ dm}^3 C_2H_4} \right| \frac{100.0 \text{ dm}^3 \text{ air}}{21.0 \text{ dm}^3 O_2} = 214 \text{ dm}^3 \text{ air}$$

Therefore, 15.0 cubic decimeters C_2H_4 will react with 214 cubic decimeters of air for complete combustion.

Example 4

How many liters of air measured at 98.5 kPa and 100°C are required to produce 200 dm³ of CO_2 measured at the same pressure and 20°C? Assume that air contains 21% oxygen by volume and that the CO_2 is being produced from CO.

Solving Process:
Write the balanced equation.

$$2CO(g) + O_2(g) \longrightarrow 2CO_2(g)$$

The conversion ratios are

$$1 \text{ dm}^3 O_2 = 2 \text{ dm}^3 CO_2$$
$$21 \text{ dm}^3 O_2 = 100 \text{ dm}^3 \text{ air}$$

Since the pressure is the same, no correction is required for pressure. The temperature increases from 20°C to 100°C, so the volume of the air increases and the absolute temperature ratio is

$$\frac{373 \text{ K}}{293 \text{ K}}$$

Convert from cubic decimeters of CO_2 at 20°C to cubic decimeters of air at 20°C; then use the absolute temperature ratio to find the volume of air at 373 K.

$$\frac{200 \text{ dm}^3 CO_2}{} \left| \frac{1 \text{ dm}^3 O_2}{2 \text{ dm}^3 CO_2} \right| \frac{100 \text{ dm}^3 \text{ air}}{21 \text{ dm}^3 O_2} \left| \frac{373 \text{ K}}{293 \text{ K}} \right. = 606 \text{ dm}^3 \text{ air}$$

Chapter Review Problems

1. In the electrolysis of water, 75.0 cm³ of oxygen gas are produced. How many cm³ of hydrogen are produced?

$$H_2O(l) \longrightarrow H_2(g) + O_2(g)$$

2. If an electric discharge produces 20.0 cm^3 of ozone, O_3, how many cubic centimeters of oxygen are required?
$$O_2(g) \longrightarrow O_3(g)$$

3. Ammonia can be produced by the Haber process. If 60.0 dm^3 of NH_3 are produced, how many dm^3 of hydrogen and nitrogen are necessary?
$$H_2(g) + N_2(g) \longrightarrow NH_3(g)$$

4. How many cm^3 of chlorine gas are required to produce 50.0 cm^3 of hydrogen chloride gas?
$$H_2(g) + Cl_2(g) \longrightarrow HCl(g)$$

5. Calculate the cubic centimeters of air required to convert 50.0 cubic centimeters of nitric oxide, NO, to nitrogen dioxide, NO_2. Assume that air contains 21% oxygen by volume.
$$NO(g) + O_2(g) \longrightarrow NO_2(g)$$

6. If 20.0 dm^3 of air burn completely a sample of carbon disulfide, how many dm^3 of carbon dioxide are produced? How many dm^3 of sulfur dioxide? Assume that air contains 21% oxygen by volume.
$$CS_2(l) + O_2(g) \longrightarrow CO_2(g) + SO_2(g)$$

7. Ammonia burns in oxygen to give nitric oxide, NO, and water. If 20.0 dm^3 of ammonia are burned, how many dm^3 of air are required? How many dm^3 of nitric oxide are produced? Assume that air contains 21% oxygen by volume.

8. In a reaction involving carbon monoxide and iron(III) oxide, the products are iron metal and carbon dioxide. If 100 dm^3 of carbon dioxide are produced, how many dm^3 of carbon monoxide are required?

9. In the reaction of hydrogen gas with nitrogen gas to produce ammonia, calculate the volume of ammonia produced if 500.0 grams of hydrogen (density 0.0900 g/dm^3) react with excess nitrogen. Assume that the actual yield of ammonia is 40.0% of the theoretical yield.

10. One of the steps in the production of sulfuric acid is the reaction of oxygen in air with sulfur dioxide to produce sulfur trioxide. How many dm^3 of oxygen and how many dm^3 of air are required to react with 75.0 dm^3 of SO_2? There are 2.1 dm^3 of oxygen in 10.0 dm^3 of air.

11. If a 50.00 gram solution of potassium hydroxide containing 40.00% water reacts with excess ammonium sulfate, calculate the following:
   a. the moles of potassium sulfate produced
   b. the grams of water produced
   c. the moles of ammonia produced
   d. the dm^3 of ammonia produced at STP
   e. the dm^3 of ammonia produced at 21°C and 98.0 kPa

12. The residue from the complete decomposition of potassium chlorate is found to contain 1.80 grams of potassium chloride. Determine the following:
   a. grams of $KClO_3$ originally present
   b. grams of oxygen produced
   c. cubic centimeters of oxygen at STP
   d. cubic centimeters of oxygen at 20°C and 98.5 kPa

13. If 15 000 cm^3 of ethane gas, C_2H_6, at STP are burned completely to form carbon dioxide and water, calculate the following:
   a. cubic centimeters of oxygen required
   b. grams of water produced
   c. moles of carbon dioxide produced
   d. cubic centimeters of air required for complete combustion (assume that air contains 21.0% O_2 by volume)
   e. grams of calcium carbonate which can be produced by bubbling the carbon dioxide produced through limewater, $Ca(OH)_2$

Limiting Reactant Problems 13

Many reactions continue until one of the reactants is consumed. The reactant which is used up first is called the **limiting reactant.** The other reactant is said to be in **excess.** In this chapter, we will deal only with nonreversible reactions. It is possible to determine whether a material is in excess or is deficient in a reaction by experiment or by calculation.

Limiting reactant problems are most easily solved by comparing the moles of the reactants present. The steps for mole comparison are

1. Change grams of reactants to moles of reactants.
2. From the balanced equation, determine the moles of one reactant that will react with a number of moles of the other reactant.
3. Convert moles of one reactant to moles of the other and compare with the original number of moles obtained in step 1. Decide which is the limiting reactant.

Example 1

Determine the limiting reactant, using the balanced equation given below, if an 80.0 gram solution of NaOH, which is 40.0% NaOH by mass, reacts with a 75.0 gram solution of H_2SO_4, which contains 45.0% water by mass.

$$2NaOH(aq) + H_2SO_4(aq) \longrightarrow Na_2SO_4(aq) + 2H_2O(l)$$

Solving Process:
When the actual masses of the reacting substances are not given, the actual masses can be found by multiplying the mass of solution by the percent of pure material.

grams pure NaOH = (80.0 g solution)(0.400) = 32.0 g NaOH

grams pure H_2SO_4 = (75.0 g solution)(0.550) = 41.3 g H_2SO_4

Change grams of reactants to moles of reactants.

$$\text{moles NaOH} = \frac{32.0 \text{ g NaOH}}{} \left| \frac{1 \text{ mol NaOH}}{40.0 \text{ g NaOH}} \right. = 0.800 \text{ mol NaOH}$$

$$\text{moles H}_2\text{SO}_4 = \frac{41.3 \text{ g H}_2\text{SO}_4}{} \left| \frac{1 \text{ mol H}_2\text{SO}_4}{98.1 \text{ g H}_2\text{SO}_4} \right. = 0.421 \text{ mol H}_2\text{SO}_4$$

From the balanced equation: 2 moles NaOH react with 1 mole H_2SO_4. Thus, the ratio is 2 moles NaOH/1 mole H_2SO_4.

Convert 0.421 mole H_2SO_4 to the moles of NaOH necessary to react with the H_2SO_4.

$$\frac{0.421 \text{ mol H}_2\text{SO}_4}{} \left| \frac{2 \text{ mol NaOH}}{1 \text{ mol H}_2\text{SO}_4} \right. = 0.842 \text{ mol NaOH}$$

Compare this answer to the moles of NaOH obtained initially. The calculation shows that 0.421 mole of H_2SO_4 will react with 0.842 mole of NaOH. The NaOH is the limiting reactant by 0.042 mole (0.842 − 0.800). The reaction will go toward completion until the NaOH is completely consumed.

After doing this mole comparison calculation you could then calculate the grams of Na_2SO_4 or the grams of H_2O, using the limiting reactant (the 0.800 mole of NaOH) as the starting point to find the moles or grams of products produced.

Example 2

If 40.0 grams of H_3PO_4 react with 60.0 grams of $MgCO_3$, calculate (a) the grams of $Mg_3(PO_4)_2$ produced, (b) the grams of CO_2 produced, and (c) the volume of CO_2 produced at STP.

Solving Process:

Part (a).

Write the balanced equation.

$$2H_3PO_4(aq) + 3MgCO_3(c) \longrightarrow Mg_3(PO_4)_2(c) + 3CO_2(g) + 3H_2O(l)$$

Change grams of reactant to moles of reactant.

$$\frac{40.0 \text{ g H}_3\text{PO}_4}{} \left| \frac{1 \text{ mol H}_3\text{PO}_4}{98.0 \text{ g H}_3\text{PO}_4} \right. = 0.408 \text{ mol H}_3\text{PO}_4$$

$$\frac{60.0 \text{ g MgCO}_3}{} \left| \frac{1 \text{ mol MgCO}_3}{84.3 \text{ g MgCO}_3} \right. = 0.712 \text{ mol MgCO}_3$$

From the balanced equation: 2 moles H_3PO_4 react with 3 moles $MgCO_3$. Thus, the ratio is 3 moles $MgCO_3$/2 moles H_3PO_4.

Determine the moles of $MgCO_3$ necessary to react with 0.408 mole of H_3PO_4. Compare this answer with the 0.712 mole of $MgCO_3$ and decide which compound is the limiting reactant.

$$\frac{0.408 \text{ mol } H_3PO_4}{} \left| \frac{3 \text{ mol } MgCO_3}{2 \text{ mol } H_3PO_4} = 0.612 \text{ mol } MgCO_3 \right.$$

Thus, 0.408 mole of H_3PO_4 will react with 0.612 mole of $MgCO_3$, but 0.712 mole of $MgCO_3$ is available. The $MgCO_3$ is in excess and the H_3PO_4 is the limiting reactant. Since the limiting compound determines how far a reaction will proceed, the 40.0 grams of H_3PO_4 or the 0.408 mole of H_3PO_4 must be used in the calculations involving the products.

Convert 0.408 mole H_3PO_4 to grams of $Mg_3(PO_4)_2$. Use moles instead of grams of H_3PO_4 to eliminate one conversion factor.

$$\frac{0.408 \text{ mol } H_3PO_4}{} \left| \frac{1 \text{ mol } Mg_3(PO_4)_2}{2 \text{ mol } H_3PO_4} \right| \frac{263 \text{ g } Mg_3(PO_4)_2}{1 \text{ mol } Mg_3(PO_4)_2}$$

$$= 53.7 \text{ g } Mg_3(PO_4)_2$$

Hence, 0.408 mole of H_3PO_4 will produce 53.7 grams of $Mg_3(PO_4)_2$.
Part (b).

Convert 0.408 mole H_3PO_4 to grams of CO_2.

$$\frac{0.408 \text{ mol } H_3PO_4}{} \left| \frac{3 \text{ mol } CO_2}{2 \text{ mol } H_3PO_4} \right| \frac{44.0 \text{ g } CO_2}{1 \text{ mol } CO_2} = 26.9 \text{ g } CO_2$$

Hence, 0.408 mole of H_3PO_4 will produce 26.9 grams of CO_2 gas.
Part (c).

Convert 0.408 mole H_3PO_4 to cm^3 of CO_2 at STP.

$$\frac{0.408 \text{ mol } H_3PO_4}{} \left| \frac{3 \text{ mol } CO_2}{2 \text{ mol } H_3PO_4} \right| \frac{22\ 400 \text{ cm}^3 \text{ } CO_2 \text{ (STP)}}{1 \text{ mol } CO_2}$$

$$= 13\ 700 \text{ cm}^3 \text{ } CO_2$$

Therefore, 0.408 mole of H_3PO_4 will produce 13 700 cm^3 of CO_2 measured at standard temperature and pressure.

The same approach for finding limiting reactants can also be used in mass-volume or volume-volume problems. It is necessary to convert from the mass or volume of the reactants to moles of the reactants. A comparison of the moles will show whether a reactant is in excess or is limiting. Once the limiting material is known, the mass and/or volume of the products can be calculated from the moles of the limiting compound.

Chapter Review Problems

1. If 20.0 grams of NaOH react with 30.0 grams of H_2SO_4 to produce Na_2SO_4, which reactant is limiting?

$$NaOH(aq) + H_2SO_4(aq) \longrightarrow Na_2SO_4(aq) + H_2O(l)$$

2. If 5.00 grams of copper metal react with a solution containing 20.0 grams of $AgNO_3$, which reactant is limiting?

$$Cu(c) + AgNO_3(aq) \longrightarrow Cu(NO_3)_2(aq) + Ag(c)$$

3. What reactant is limiting if $3000 \, cm^3$ of Cl_2 at STP react with a solution containing 25.0 grams of NaBr?

4. If 20.0 grams of KOH react with 15.0 grams of $(NH_4)_2SO_4$, calculate the following:
   a. the moles of K_2SO_4 produced
   b. the grams of NH_3 produced
   c. the cm^3 of NH_3 produced at STP
   d. the cm^3 of NH_3 produced, measured at 20°C and 99.2 kPa

5. A $CaCl_2$ solution with a mass of 50.0 grams contains 30.0% $CaCl_2$. This solution reacts with 35.0 grams of $AgNO_3$, one of the products is the precipitate, AgCl. Calculate the following:
   a. the excess material and the grams of excess material
   b. the moles of AgCl produced
   c. the grams of $Ca(NO_3)_2$ produced

6. If 20.0 grams of hydrogen gas (density $0.0900 \, g/dm^3$) react with 15.0 grams of nitrogen (density $1.25 \, g/dm^3$), what gas is limiting? How many dm^3 of ammonia (density $0.759 \, g/dm^3$) will be produced?

7. A zinc sample, which has a mass of 40.0 grams and contains 10.0% inert material, reacts with a hydrochloric acid solution that contains 20.0 grams of pure HCl. Zinc chloride and hydrogen gas are produced. Calculate the following:
   a. the moles of $ZnCl_2$ produced
   b. the molecules of H_2 produced
   c. the cm^3 of H_2 produced at 98.5 kPa and 27°C
   d. the cm^3 of dry H_2 produced if the gas was collected over water at 20°C and 97.6 kPa

8. If $20.0 \, dm^3$ of methane, CH_4, react with $200.0 \, dm^3$ of air, calculate the following:
   a. the dm^3 of carbon dioxide gas
   b. the grams of CO_2 produced
   c. the grams of H_2O produced
   Assume that all volumes are measured at STP and that air contains 20.0% oxygen by volume.

9. A solution of KOH with a mass of 50.0 grams and containing 70.0% water is neutralized by 20.0 grams of H_2SO_4. The products are potassium sulfate and water. Calculate the following:
    a. the moles of K_2SO_4 produced
    b. the grams of water produced
    c. the total mass of water in the reaction mixture after the reaction is finished

10. Magnesium acetate can be prepared by a reaction involving 15.0 grams of iron(III) acetate with either 10.0 grams of $MgCrO_4$ or 15.0 grams of $MgSO_4$. Which reaction will give the greatest yield of $Mg(C_2H_3O_2)_2$? How many grams of $Mg(C_2H_3O_2)_2$ will be produced?

    $$2Fe(C_2H_3O_2)_3(aq) + 3MgCrO_4(c) \longrightarrow$$
    $$3Mg(C_2H_3O_2)_2(aq) + 2Fe_2(CrO_4)_3(c)$$

    $$2Fe(C_2H_3O_2)_3(aq) + 3MgSO_4(c) \longrightarrow$$
    $$3Mg(C_2H_3O_2)_2(aq) + 2Fe_2(SO_4)_3(c)$$

11. In the reaction between hydrogen and nitrogen to produce ammonia, $50.0 \, dm^3$ of hydrogen (density $0.0900 \, g/dm^3$) react with $15.0 \, dm^3$ of nitrogen (density $1.25 \, g/dm^3$). Calculate the grams of ammonia (density $0.759 \, g/dm^3$) produced if the yield is 35.0% of ammonia.

12. A solution containing 20.0 grams of sodium sulfite reacts with 7.00 cubic centimeters of phosphoric acid (density $1.83 \, g/cm^3$). Determine the following:
    a. the excess reactant and its mass
    b. grams of water produced
    c. moles of sodium phosphate produced
    d. grams of sulfur dioxide produced
    e. cubic decimeters of sulfur dioxide at STP
    f. cubic decimeters of sulfur dioxide at $103\,000 \, Pa$ and $-10°C$

13. A zinc sample which has a mass of 20.0 grams and contains 90.0% zinc reacts with 20.0 cubic centimeters of hydrochloric acid (density $1.19 \, g/cm^3$). Calculate the following:
    a. grams of zinc chloride produced
    b. grams of H_2 produced at STP
    c. cubic centimeters of H_2 at STP
    d. cubic centimeters of dry H_2 at $98\,000 \, Pa$ and $19°C$
    e. If the cubic centimeters of H_2 calculated in Part d were burned in air, determine the cubic centimeters of air required if the same conditions are maintained. Assume that air contains 21.0% oxygen by volume.

14. Calcium carbide (CaC_2) reacts with water to produce calcium hydroxide and acetylene (C_2H_2). What volume of the gas at STP could be produced from the reaction of 50.0 grams of CaC_2 and 50.0 grams of water?

15. Methyl orange is a colored substance which, in solution, is red in the presence of acids and yellow in the presence of bases. What will be the final color of a solution which results from mixing two separate solutions containing 10.0 grams H_2SO_4 and 7.00 grams NaOH after a small amount of methyl orange is added?

16. Hydrogen burns to give water. If 200 cm³ of H_2 reacts with 150 cm³ of O_2, what volume of water vapor is produced? How many cubic centimeters of gas remain unreacted and what gas remains? Assume that all volumes are measured at any given temperature above the normal boiling point of water.

17. Under certain extreme conditions, nitrogen and oxygen react to produce nitric oxide, NO. If a total volume of 1 liter of nitrogen and oxygen in the same ratio as that found in air react, what gas and how much of that gas will not react? How many cm³ of NO are produced? Assume that air contains 20% oxygen and 80% nitrogen.

Thermochemistry_____14

When a substance is heated, the energy of its constituent particles is increased. If the kinetic energy is increased, the result is an increase in the temperature of the substance. If the increase is in potential energy, the physical state of the substance will change. The change, or combination of changes, that will take place, depends upon the starting temperature of the substance. Similar considerations can be applied to removing heat from (cooling) a substance.

14:1 Changes of State

The changes of state from solid to liquid and liquid to solid take place at the same temperature which is labeled the **melting point** or **freezing point.** The changes from liquid to gas and gas to liquid take place at the same temperature which is labeled the **boiling point** or **condensing point.** The amount of heat required for a state change depends on the specific substance and the amount of that substance. If we use ΔH to represent the quantity of heat needed to melt a substance, then

$$\Delta H = m(H_f)$$

where m is the mass of the substance and H_f is a property of a substance called its **heat of fusion.** Similarly, to boil a substance, the relationship is

$$\Delta H = m(H_v)$$

where H_v is a property of a substance called its heat of vaporization.

A table of H_f and H_v values is included in the Appendix of this book and should be used for the solution of problems in this chapter.

Example 1

How much heat is required to melt 86.3 grams of iron at its melting point?

Solving Process:

The heat required for a phase change depends upon the mass (86.3 g) and heat of fusion or vaporization. In the present case the heat of fusion of iron is 15.4 kJ/mol. To make use of the H_f value, the quantity of iron must be in units of moles. Thus, the solution is

$$\frac{86.3 \text{ g Fe}}{} \left| \frac{1 \text{ mol Fe}}{55.8 \text{ g Fe}} \right| \frac{15.4 \text{ kJ}}{1 \text{ mol Fe}} = 23.8 \text{ kJ}$$

Example 2

How much heat is released when 79.1 grams selenium vapor condense to selenium liquid at its boiling point?

Solving Process:

The heat involved in the condensation depends upon the mass (79.1 g) and the heat of vaporization of selenium (86.2 kJ/mol). The solution requires the conversion of the quantity of selenium from grams to moles.

$$\frac{79.1 \text{ g Se}}{} \left| \frac{1 \text{ mol Se}}{79.0 \text{ g Se}} \right| \frac{86.2 \text{ kJ}}{1 \text{ mol Se}} = 86.3 \text{ kJ}$$

Problems

1. How much heat is released upon the solidification of 387 grams of arsenic at its freezing point?

2. How much heat is required to boil 47.5 grams of helium at its boiling point?

14:2 Changes of Temperature

The amount of heat required to change the temperature of a substance depends upon the amount and nature of the substance as well as the extent of the temperature change. In symbols

$$\Delta H = m(\Delta T)C_p$$

where ΔH is the heat added (or removed), m is the mass of the substance, ΔT is the change in temperature, and C_p is a property of the substance called its **specific heat capacity.** The specific heat capacity of a substance varies with the temperature. However, the variation for liquids and solids is small enough to be neglected in elementary work. For gases, the variation is greater, but for simple calculations an average value for the temperature range of interest is sufficient. Values of specific heat capacities are given in the Appendix.

Example 3

How much heat is required to raise the temperature of 68.0 grams of tin from 25.0°C to 80.0°C?

Solving Process:

In addition to the temperature change and mass given in the statement of the problem, we must consult the table in the Appendix to obtain the specific heat capacity of tin, 0.222 J/g · C°.

$$\Delta H = m(\Delta T)C_p$$

$$\Delta H = \frac{68.0\,g \mid (80 - 25)\,C° \mid 0.222\,J}{\mid \mid g \cdot C°} = 830\,J$$

Example 4

How much heat is released by 147 grams of water cooling from 100.0°C to 27.0°C?

Solving Process:

From the table in Appendix A, the specific heat capacity of water is 4.18 J/g · C°. Thus,

$$\frac{147\,g \mid 73.0\,C° \mid 4.18\,J}{\mid \mid g \cdot C°} = 44\,900\,J$$

Problems

3. How much heat is required to raise the temperature of 789 grams of acetic acid from 25.0° to 82.7°C?

4. How much heat is released when 432 grams of water cool from 71.0°C to 18.0°C?

14:3 Combination Changes

Many times problems are encountered that involve both temperature and state changes. For such problems, each step (temperature or state change) is solved as in the preceding examples. The sum of the heat changes for all the steps is the solution to the original problem.

The most complex case would be to start with a solid substance below its melting point and change that substance to a gas above its boiling point. Consider the steps to be taken in such a change:

1. Heat the solid to its melting point.
2. Melt the solid.
3. Heat the liquid to its boiling point.
4. Boil the liquid.
5. Heat the gas to the required temperature.

Steps 1, 3, and 5 are solved in the usual manner with the relationship $\Delta H = m(\Delta T)C_p$. Steps 2 and 4 require H_f and H_v, respectively, as well as m. The sum of the heat changes in steps 1 through 5 would then be the answer to the original problem.

Example 5

How much heat is required to heat 25.6 grams of indium from 100.0°C to 200.0°C?

Solving Process:
Reference to a table of elementary properties shows that indium melts at 155.0°C. Thus, solid indium must be heated from 100.0°C to 155.0°C. Second, the indium must be melted. Finally, the liquid indium is heated from 155.0°C to 200.0°C. References show that the specific heat capacity of solid indium is 0.238 J/g·C° and of liquid indium 0.216 J/g·C°. The heat of fusion of indium is 3.27 kJ/mol.
Step 1: To heat the indium to the melting point.

$$\frac{25.6 \ g \mid 55.0 \ C° \mid 0.238 \ J}{\mid \mid g \cdot C°} = 335 \ J$$

Step 2: To melt the indium.

$$\frac{25.6 \ g \ In \mid 1 \ mol \ In \mid 3.27 \ kJ}{\mid 115 \ g \ In \mid 1 \ mol \ In} = 0.728 \ kJ = 728 \ J$$

Step 3: Heat the liquid indium to 200.0°C.

$$\frac{25.6 \ g \mid 45.0 \ C° \mid 0.216 \ J}{\mid \mid g \cdot C°} = 249 \ J$$

The heat required is the sum of steps 1, 2, and 3.

$$335 \ J + 728 \ J + 249 \ J = 1312 \ J$$

Example 6

How much heat is released when 42.5 grams of aluminum are cooled from 5000 K to 298 K?

Solving Process:
Step 1: The Al gas is cooled to the condensing point, 2600 K or 2327°C.

$$\frac{42.5\,g}{}\Bigg|\frac{2127\,°\!C}{}\Bigg|\frac{0.903\ \text{J}}{g\cdot°\!C} = 81\ 629\ \text{J} = 81.6\ \text{kJ}$$

Step 2: The Al gas is condensed.

$$\frac{42.5\,g}{}\Bigg|\frac{1\ mol}{27.0\,g}\Bigg|\frac{284\ \text{kJ}}{1\ mol} = 447\ \text{kJ}$$

Step 3: The liquid Al is cooled to the freezing point, 933 K or 660°C.

$$\frac{42.5\,g}{}\Bigg|\frac{1667\,°\!C}{}\Bigg|\frac{0.903\ \text{J}}{g\cdot°\!C} = 63\ 975\ \text{J} = 63.9\ \text{kJ}$$

Step 4: The liquid Al is frozen.

$$\frac{42.5\,g}{}\Bigg|\frac{1\ mol}{27.0\,g}\Bigg|\frac{10.8\ \text{kJ}}{1\ mol} = 17.0\ \text{kJ}$$

Step 5: The solid Al is cooled to 298 K or 25°C.

$$\frac{42.5\,g}{}\Bigg|\frac{635\,°\!C}{}\Bigg|\frac{0.903\ \text{J}}{g\cdot°\!C} = 24\ 400\ \text{J} = 24.4\ \text{kJ}$$

The total heat released is the sum of all steps.

$$81.6 + 447 + 63.9 + 17.0 + 24.4 = 634\ \text{kJ}$$

Chapter Review Problems

5. Compute the heat changes associated with the following transitions:
   a. melting 55.8 grams Ti at 1677°C.
   b. condensing 14.2 grams H_2O at 100°C.
   c. boiling 53.5 grams C_6H_6 at 80.1°C.
   d. freezing 27.3 grams Al at 660°C.
   e. melting 76.4 grams Au at 1065°C.

6. Compute the heat changes associated with the following transitions:
   a. 49.2 grams acetic acid from 24.1°C to 67.3°C.
   b. 9.61 grams toluene from 19.6°C to 75.0°C.
   c. 2.47 grams kerosene from 17.1°C to 46.7°C.
   d. 31.9 grams chalk from 83.2°C to 55.5°C.
   e. 63.6 grams glass from 95.5°C to 42.3°C.

7. How much heat must be removed from 6.81 kilograms of steel to cool it from 2720°C to 625°C? Assume a freezing point of 1300°C.

8. How much heat is required to change 34.4 grams of ice at −5.44°C to steam at 249°C?

Thermodynamics_____15

All chemical changes are accompanied by energy changes and changes in the degree of disorder for the particles involved. Calculations based on these changes can be kept simple if we reduce all variables to a set of standard conditions. These standards are 25°C, 1.013 bars, and 1 molar solutions.

15:1 Changes Accompanying a Reaction

The variables of interest to the chemist include:

H, the **enthalpy,** or heat content, of a substance
S, the **entropy,** or disorder, of a substance
G, the **free energy,** or chemical potential, of a substance

For each of these variables, the change in the quantity during a reaction is the difference between the values for the products and the reactants. Thus,

$$\Delta H = H_{(products)} - H_{(reactants)}$$
$$\Delta S = S_{(products)} - S_{(reactants)}$$
$$\Delta G = G_{(products)} - G_{(reactants)}$$

Chemists are interested in ΔH since if $\Delta H < 0$ the reaction is **exothermic,** that is, energy is given off. On the other hand if $\Delta H > 0$, the reaction is **endothermic,** that is, energy is taken in. Changes in entropy are of little value in themselves. The chief use of ΔS is as a step in determining ΔG. ΔG is important because if $\Delta G < 0$ the reaction is spontaneous and if $\Delta G > 0$ the reaction is not spontaneous. Of course, if $\Delta S > 0$ there is an increase in disorder (decrease in order) and if $\Delta S < 0$ there is a decrease in disorder (increase in order). Enthalpy and free energy quantities are relative values compared to free elements defined as having zero enthalpy and zero free energy. The enthalpy and free energy of each substance are therefore represented by ΔH_f° and ΔG_f°, respectively. The superscript "°" designates standard conditions. The subscript "f" designates "of formation" since the formation of the substance from the free elements is the enthalpy or free energy. The reactants (in this case the free elements) would be equal to zero. At standard conditions, then, the equations become

$$\Delta H^\circ_{(reaction)} = \Sigma\Delta H^\circ_{f(products)} - \Sigma\Delta H^\circ_{f(reactants)}$$
$$\Delta G^\circ_{(reaction)} = \Sigma\Delta G^\circ_{f(products)} - \Sigma\Delta G^\circ_{f(reactants)}$$
$$\Delta S^\circ_{(reaction)} = \Sigma S^\circ_{(products)} - \Sigma S^\circ_{(reactants)}$$

Example 1

What is the enthalpy change for the following reaction?

$$Cl_2(g) + 2HBr(g) \longrightarrow 2HCl(g) + Br_2(g)$$

Solving Process:
From the table of thermodynamic values in the Appendix, we find the following ΔH_f° values:

$$HBr = -53.4 \text{ kJ/mol}$$
$$HCl = -92.3 \text{ kJ/mol}$$

By definition, the heat of formation for the free elements Cl_2 and Br_2 is 0.

$$\Delta H^\circ = \Sigma\Delta H^\circ_{f(products)} - \Sigma\Delta H^\circ_{f(reactants)}$$

$$\Delta H^\circ = \left[\frac{1 \text{ mol Br}_2}{} \cdot \frac{0 \text{ kJ}}{\text{mol Br}_2} + \frac{2 \text{ mol HCl}}{} \cdot \frac{(-92.3)\text{kJ}}{\text{mol HCl}} \right]$$
$$- \left[\frac{1 \text{ mol Cl}_2}{} \cdot \frac{0 \text{ kJ}}{\text{mol Cl}_2} + \frac{2 \text{ mol HBr}}{} \cdot \frac{(-53.4)\text{kJ}}{\text{mol HBr}} \right]$$

$$\Delta H^\circ = +77.8 \text{ kJ}$$

The positive sign indicates that the products have more enthalpy, or heat content, than the reactants. Thus, energy must have been absorbed, and the reaction is said to be endothermic. If ΔH had been negative, energy would have been released and the reaction would have been exothermic.

Example 2

For the reaction

$$Ca(c) + 2H_2O(l) \longrightarrow Ca(OH)_2(c) + H_2(g)$$
$$\Delta S° = 25.7 \text{ J/K}$$

What is $S°$ for $Ca(OH)_2(c)$?

Solving Process:

From a table of thermodynamic values in the Appendix, we find the following $S°$ values:

$$Ca(c) = 41.6 \text{ J/mol} \cdot K$$
$$H_2O(l) = 69.9 \text{ J/mol} \cdot K$$
$$H_2(g) = 131 \text{ J/mol} \cdot K$$

$$\Delta S° = \Sigma S°_{(products)} - \Sigma S°_{(reactants)}$$

$$25.7 \text{ J/K} = \left[\frac{1 \text{ mol } Ca(OH)_2 \mid x}{} + \frac{1 \text{ mol } H_2 \mid 131 \text{ J}}{\mid mol H_2 \cdot K} \right]$$

$$- \left[\frac{1 \text{ mol } Ca \mid 41.6 \text{ J}}{\mid mol Ca \cdot K} + \frac{2 \text{ mol } H_2O \mid 69.9 \text{ J}}{\mid mol H_2O \cdot K} \right]$$

$$x = 76.1 \text{ J/mol} \cdot K$$

15:2 Spontaneous Reactions

An American chemist, J. Willard Gibbs, discovered the relationship among these variables.

$$\Delta G° = \Delta H° - T\Delta S°$$

where T is the absolute temperature. A spontaneous reaction is one in which ΔG is negative. Using tables of thermodynamic values, then, we can predict whether a reaction is spontaneous at standard conditions. If a table includes values of $\Delta G_f°$, the $\Delta G°$ for the reaction can be calculated directly as in the previous section. $\Delta G°$ can also be calculated using $\Delta H°$, T, and $\Delta S°$.

Example 3

Is the following reaction spontaneous?

$$2H_2O_2 \longrightarrow 2H_2O + O_2$$

Solving Process:

From the table of thermodynamic values in the Appendix, we obtain the following $\Delta G_f°$ values:

$$H_2O_2 = -120 \text{ kJ/mol}$$
$$H_2O = -237 \text{ kJ/mol}$$

By definition ΔG_f° for O_2 (a free element) $= 0$.

$$\Delta G^\circ = \Sigma \Delta G_{f\,(products)}^\circ - \Sigma \Delta G_{f\,(reactants)}^\circ$$

$$\Delta G^\circ = \left[\frac{2 \text{ mol } H_2O}{} \left| \frac{(-237) \text{ kJ}}{\text{mol } H_2O} + \frac{1 \text{ mol } O_2}{} \right| \frac{0 \text{ kJ}}{\text{mol } O_2}\right]$$
$$- \left[\frac{2 \text{ mol } H_2O_2}{} \left| \frac{(-120) \text{ kJ}}{\text{mol } H_2O_2}\right.\right]$$

$$\Delta G^\circ = -234 \text{ kJ}$$

ΔG° is negative, so the reaction is spontaneous at standard conditions. Note, however, the term spontaneous tells us nothing about how long a reaction will take.

Example 4

For the reaction

$$P_4O_{10}(c) + 6H_2O(l) \longrightarrow 4H_3PO_4(aq)$$
$$\Delta H^\circ = -416 \text{ kJ}$$
$$\Delta S^\circ = -208 \text{ J/K}$$

Is the reaction spontaneous?

Solving Process:
The spontaneity of a reaction is indicated by ΔG° and $\Delta G^\circ = \Delta H^\circ - T\Delta S^\circ$.

$$\Delta G^\circ = -416 \text{ kJ} - [(298 \text{ K})(-208 \text{ J/K})]$$
$$\Delta G^\circ = -416 \text{ kJ} + 62\,000 \text{ J} = -416 \text{ kJ} + 62 \text{ kJ}$$
$$\Delta G^\circ = -354 \text{ kJ}$$

The reaction is spontaneous.

Chapter Review Problems

1. Find ΔG° for the following reactions and predict the spontaneity at standard conditions. Use the Thermodynamic Properties table in the Appendix of this book.
   a. $Ca(OH)_2(c) + 2NH_4Cl(aq) \rightarrow CaCl_2(aq) + 2NH_3(g) + 2H_2O(l)$
   b. $2NaCl(c) + H_2SO_4(l) \rightarrow Na_2SO_4(aq) + 2HCl(g)$
   c. $CaCl_2(aq) + 2NaOH(aq) \rightarrow Ca(OH)_2(c) + 2NaCl(aq)$
   d. $3Mg(c) + N_2(g) \rightarrow Mg_3N_2(c)$
   e. $3Cu(c) + 8HNO_3(aq) \rightarrow 3Cu(NO_3)_2(aq) + 4H_2O(l) + 2NO(g)$

2. Find $\Delta H°$ for the following reactions.
    a. $2KBr(c) + H_2SO_4(l) \rightarrow K_2SO_4(aq) + 2HBr(g)$
    b. $Mg_3N_2(c) + 6H_2O(l) \rightarrow 3Mg(OH)_2(c) + 2NH_3(g)$
    c. $NH_4NO_3(c) \rightarrow N_2O(g) + 2H_2O(l)$
    d. $2NO(g) + O_2(g) \rightarrow 2NO_2(g)$
    e. $4Zn(c) + 9HNO_3(aq) \rightarrow 4Zn(NO_3)_2(aq) + NH_3(g) + 3H_2O(l)$

3. Find $\Delta S°$ for the following reactions.
    a. $Zn(NO_3)_2(aq) + 2NaOH(aq) \rightarrow Zn(OH)_2(c) + 2NaNO_3(aq)$
    b. $2NO_2(g) + H_2O(l) \rightarrow HNO_2(aq) + HNO_3(aq)$
    c. $Mg(c) + 2HNO_3(aq) \rightarrow Mg(NO_3)_2(aq) + H_2(g)$
    d. $4HBr(g) + O_2(g) \rightarrow 2H_2O(l) + 2Br_2(l)$
    e. $Cu(c) + Ag_2SO_4(aq) \rightarrow CuSO_4(aq) + 2Ag(c)$

4. Predict the spontaneity of the following reactions at 298 K.
    a. $Sn(c) + 4HNO_3(aq) \rightarrow SnO_2(c) + 4NO_2(g) + 2H_2O(l)$
          $(\Delta H° = -192 \text{ kJ}, \Delta S° = 887 \text{ J/K})$
    b. $2N_2O_5(g) \rightarrow 4NO_2(g) + O_2(g)$
          $(\Delta H° = 110 \text{ kJ}, \Delta S° = 839 \text{ J/K})$
    c. $Mn(c) + 2HCl(aq) \rightarrow MnCl_2(aq) + H_2(g)$
          $(\Delta H° = -221 \text{ kJ}, \Delta S° = 79.7 \text{ J/K})$
    d. $I_2(c) + Cl_2(g) \rightarrow 2ICl(l)$
          $(\Delta H° = -47.8 \text{ kJ}, \Delta S° = -16.45 \text{ J/K})$
    e. $Na_2O(c) + SiO_2(c) \rightarrow Na_2SiO_3(c)$
          $(\Delta H° = -192 \text{ kJ}, \Delta S° = -0.837 \text{ J/K})$

Concentration of Solutions 16

16:1 Solute-Solvent

A solution consists of a dissolved substance, the **solute,** and a dissolving medium, the **solvent.** A solution is a homogeneous mixture and has a constant composition throughout. A solute need not be a solid. It can be a gas as HCl in hydrochloric acid or a liquid as the alcohol in a car's cooling system. If the solution contains two liquids, the liquid that is in excess is conventionally called the solvent. The most common solvent is water.

Knowing the actual strength of a solution is more useful than knowing in general terms that it is dilute or concentrated. The concentration of solutions can be described quantitatively in many ways. Molarity, normality, and mass percent concentration are discussed in this chapter. Molality is considered in Chapter 19.

16:2 Molarity

A solution for which a precise concentration is known is called a **standard solution.** Its strength is often expressed in terms of molarity. A **1 molar solution** contains 1 mole of solute dissolved in enough solvent (usually water) to make 1 cubic decimeter of solution.

$$molarity\ (M) = \frac{\text{number of moles of solute}}{\text{cubic decimeters of solution}}$$

Chemists express concentration in terms of molarity because they measure out solutions by volume. Yet, they are most interested in obtaining a certain number of particles. One mole of sodium chloride, NaCl, is 58.5 grams. If 58.5 grams of NaCl are dissolved in enough water to make 1 cubic decimeter of solution, the solution is a $1M$ solution of NaCl. Similarly, if 2 moles of NaCl (117.0 grams) are dissolved in enough water to make 1 cubic decimeter of solution, the solution is a $2M$ solution. Fifty cubic centimeters of a solution with a $2M$ concentration and 500 cubic centimeters of the same solution will have the same concentration, $2M$. The total number of particles changes when the volume is changed but the concentration of particles (the number of particles per unit volume) does not change. When chemists see the symbol M, they translate this symbol into moles of solute per cubic decimeter of solution.

Example 1

Calculate the molarity of a 1500 cubic centimeter solution that contains 200.0 grams of $MgCl_2$.

Solving Process:

The problem requires the calculation of molarity. Molarity is moles of solute per (divided by) liter of solution. Therefore, the data concerning solute is placed in the numerator, and the data concerning the solution in the denominator. The solute data in the numerator is then converted to moles, and the solution data in the denominator to liters.

$$\text{molarity} = \frac{200.0 \text{ g MgCl}_2}{1500 \text{ cm}^3} \left| \frac{1 \text{ mol MgCl}_2}{95.2 \text{ g MgCl}_2} \right| \frac{1000 \text{ cm}^3}{1 \text{ dm}^3}$$

$$= 1.40 \text{ mol/dm}^3 = 1.40M$$

Example 2

Calculate the molarity of a 500 cubic centimeter solution that contains 10.0 grams of sodium hydroxide.

Solving Process:

Convert 10.0 grams of NaOH per 500 cubic centimeters to moles of NaOH per cubic decimeter of solution.

$$\frac{10.0 \text{ g NaOH}}{500 \text{ cm}^3} \left| \frac{1 \text{ mol NaOH}}{40.0 \text{ g NaOH}} \right| \frac{1000 \text{ cm}^3}{1 \text{ dm}^3} = 0.500 \text{ mol/dm}^3 = 0.500M$$

Example 3

If 160 grams of sodium hydroxide are used to prepare a $2.00M$ NaOH solution, what volume (in dm^3) of solution can be made?

Solving Process:
Convert from grams of NaOH to moles of NaOH. Then convert moles of NaOH to dm^3 of solution, using the concentration expression. That expression is 1 dm^3/2 mol NaOH.

$$\text{cubic decimeters of soln} = \frac{160 \text{ g NaOH}}{} \left| \frac{1 \text{ mol NaOH}}{40.0 \text{ g NaOH}} \right| \frac{1 \text{ dm}^3}{2.00 \text{ mol NaOH}}$$

$$= 2.00 \text{ dm}^3 \text{ soln}$$

Example 4

Calculate the mass of solute required to make 750 cubic centimeters of a 2.50*M* sodium chloride solution.

Solving Process:
Convert the volume of solution to moles using the given concentration. The 2.50*M* solution contains 2.50 moles of sodium chloride per cubic decimeter of solution. Convert the moles of NaCl to grams of NaCl, using the formula mass of NaCl.

$$\text{grams of solute} = \frac{750 \text{ cm}^3}{} \left| \frac{1 \text{ dm}^3}{1000 \text{ cm}^3} \right| \frac{2.50 \text{ mol NaCl}}{1 \text{ dm}^3} \left| \frac{58.5 \text{ g NaCl}}{1 \text{ mol NaCl}} \right.$$

$$= 110 \text{ g NaCl}$$

Example 5

What mass of $AgNO_3$ must be used to make 2.00 cubic decimeters of a 0.100*M* solution of silver nitrate?

Solving Process:
Convert dm^3 of solution to moles of $AgNO_3$ using the given concentration. Then convert moles of $AgNO_3$ to grams.

$$\frac{2.00 \text{ dm}^3}{} \left| \frac{0.100 \text{ mol AgNO}_3}{1 \text{ dm}^3} \right| \frac{170 \text{ g AgNO}_3}{1 \text{ mol AgNO}_3} = 34.0 \text{ g AgNO}_3$$

Example 6

How many cubic centimeters of a 1.50*M* sulfuric acid solution can be made using 36.0 grams of sulfuric acid?

Solving Process:
Convert grams of sulfuric acid to moles of sulfuric acid. The moles of H_2SO_4 can be converted to dm^3 of H_2SO_4 using the concentration. Finally, volume is converted to cubic centimeters.

$$\frac{36.0 \text{ g H}_2\text{SO}_4}{} \left| \frac{1 \text{ mol H}_2\text{SO}_4}{98.1 \text{ g H}_2\text{SO}_4} \right| \frac{1 \text{ dm}^3}{1.50 \text{ mol H}_2\text{SO}_4} \left| \frac{1000 \text{ cm}^3}{1 \text{ dm}^3} \right. = 245 \text{ cm}^3$$

Example 7

A test solution used in qualitative analysis must contain 15.0 mg/cm³ of Cu^{2+}. What mass of copper(II) nitrate, $Cu(NO_3)_2$, must be used to make 500 cm³ of the solution?

Solving Process:

The $Cu(NO_3)_2$ ionizes in solution according to the equation:

$$Cu(NO_3)_2(c) \longrightarrow Cu^{2+}(aq) + 2NO_3^-(aq)$$

To calculate the grams of $Cu(NO_3)_2$ needed to furnish 15.0 mg/cm³ of Cu^{2+} start with the volume of solution and convert to mg of Cu^{2+}. Then convert to grams to Cu^{2+} by using the relationship between milligrams and grams. Convert from grams Cu^{2+} to moles Cu^{2+} using the atomic mass of copper. Convert to moles of $Cu(NO_3)_2$ and then to grams of $Cu(NO_3)_2$.

$$\frac{500 \text{ cm}^3}{} \left| \frac{15.0 \text{ mg } Cu^{2+}}{1 \text{ cm}^3} \right| \frac{1 \text{ g } Cu^{2+}}{1000 \text{ mg } Cu^{2+}} \left| \frac{1 \text{ mol } Cu^{2+}}{63.5 \text{ g } Cu^{2+}} \right|$$

$$\frac{1 \text{ mol } Cu(NO_3)_2}{1 \text{ mol } Cu^{2+}} \left| \frac{188 \text{ g } Cu(NO_3)_2}{1 \text{ mol } Cu(NO_3)_2} \right. = 22.2 \text{ g } Cu(NO_3)_2$$

Example 8

Calculate the molarity of the test solution in Example 7.

Solving Process:

The molarity can be calculated either of two ways. Use the grams of $Cu(NO_3)_2$ calculated in the previous problem and convert to molarity.

$$\frac{22.2 \text{ g } Cu(NO_3)_2}{500 \text{ cm}^3} \left| \frac{1 \text{ mol } Cu(NO_3)_2}{188 \text{ g } Cu(NO_3)_2} \right| \frac{1000 \text{ cm}^3}{1 \text{ dm}^3} = 0.236 \text{ mol/dm}^3$$

$$= 0.236M$$

Alternate Method:

The molarity of the solution is equal to the molarity of the Cu^{2+}, since each mole of $Cu(NO_3)_2$ gives one mole of Cu^{2+}. Convert from 15.0 mg/cm³ to moles per cubic decimeter.

$$\frac{15 \text{ mg } Cu^{2+}}{1 \text{ cm}^3} \left| \frac{1000 \text{ cm}^3}{1 \text{ dm}^3} \right| \frac{1 \text{ g}}{1000 \text{ mg}} \left| \frac{1 \text{ mol } Cu^{2+}}{63.5 \text{ g } Cu^{2+}} \right. = 0.236 \text{ mol/dm}^3$$

$$= 0.236M \text{ } Cu^{2+}$$

Example 9

Calculate the molarity of the nitrate ion in Example 7.

Solving Process:

Each mole of $Cu(NO_3)_2$ gives two moles of NO_3^-

$$Cu(NO_3)_2(c) \longrightarrow Cu^{2+}(aq) + 2NO_3^-(aq)$$

Thus, the molarity of the NO_3^- will be twice the molarity of the Cu^{2+}

$$\frac{0.236 \ \text{mol Cu}^{2+}}{1 \ dm^3} \left| \frac{2 \ \text{mol NO}_3^-}{1 \ \text{mol Cu}^{2+}} \right. = 0.472M \ NO_3^-$$

Problems

1. Calculate the molarity of the following solutions:
   a. $800 \ cm^3$ which contains 30.0 g of acetic acid (CH_3COOH)
   b. $2000 \ cm^3$ which contains 49.0 g of phosphoric acid (H_3PO_4)
   c. $1.50 \ cm^3$ which contains 102 g of potassium hydroxide
   d. $500.0 \ cm^3$ which contains 82.0 g calcium nitrate
   e. $250.0 \ cm^3$ which contains 50.0 g copper(II) sulfate pentahydrate
   f. $1000.0 \ cm^3$ which contains 116 g sodium carbonate heptahydrate

2. Calculate the mass of solute in the following solutions:
   a. $750.0 \ cm^3$ of $CaCl_2$ solution which is $0.500M$
   b. $3000.0 \ cm^3$ of a KOH solution which is $2.50M$
   c. $250.0 \ cm^3$ of a Na_2SO_4 solution which is $2.00M$
   d. $250.0 \ cm^3$ of a $Na_2SO_4 \cdot 7H_2O$ solution which is $2.00M$
   e. $1.500 \ dm^3$ of KH_2PO_4 solution which is $0.240M$
   f. $2500.0 \ cm^3$ of a HNO_3 solution which is $4.00M$

3. How many grams of lead(II) acetate, $Pb(C_2H_3O_2)_2$, must be used to make $500.0 \ cm^3$ of a solution that is to contain $10.0 \ mg/cm^3$ of lead ion? What is the molarity of this solution?

4. How many cubic decimeters of solution can be made from each of the following?
   a. a $2.00M$ solution using 80.0 g sodium hydroxide
   b. a $0.500M$ solution using 80.0 g sodium hydroxide
   c. a $6.00M$ solution using 126 g nitric acid
   d. a $0.100M$ solution using 117 g sodium chloride
   e. a $1.00M$ solution using 50.0 g copper(II) sulfate pentahydrate
   f. a $0.200M$ solution using 200.0 g sodium sulfide

5. A test solution of aluminum nitrate, $Al(NO_3)_3$, must be made that contains $20.0 \ mg/cm^3$ of the metal ion. If $1500.0 \ cm^3$ of the solution is desired, how many grams of the solute with mass measured as $Al(NO_3)_3 \cdot 9H_2O$ must be used? What is the molarity of the solution? What is the molarity of the aluminum ion? What is the molarity of the nitrate ion?

16:3 Normality

Another quantitative method of expressing the concentration of solutions is **normality**. A $1N$ solution contains one equivalent mass of solute per liter of solution.

$$\text{normality } (N) = \frac{\text{number of equivalents of solute}}{\text{liters of solution}}$$

What is an equivalent? One equivalent provides 1 mole of charge. Consider these three substances.

$$NaNO_3 \longrightarrow Na^+ + NO_3^-$$
$$Na_2SO_4 \longrightarrow 2Na^+ + SO_4^{2-}$$
$$Na_3PO_4 \longrightarrow 3Na^+ + PO_4^{3-}$$

$NaNO_3$ contains 1 equivalent per mole; Na_2SO_4 contains 2 equivalents; and Na_3PO_4 contains 3 equivalents.

Table 16-1
Equivalent Masses of Compounds

Compound	Formula mass	Total + or − charge	Equivalent mass (grams)	Number of equivalents/ mole
HCl	36.5	1	36.5	1
HNO_3	63	1	63	1
H_2SO_4	98	2	49 (98/2)	2
H_3PO_4	98	3	32.7 (98/3)	3
KOH	56	1	56	1
$Ca(OH)_2$	74	2	37 (74/2)	2
$MgCl_2$	95	2	47.5 (95/2)	2
$CaSO_4$	136	2	68 (136/2)	2
$Al(NO_3)_3$	218	3	72.6 (218/3)	3
$Al_2(SO_4)_3$	342	6	57 (342/6)	6
$Ca_3(PO_4)_2$	310	6	51.6 (310/6)	6

Example 10

In a laboratory, three standard solutions have labels marked 0.500M NaCl, 0.300M $Mg(NO_3)_2$, and $1.20M$ H_3PO_4. What is the normality of each solution?

Solving Process:

Determine the number of equivalents per 1 mole of compound and convert.

$$0.500M \text{ NaCl} = \frac{0.500 \text{ mol NaCl}}{1 \text{ L}} \left| \frac{1 \text{ equivalent NaCl}}{1 \text{ mol NaCl}} \right. = 0.500N$$

$$0.300\,M\ Mg(NO_3)_2 = \frac{0.300\ \text{mol Mg(NO}_3)_2}{1\ L}\ \Big|\ \frac{2\ \text{equivalents Mg(NO}_3)_2}{1\ \text{mol Mg(NO}_3)_2}$$

$$= 0.600N$$

$$1.20\,M\ H_3PO_4 = \frac{1.20\ \text{mol H}_3PO_4}{1\ L}\ \Big|\ \frac{3\ \text{equivalents H}_3PO_4}{1\ \text{mol H}_3PO_4} = 3.60N$$

Example 11

Calculate the normality if 1.89 grams of $Ca(OH)_2$ are dissolved in enough water to make 1.00 liter of solution.

Solving Process:

One mole $Ca(OH)_2$ contains two equivalents.

$$\text{normality} = \frac{1.89\ \text{g Ca(OH)}_2}{1\ L}\ \Big|\ \frac{1\ \text{mol Ca(OH)}_2}{74.1\ \text{g Ca(OH)}_2}\ \Big|\ \frac{2\ \text{eq Ca(OH)}_2}{1\ \text{mol Ca(OH)}_2}$$

$$= 0.0510N$$

Example 12

Determine the grams of sodium sulfate, Na_2SO_4, in 500 cm³ of solution that has a concentration of 0.250N.

Solving Process:

One mole of Na_2SO_4 contains two equivalents.

$$\text{grams solute} = \frac{500\ \text{cm}^3\ \text{soln}}{}\ \Big|\ \frac{1\ L}{1000\ \text{cm}^3}\ \Big|\ \frac{0.250\ \text{eq Na}_2SO_4}{1\ L}$$

$$\frac{1\ \text{mol Na}_2SO_4}{2\ \text{eq Na}_2SO_4}\Big|\frac{142\ \text{g Na}_2SO_4}{1\ \text{mol Na}_2SO_4} = 8.88\ \text{g Na}_2SO_4$$

Example 13

How many liters of a 0.100N solution can be made from 85.5 grams of aluminum sulfate?

Solving Process:

Start with the grams of solute and convert to moles of solute. One mole of $Al_2(SO_4)_3$ contains 6 equivalents.

$$\frac{85.5\ \text{g Al}_2(SO_4)_3}{}\ \Big|\ \frac{1\ \text{mol Al}_2(SO_4)_3}{342\ \text{g Al}_2(SO_4)_3}\ \Big|\ \frac{6\ \text{eq Al}_2(SO_4)_3}{1\ \text{mol Al}_2(SO_4)_3}\ \Big|\ \frac{1\ L\ \text{soln}}{0.100\ \text{eq Al}_2(SO_4)_3}$$

$$= 15.0\ \text{liters}$$

Problems

6. Calculate the number of equivalents of solute in each of the following solutions:

   a.   1.00 liter of solution which is $1.00N$ NaOH
   b.   1.00 liter of solution which is $3.00N$ NaOH
   c.   1.00 liter of solution which is $1.00N$ H_2SO_4
   d.   1.00 liter of solution which is $3.00N$ H_2SO_4
   e.   1.00 liter of solution which is $1.00N$ H_3PO_4
   f.   1.00 liter of solution which is $3.00N$ H_3PO_4

7. Determine the normality of the following solutions. Also determine the molarity for each solution from the normality.

   a.   9.50 grams of $MgCl_2$ in 500.0 cm^3 of solution
   b.   80.0 grams of NaOH in 1000.0 cm^3 of solution
   c.   24.2 grams of $Cu(NO_3)_2 \cdot 3H_2O$ in 500.0 cm^3 of solution
   d.   196.0 grams of H_3PO_4 in 2.00 liters of solution
   e.   30.0 grams of oxalic acid, $H_2C_2O_4$, in 500.0 cm^3 of solution

8. For each of the following solutions calculate the concentration term needed:

		Molarity	Normality
a.	KOH	2.00	?
b.	NaH_2PO_4	?	0.600
c.	$CuSO_4$	0.100	?
d.	NaCl	?	1.50
e.	K_2S	?	3.00
f.	NH_4Cl	0.500	?
g.	$Mg(NO_3)_2$	?	4.00
h.	H_3PO_4	1.50	?
i.	$CuSO_4 \cdot 5H_2O$	?	1.00
j.	$Al_2(SO_4)_3$	0.100	?
k.	$(NH_4)_2SO_4$	?	3.00

9. From your knowledge of molarity and normality, fill in the missing blanks in the following table:

Solute	Grams Solute	Moles Solute	Equivalents Solute	Volume of Solution (cm^3)	Molarity	Normality
HCl	74.0			500.0		
NaOH			0.500		0.100	
K_2SO_4		1.5				1.00
$Mg(NO_3)_2$			2.00	750.0		
H_3PO_4		0.500			2.00	
$Al_2(SO_4)_3$	49.0					6.00

16:4 Percentage Concentration

The percent of a solute in a solution is defined as the mass of solute in 100 grams of solution. A 20% solution of sulfuric acid contains 20% pure H_2SO_4 by mass and 80% pure H_2O by mass. In 100 grams of H_2SO_4 there are 20 grams of sulfuric acid and 80 grams of water. Unless otherwise stated, assume that water is the solvent.

Example 14

If 18.0 grams of sodium sulfate are dissolved in 207.0 grams of water, what is the percent concentration of this solution?

Solving Process:

Since the percent concentration is the grams of solute per grams of solution, the grams of solute are divided by the grams of solution.

$$\% \text{ concentration} = \frac{18.0 \text{ g solute}}{225 \text{ g solution}} \left| 100\% \right. = 8.00\%$$

Example 15

Calculate the mass of sodium chloride in 5.00% solution which has a mass of 750.0 grams.

Solving Process:

A 5.00% solution contains 5.00 grams of NaCl in each 100 grams of solution.

$$\text{grams NaCl} = \frac{750.0 \text{ g solution}}{} \left| \frac{5.00 \text{ g NaCl}}{100 \text{ g solution}} \right. = 37.5 \text{ g NaCl}$$

Example 16

What is the mass of solute in 300.0 cm³ of a solution if the solution is 85.0% water? The density of the solution is 1.60 g/cm³.

Solving Process:

Since the solution contains 85.0% water, it contains 15.0 grams solute per 100 grams of solution.

$$\text{grams solute} = \frac{300.0 \text{ cm}^3 \text{ soln}}{} \left| \frac{1.60 \text{ g soln}}{\text{cm}^3 \text{ soln}} \right| \frac{15.0 \text{ g solute}}{100 \text{ g soln}} = 72.0 \text{ g}$$

Problems

10. Calculate the mass of solute for the following solutions:
    a. a 4.00% solution which has a mass of 800.0 grams
    b. a 20.0% solution which has a mass of 500.0 grams
    c. a 12.0% solution which has a mass of 600.0 grams

11. Calculate the percentage concentration for the following solutions:
    a. 25.0 grams of solute in 75.0 grams of water
    b. 15.0 grams of solute in 150.0 grams of solvent
    c. 40.0 grams of solute in 200.0 grams of solution

12. Determine the mass of solvent for the following solutions:
    a. a 3.00% solution which has a mass of 150.0 grams
    b. a 15.0% solution which has a mass of 120.0 grams
    c. a 10.0% solution which has a mass of 200.0 grams

Chapter Review Problems

13. A test solution of sodium acetate is to contain 10.0 mg/cm³ of the metal ion. If 750.0 cm³ of the solution is needed, how many grams of sodium acetate must be used? What is the molarity of this solution?

14. What is the molarity of a hydrochloric acid solution which has a density of 1.12 g/cm³ and contains 25.0% HCl?

15. Calculate the number of moles of H_2SO_4 on 500 cm³ of a solution that has a density of 1.50 g/cm³ and contains 60.0% H_2SO_4. What is the molarity of this solution?

16. How many molecules of ethanol, C_2H_5OH, are in 500.0 cm³ of a solution which is 2.00 M? How many grams of ethanol are in this solution? What volume of ethanol is dissolved in the water? The density of ethanol is 0.789 g/cm³.

Chemical Equilibrium _____17

In the previous chapters we have assumed that the reactions have gone to completion. Reactions tend to go to completion because of the formation of a gas (CO_2, SO_2), a precipitate (AgCl, $PbSO_4$) or a slightly ionized substance (H_2O). Formation of these or similar species causes the ions from the initial reactants to be removed from the reaction.

$$2KClO_3(c) \longrightarrow 2KCl(c) + 3O_2(g)$$
(formation of a gas)

$$Na_2CO_3(aq) + H_2SO_4(aq) \longrightarrow Na_2SO_4(aq) + H_2CO_3(aq)$$
(formation of a slightly ionized substance)

$$AgNO_3(aq) + NaCl(aq) \longrightarrow NaNO_3(aq) + AgCl(c)$$
(formation of a precipitate)

17:1 Reversible Reactions

It has been determined experimentally that the conversion of some reactants to products is often incomplete, regardless of the reaction time. Initially the reactants are present at a definite concentration. As the reaction proceeds, the reactant concentration decreases. However, a point is reached at which the reactant concentration levels off and becomes constant. The concentration levels for the reactants and products no longer change. A state of **chemical equilibrium** has been established.

An example of a reaction which can proceed in either direction is the equilibrium system involving nitrogen, hydrogen, and ammonia gases. The reversible reaction is written as:

$$N_2(g) + 3H_2(g) \underset{reverse}{\overset{forward}{\rightleftharpoons}} 2NH_3(g) + heat$$

A reversible chemical reaction is in chemical equilibrium when the rates of the opposing reactions are equal and the overall concentrations remain constant. Such a system is said to be in a state of **dynamic chemical equilibrium.**

17:2 Le Chatelier's Principle and Reactants

Sometimes, systems initially at equilibrium are subjected to an outside influence or stress. Le Chatelier's Principle states: If a system in equilibrium is subjected to a stress, the equilibrium will shift in an attempt to reduce the stress.

Concentration, pressure, and temperature changes affect equilibrium because they produce a stress. If more reactant is added to a system which is in equilibrium, the reaction shifts to the right (the product side) and more product is formed. For example, in the ammonia equation considered above, the addition of N_2 puts a stress on the system. The stress is too much N_2. The system can relieve the stress by consuming N_2. The system shifts to the right to consume N_2, and in the process, produces more NH_3. If a reactant is removed, the reaction shifts to the left. In the ammonia synthesis, if we remove some H_2, the stress we have placed on the system is not enough H_2. The system can relieve a stress of not enough H_2 by producing H_2. When the system shifts left to replace the missing H_2, it also produces more N_2 and consumes NH_3.

Pressure affects only gaseous equilibrium systems. As pressure on the reactant gases is increased, the reaction shifts toward the side with the least volume. In the ammonia synthesis, an increase of pressure would shift the equilibrium to the right. In the process of shifting, four particles ($N_2 + 3H_2$) are converted to two particles ($2NH_3$). The number of particles colliding is thereby reduced, and thus also, the pressure, relieving the stress. If temperature is increased, the reaction shifts in such a way that the endothermic reaction is favored. In the ammonia synthesis, the reaction from left to right is exothermic, while the reaction from right to left is endothermic. Consequently, a rise in temperature will shift the reaction to the left.

The effects of Le Chatelier's Principle and changing conditions is illustrated with these reversible gaseous reactions.

1. $N_2 + 3H_2 \rightleftharpoons 2NH_3 + heat$
2. $H_2 + I_2 \rightleftharpoons 2HI + heat$
3. $2NO + O_2 \rightleftharpoons 2NO_2 + heat$

Concentration

Equation	Stress	Results increase	decrease
1	increase N_2	NH_3	H_2
2	decrease H_2	I_2	HI
3	increase O_2	NO_2	NO
	decrease NO_2		NO, O_2

Pressure

Equation	Stress	Results increase	decrease
1	increase	NH_3	N_2, H_2
	decrease	N_2, H_2	NH_3
2	increase or	no change (same number	
	decrease	of particles on each side)	
3	increase	NO_2	NO, O_2
	decrease	NO, O_2	NO_2

Temperature

Equation	Stress	Results increase	decrease
1	increase	N_2, H_2	NH_3
	decrease	NH_3	N_2, H_2
2	increase	H_2, I_2	HI
	decrease	HI	H_2, I_2
3	increase	NO, O_2	NO_2
	decrease	NO_2	NO, O_2

17:3 Equilibrium Constant

The rate of a chemical reaction varies directly as the concentration of the reactants. The concentration is expressed in moles per liter and is indicated by brackets [   ]. For the reaction

$$N_2 + 3H_2 \rightleftharpoons 2NH_3$$

the rate of forward reaction = $k_f[N_2][H_2]^3$

the rate of reverse reaction = $k_r[NH_3]^2$

At equilibrium, the two rates are equal.

$$k_f[N_2][H_2]^3 = k_r[NH_3]^2$$

Solving for the constants, k_f/k_r, gives a new constant termed the equilibrium constant, K_{eq}.

$$K_{eq} = \frac{[\text{products}]}{[\text{reactants}]} = \frac{[NH_3]^2}{[N_2][H_2]^3}$$

There is a unique value of K_{eq} for each reaction and for each temperature. At equilibrium, if K_{eq} is much greater than 1 the products are favored. If the K_{eq} is much less than 1 the reactants are favored. Note that the coefficients from the balanced equation are used as exponents in the expression for the equilibrium constant.

Example 1

What is the equilibrium constant, K_{eq}, for the following reaction if the equilibrium concentrations at 25°C are $[N_2O_4] = 0.0450M$ and $[NO_2] = 0.0161M$?

$$N_2O_4(g) \rightleftharpoons 2NO_2(g)$$

Solving Process:

$$K_{eq} = \frac{[NO_2]^2}{[N_2O_4]} = \frac{[0.0161]^2}{[0.0450]} = 0.00576$$

The low value indicates that, at equilibrium most of the oxygen and nitrogen will be in the form N_2O_4.

Example 2

For the following reaction the concentrations are experimentally determined to be $[HI] = 0.00998$, $[H_2] = 0.000867$ and $[I_2] = 0.00264$. Determine the equilibrium constant.

$$H_2(g) + I_2(g) \rightleftharpoons 2HI(g)$$

Solving Process:

$$K_{eq} = \frac{[HI]^2}{[H_2][I_2]} = \frac{[0.00998]^2}{[0.000867][0.00264]} = 43.5$$

The high value indicates that at equilibrium most of the hydrogen and iodine will be in the form HI.

Example 3

If at a certain temperature exactly 1 mole of CO_2 and exactly 1 mole of H_2 are mixed in a one liter container, the equilibrium constant is 0.803. For the following gaseous reaction what are the equilibrium concentrations of all species?

$$CO_2(g) + H_2(g) \rightleftharpoons CO(g) + H_2O$$

Solving Process:
    The same number of moles of reactants produce the same number of moles of products. Let $x = [CO] = [H_2O]$; then $(1 - x) = [CO_2] = [H_2]$.

$$CO_2(g) + H_2(g) \rightleftharpoons CO(g) + H_2O(l)$$
$$\underset{1-x}{} \underset{1-x}{} \underset{x}{} \underset{x}{}$$

Substitute into the K_{eq} expression.

$$K_{eq} = \frac{[CO][H_2O]}{[CO_2][H_2]} = 0.803$$

$$= \frac{[x][x]}{[1 - x][1 - x]} = 0.803$$

$$= \frac{[x]^2}{[1 - x]^2} = 0.803$$

Extract the square root from both sides of the equation and solve for x. The square root of 0.803 is 0.896.

$$\frac{x}{1 - x} = 0.896 \qquad \text{or} \qquad x = 0.473$$

Substituting the value of x gives,

$$[CO] = [H_2O] = x = 0.473 \text{ moles/liter}$$
$$[CO_2] = [H_2O] = (1 - x) = 0.527 \text{ moles/liter}$$

Example 4

    The K_{eq} is 52.4 for the equilibrium system, $H_2(g) + I_2(g) \rightleftharpoons 2HI(g)$, at a specific temperature. The initial reactant concentrations of H_2 and I_2 are $0.010M$. If an HI concentration of $0.100M$ is introduced, what are the concentrations of all species when equilibrium is re-established?

Solving Process:
    Based on the equation, let $2x$ equal the additional moles of HI dissociated, then x equals the additional moles of H_2 and I_2.

	$H_2(g)$	$+$	$I_2(g)$	$\rightleftharpoons$	$2HI(g)$
initial	0.0100		0.0100		
final	$0.0100 + x$		$0.0100 + x$		$0.1000 - 2x$

Substitute into the K_{eq} expression,

$$K_{eq} = \frac{[HI]^2}{[H_2][I_2]} = 52.4$$

$$= \frac{[0.1000 - 2x][0.1000 - 2x]}{[0.0100 + x][0.0100 + x]} = 52.4$$

Extract the square root from both sides of the equation and solve for x. The square root of 52.4 is 7.24.

$$\frac{[0.1000 - 2x]}{[0.0100 + x]} = 7.24 \qquad \text{or} \qquad x = 0.00299$$

Substituting the value of x gives,

$$[H_2] = [I_2] = (0.0100 + x) = 0.0130M$$
$$[HI] = (0.1000 - 2x) = 0.0940M$$

Example 5

At a certain temperature, the K_{eq} for the phosgene, $COCl_2$, equilibrium system is 0.680. If the initial concentration of the phosgene is $0.0500M$, calculate the concentration of all species at equilibrium.

$$COCl_2(g) \rightleftharpoons CO(g) + Cl_2(g)$$

Solving Process:

Let x represent the moles per liter of $COCl_2$ that dissociate. The initial concentration of the products is zero, so their final concentration equals x. Then $[COCl_2] = 0.0500 - x$ and $[CO] = [Cl_2] = x$. Substitute into the K_{eq} expression.

$$K_{eq} = \frac{[CO][Cl_2]}{[COCl_2]} = 0.680$$

$$= \frac{[x][x]}{[0.0500 - x]} = 0.680$$

The assumption could be made that x is very small compared to 0.0500. That is $0.0500 - x \approx 0.0500$. If this assumption were made

$$\frac{[x]^2}{[0.050]} = 0.680$$

$$x^2 = (0.680)(0.0500) = 0.0340$$

$$x = 0.184 \ M$$

Since $[COCl_2] = (0.0500 - 0.184)$ gives a negative value, the assumption cannot be made. In chemistry, a negative concentration has no meaning so we must try another approach to solve the problem. It is necessary to use the quadratic formula to solve for x in the initial K_{eq} expression.

An algebraic equation in the form $ax^2 + bx + c = 0$, where a, b, and c are constants, can be solved in terms of the unknown x using the quadratic formula.

$$x = \frac{-b \pm \sqrt{b^2 - 4ac}}{2a}$$

$$K_{eq} = \frac{x^2}{0.0500 - x} = 0.680 \qquad \text{or} \qquad x^2 + 0.680x - 0.0340$$

Substitution into the quadratic formula gives

$$x = \frac{-0.680 \pm \sqrt{(0.680)^2 - 4(1)(-0.0340)}}{2(1)}$$

$$= \frac{-0.680 \pm \sqrt{.462 + .136}}{2}$$

$$= \frac{-0.680 \pm \sqrt{.598}}{2}$$

$$= \frac{-0.680 \pm 0.773}{2}$$

$$x = -0.727 \text{ or } 0.0465$$

Since the negative number has no significance in concentrations, the answer is $x = 0.0465\ M$

Substituting the meaningful value of x gives,

$[CO] = [Cl_2] = x = 0.0465$ moles/liter

$[COCl_2] = (0.0500 - x) = (0.0500 - 0.0465) = 0.004$ moles/liter

Chapter Review Problems

1. For the gaseous equilibrium reactions, indicate what happens to the equilibrium position (shift to right or left) when the indicated stress or condition change occurs.

   a. remove NH_3 gas   **b.** decrease pressure

   $$N_2 + 3H_2 \rightleftharpoons 2NH_3 + heat$$

   c. decrease temperature   **d.** add a catalyst

   $$CO_2 + H_2 + heat \rightleftharpoons CO + H_2O$$

   e. increase SO_2 concentration   **f.** increase temperature

   $$2SO_2 + O_2 \rightleftharpoons 2SO_3 + heat$$

   g. increase temperature   **h.** increase CO concentration

   $$CO_2 + C + heat \rightleftharpoons 2CO$$

   i. decrease pressure   **j.** remove N_2O_4

   $$N_2O_4 + heat \rightleftharpoons 2NO_2$$

   k. increase H_2 concentration   **l.** increase pressure

   $$H_2 + Cl_2 \rightleftharpoons 2HCl + heat$$

   m. decrease O_2 concentration   **n.** add catalyst

   $$N_2 + O_2 + heat \rightleftharpoons 2NO$$

    o. increase Cl_2 concentration   **p.** decrease pressure
$$PCl_3 + Cl_2 \rightleftharpoons PCl_5 + heat$$

2. Determine the equilibrium constant for the following reaction if the concentration of $[N_2O_4] = 1.50 \times 10^{-3}$ and $[NO_2] = 0.571$
$$N_2O_4(g) \rightleftharpoons 2NO_2(g)$$

3. For the reaction, $2SO_2(g) + O_2(g) \rightleftharpoons 2SO_3(g)$, the concentrations of the sulfur oxides are $[SO_2] = 2.00$ and $[SO_3] = 10.0$. What is the concentration of the oxygen when the K_{eq} is 800.0 for the reaction?

4. Determine the equilibrium concentration when 1.00 mole of I_2 and 1.00 mole of H_2 are put into a 5 liter container. At the reaction temperature, the K_{eq} is 64.0.
$$H_2(g) + I_2(g) \rightleftharpoons 2HI(g)$$

5. At a specific temperature, 0.0750 mole of each reactant (CO and H_2O) is added to a 1 liter container. At equilibrium, the [CO] is 0.0210. What is the value of K_{eq} for the reaction?
$$CO(g) + H_2O(g) \rightleftharpoons CO_2(g) + H_2(g)$$

6. Using the information in problem 5, determine the new equilibrium concentrations if an additional 0.0050 mole/liter of each reactant is added to the container.

7. At a specific temperature, the equilibrium constant for the reaction given is 43.8. If 2.00 moles of I_2 and 1.00 mole of H_2 are put into a container measuring exactly five liters, what are the equilibrium concentrations of all the species?
$$H_2(g) + I_2(g) \rightleftharpoons 2HI(g)$$

8. For problem 7, what happens to the concentrations if the volume is expanded to exactly ten liters?

9. Considering the equation in problem 7, the K_{eq} is 45.9 at a different temperature. If 1.000 mole of each reactant is added to a container which measures exactly one liter, what is the final concentration when equilibrium has been established?

10. The K_{eq} is 0.0420 for the equilibrium reaction $PCl_5(g) \rightleftharpoons PCl_3(g) + Cl_2(g)$. Determine the equilibrium concentrations of all the species if the initial concentration of PCl_5 is $0.0500M$.

Dilution Problems_____18

It is sometimes necessary to prepare a solution of a specific concentration by diluting a solution of known concentration.

There are two ways to solve such a dilution problem: You may use the factor-label method or the mole-volume equation. For either method, the actual dilution is the same. The moles or grams of solute must remain the same. Only the solvent (usually water) is added in dilution.

Example 1 _____

It is necessary to make a 0.500M solution of hydrochloric acid from 250.0 cm^3 of a 2.00M solution of HCl. What is the volume of the new solution?

Solving Process:

The number of moles of HCl is the same in both the original and new solutions. Thus, the moles of HCl in the original solution can be converted to cubic decimeters of the new solution.

$$\frac{250 \text{ cm}^3 \text{ old soln}}{} \left| \frac{1 \text{ dm}^3}{1000 \text{ cm}^3} \right| \frac{2.00 \text{ mol HCl}}{1 \text{ dm}^3 \text{ solution}} \left| \frac{1 \text{ dm}^3 \text{ new soln}}{0.500 \text{ mol HCl}} \right. = 1.00 \text{ dm}^3$$

Alternate Method: Moles of solute in the initial solution are equal to the moles of solute in the new solution, giving the following relationship:

$$\underset{\text{Original solution}}{\frac{\text{moles solute}}{\text{cubic decimeters}} \times \text{volume (dm}^3)} = \underset{\text{Final solution}}{\frac{\text{moles solute}}{\text{cubic decimeters}} \times \text{volume (dm}^3)}$$

This expression can be represented by

$$M_i \times V_i = M_f \times V_f$$

M stands for the molarity and i stands for initial and f stands for final. Substituting the data given in the problem into the preceding equation gives:

$$(2.00M)(0.250 \text{ dm}^3) = (0.500M)(V_f) \quad \text{or} \quad V_f = \frac{(2.00\cancel{M})(0.250 \text{ dm}^3)}{0.500\cancel{M}}$$

$$= 1.00 \text{ dm}^3$$

The solution would be prepared by diluting 250 cm³ of the original solution with enough water to make 1.00 dm³ of the new solution, which would have a concentration of 0.500M.

Example 2

What is the final volume of a solution if 500.0 cm³ of a 3.00M solution of H_2SO_4 is to be diluted to a concentration of 0.500M?

Solving Process:

$$\frac{500.0 \text{ cm}^3 \cancel{\text{ old soln}}}{} \left| \frac{1 \cancel{\text{ dm}^3}}{1000 \cancel{\text{ cm}^3}} \right| \frac{3.00 \cancel{\text{ mol } H_2SO_4}}{1 \cancel{\text{ dm}^3 \text{ old soln}}} \left| \frac{1 \text{ dm}^3 \text{ new soln}}{0.500 \cancel{\text{ mol } H_2SO_4}} \right.$$

$$= 3.00 \text{ dm}^3 \text{ new solution}$$

Alternate Method:

$$M_i \times V_i = M_f \times V_f$$

$$\frac{3.00\cancel{M}}{0.500\cancel{M}} \left| 0.500 \text{ dm}^3 \text{ solution} \right. = 3.00 \text{ dm}^3 \text{ soln}$$

Example 3

What is the molarity of a solution which has a volume of 1500.0 cm³ if it was obtained by diluting 250 cm³ of a 6.0M solution of H_2SO_4?

Solving Process:

$$\frac{250 \text{ cm}^3 \cancel{\text{ old soln}}}{1500 \text{ cm}^3 \text{ new soln}} \left| \frac{6.00 \text{ mol } H_2SO_4}{1000 \cancel{\text{ cm}^3 \text{ old soln}}} \right.$$

$$M_i = \frac{6M}{} \left| \frac{0.250 \cancel{\text{ dm}^3}}{1.5 \cancel{\text{ dm}^3}} \right. = 1M$$

Example 4

An aqueous ammonia solution contains 20.00% ammonia by mass and has a density of 0.923 g/cm³. What volume of the solution is used to prepare 2.00 dm³ of a 6.00M solution?

Solving Process:

$$\frac{2.00 \text{ dm}^3 \cancel{\text{ soln}}}{} \left| \frac{6.00 \cancel{\text{ mol } NH_3}}{1 \cancel{\text{ dm}^3 \text{ soln}}} \right| \frac{17.0 \cancel{\text{ g } NH_3}}{1 \cancel{\text{ mol } NH_3}} \left| \frac{100 \cancel{\text{ g soln}}}{20.00 \cancel{\text{ g } NH_3}} \right| \frac{1 \text{ cm}^3 \text{ soln}}{0.923 \cancel{\text{ g soln}}}$$

$$= 1110 \text{ cm}^3$$

Chapter Review Problems

1. What is the final volume of a solution if it is necessary to make a 0.0500M solution using 10.0 cm^3 of a 2.00M solution of NaCl?

2. To prepare 250.0 cm^3 of a 0.100M solution, how many cubic centimeters of a 4.00M Ca(NO$_3$)$_2$ solution must be used?

3. When 400.0 cm^3 of 2.00M solution of NaOH is diluted to make 0.10M solution, what will be the final volume?

4. Calculate the normality of 500 mL of NaC$_2$H$_3$O$_2$ if it was prepared by diluting 100 mL of a 4.00M solution.

5. What is the molarity of a solution if 10.0 cm^3 of a 6.00M solution of NaCl is diluted to a volume of 200.0 cm^3?

6. Calculate the molarity of a solution if 30.0 cm^3 of a 4.00N solution of Na$_2$SO$_4$ is diluted to a volume of 150.0 cm^3.

7. An ammonium sulfate solution has a density of 1.17 g/cm^3 and contains 30.0% solute. What volume of this solution is needed to make 1.50 dm^3 of a 0.500M solution?

8. What is the molarity of a phosphoric acid solution if 200.0 cm^3 of an 85.0% H$_3$PO$_4$ solution is diluted to 1.000 dm^3? The density of the original solution is 1.689 g/cm^3.

9. An experiment requires 0.500M solutions of each of the following. Determine the volume of the original solution required to prepare 2.00 dm^3 of the 0.500M solution:
    a. KCl   1.13 g/cm^3 20.0% solute
    b. KBr   1.07 g/cm^3 10.0% solute
    c. KI   1.27 g/cm^3 30.0% solute
    d. Na$_2$CrO$_4$ 1.19 g/cm^3 20.0% solute
    e. Na$_2$Cr$_2$O$_7$ 1.16 g/cm^3 20.0% solute

10. An experiment requires 0.500M solutions of each of the following. Calculate the volume of the original solution necessary to make 100.00 cm^3 of each solution.
    a. NaNO$_3$ 2.00M
    b. Mg(C$_2$H$_3$O$_2$)$_2$ 4.00M
    c. Cu(NO$_3$)$_2$ 3.00M
    d. AgNO$_3$ 1.50M
    e. Fe(C$_2$H$_3$O$_2$)$_3$ 6.00M

Molality and
Colligative Properties___19

19:1   Molality

Some properties of a solution depend only on the number of particles, not on the type of particles. The number of particles in a mass of solvent can affect the boiling or freezing point of the solvent. The study of this behavior is the study of **colligative properties.** Molality (m) is used in place of molarity when dealing with colligative properties. **Molality** is the number of moles of solute per 1000 grams or 1 kilogram of solvent. A one molal ($1m$) solution contains one mole of solute in each 1000 grams of solvent. A two molal ($2m$) solution contains two moles of solute dissolved in each 1000 grams of solvent.

For example:

dextrose   1 mole $C_6H_{12}O_6$
$$= 180 \text{ grams } C_6H_{12}O_6 = 6.02 \times 10^{23} \text{ molecules } C_6H_{12}O_6$$

acetic acid   1 mole $HC_2H_3O_2$
$$= 60 \text{ grams } HC_2H_3O_2 = 6.02 \times 10^{23} \text{ molecules } HC_2H_3O_2$$

Example 1 _____

Calculate the molality of a solution made by dissolving 45.0 grams of dextrose, $C_6H_{12}O_6$, in 500.0 grams of water.

Solving Process:
Convert grams of dextrose to moles of dextrose. The molality expression gives the number of moles of solute per 1000 grams of solvent (water). The molecular mass of dextrose is 180.

$$\text{molality} = \frac{45.0 \text{ g } C_6H_{12}O_6}{500.0 \text{ g } H_2O} \left| \frac{1000 \text{ g } H_2O}{1 \text{ kg } H_2O} \right| \frac{1 \text{ mol } C_6H_{12}O_6}{180.0 \text{ g } C_6H_{12}O_6}$$

$$= \frac{0.500 \text{ mol}}{1 \text{ kg } H_2O} = 0.500m$$

Example 2

If 60.0 grams of NaOH are dissolved in 1500 grams of water, what is the concentration of this solution expressed in molality?

Solving Process:

To find molality, convert to moles of NaOH per 1000 grams H_2O.

$$\frac{60.0 \text{ g NaOH}}{1500 \text{ g } H_2O} \left| \frac{1 \text{ mol NaOH}}{40.0 \text{ g NaOH}} \right| \frac{1000 \text{ g } H_2O}{1 \text{ kg } H_2O} = \frac{1.00 \text{ mol NaOH}}{1 \text{ kg } H_2O} = 1.00m$$

Example 3

Calculate the mass of ethanol which must be dissolved in 750.0 grams of water to make a 2.00m solution.

Solving Process:

The concentration unit 2.00m can be written as

$$\frac{2.00 \text{ mol } C_2H_5OH}{1000 \text{ g } H_2O}$$

To obtain the mass of C_2H_5OH, multiply the mass of water by the concentration unit and then convert to grams of ethanol by using the molecular mass of the solute.

$$\frac{750 \text{ g } H_2O}{} \left| \frac{2.00 \text{ mol } C_2H_5OH}{1000 \text{ g } H_2O} \right| \frac{46.1 \text{ g } C_2H_5OH}{1 \text{ mol } C_2H_5OH} = 69.2 \text{ g } C_2H_5OH$$

Example 4

Determine the mass of H_2SO_4 which must be dissolved in 2500 grams of water to make a 4.00m solution.

Solving Process:

Multiply the mass of H_2O by the concentration ratio. Then convert from moles to grams of sulfuric acid, using the formula mass of the acid:

$$\text{grams } H_2SO_4 = \frac{2500 \text{ g } H_2O}{} \left| \frac{4.00 \text{ mol } H_2SO_4}{1000 \text{ g } H_2O} \right| \frac{98.1 \text{ g } H_2SO_4}{1 \text{ mol } H_2SO_4}$$

$$= 981 \text{ g } H_2SO_4$$

Example 5

How many molecules of ethanol, C_2H_5OH, must be dissolved in 500.0 grams of water to make a $1.00m$ solution?

Solving Process:

Multiply the mass of water by the concentration. Then multiply by a conversion ratio which involves Avogadro's number.

$$\frac{\text{molecules}}{C_2H_5OH} = \frac{500.0 \text{ g } H_2O}{} \left| \frac{1.00 \text{ mol } C_2H_5OH}{1000 \text{ g } H_2O} \right| \frac{6.02 \times 10^{23} \text{ molecules}}{1 \text{ mol}}$$

$$= 3.01 \times 10^{23} \text{ molecules } C_2H_5OH$$

Example 6

What is the percentage by mass of $Mg(NO_3)_2$ in a $2.50m$ solution?

Solving Process:

The concentration expression involves 1000 grams of water. Find the grams of $Mg(NO_3)_2$ and add these two masses together to obtain the total mass. Then calculate the percent of magnesium nitrate.

$$\text{grams } Mg(NO_3)_2 = \frac{2.50 \text{ mol } Mg(NO_3)_2}{1000 \text{ g } H_2O} \left| \frac{148.0 \text{ g } Mg(NO_3)_2}{1 \text{ mol } Mg(NO_3)_2} \right.$$

$$= \frac{370.0 \text{ g } Mg(NO_3)_2}{1000 \text{ g } H_2O}$$

The mass of the solution is (370.0 g + 1000 g) 1370 grams.

$$\text{percent } Mg(NO_3)_2 = \frac{370 \text{ g}}{1370 \text{ g}} \left| \frac{100\%}{1} \right. = 27.0\%$$

Example 7

How many grams of water are required to dissolve 41.0 grams of $NaC_2H_3O_2$ to make a $3.00m$ solution?

Solving Process:

Convert grams of $NaC_2H_3O_2$ to moles and then multiply by the concentration ratio to get solvent volume.

$$\frac{41.0 \text{ g } NaC_2H_3O_2}{} \left| \frac{1 \text{ mol } NaC_2H_3O_2}{82.0 \text{ g } NaC_2H_3O_2} \right| \frac{1000 \text{ g } H_2O}{3.00 \text{ mol } NaC_2H_3O_2} = 167 \text{ g } H_2O$$

Problems

1. Calculate the molality of the following solutions:
   a. 1.50 moles $NaC_2H_3O_2$ dissolved in 750.0 grams of water
   b. 3.00 moles H_2SO_4 dissolved in 1250.0 grams of water

    c. 50.0 grams acetic acid dissolved in 500.0 grams of water

    d. 15.0 grams ethanol dissolved in 250.0 grams of water

    e. 10.0 grams glucose, $C_6H_{12}O_6$, dissolved in 500.0 grams of water

    f. 1.204×10^{24} molecules $HC_2H_3O_2$ dissolved in 1500.0 grams of water

2. Determine the grams of solute required to prepare the following solutions:

    a. 3.00m solution of KOH containing 1500.0 grams of water

    b. 0.500m solution $HC_2H_3O_2$ containing 750.0 grams of water

    c. 2.50m solution of $C_6H_{12}O_6$ containing 2000.0 grams of water

    d. 1.25m solution of NaCl containing 250.0 grams of water

3. Calculate the grams of water required to make a 0.500m solution which contains 20.0 grams of NaCl.

4. How many molecules of glycerol, $C_3H_5(OH)_3$, dissolved in 750.0 grams of water are needed to make a 1.50m solution?

5. Determine the mass of ethylene glycol, $C_2H_4(OH)_2$, which must be dissolved in 2500.0 grams of water to make a 4.00m solution. How many molecules is this?

6. What is the percentage by mass of ethylene glycol in a 3.50m solution?

19:2 Moles of Solute

When a solute is dissolved in a solvent, the vapor pressure of the solvent is reduced. The amount of the reduction depends upon the number of solute particles in a given amount of solvent. The French chemist, Raoult, first discovered the vapor pressure lowering relationship experimentally in 1882. Since both the freezing point and boiling point of a liquid depend on its vapor pressure, introduction of a solute into a solvent will change the solvent's freezing and boiling points. The freezing point of the solvent is lowered by the addition of the solute. The addition of a solute also increases the boiling point of a solvent.

The change in freezing point and boiling point varies directly as the concentration of solute particles. One mole or 6.02×10^{23} particles of a molecular solute dissolved in 1000 grams of water (a 1 molal solution) lowers the freezing point of the water by 1.86C°.* This temperature interval (1.86C°) is the **molal freezing point constant** for water. One mole

---

*A distinction must be made between °C and C°. °C indicates a temperature; whereas C° indicates a temperature interval, a certain number of degrees regardless of the actual temperature.

of the ionic solute, NaCl, contains 2 moles of solute particles (1 mole Na^+ and 1 mole Cl^-). The freezing point of the water is lowered by 2 × 1.86C°.

One mole of a molecular solute dissolved in 1000 grams of water (a 1 molal solution) raises the boiling point of the water by 0.512C°. This temperature interval is called the **molal boiling point constant** for water. One mole of the ionic substance $BaCl_2$ contains 3 moles of solute particles (1 mole Ba^{2+} and 2 moles Cl^-). The boiling point of the water is raised by 3 × 0.512C°.

Both neutral molecules and electrically charged ions change the boiling and freezing points of a solution. Pure substances which act as solvents have fixed boiling and freezing points.

Unless otherwise stated, the solvent used is water. Other solvents can be used, but each solvent has a different and characteristic molal freezing point depression constant and molal boiling point elevation constant.

Boiling and freezing point constants for water (1.86C° and 0.512C°) can be used to calculate:

1. the freezing point of the water
2. the boiling point of the water
3. the molecular mass of the solute from the freezing point or the boiling point

Table 19-1
Molal Freezing and Boiling Point Constants
(C°/mol/1000 g Solvent)

Substance	Freezing Point (°C)	Molal Freezing Point Constant	Boiling Point (°C)	Molal Boiling Point Constant
Acetic Acid	16.6	−3.90	118	3.07
Benzene	5.5	−5.12	80.1	2.53
Camphor	178.4	−37.7	208.25	5.95
Cyclohexane	6.5	−20.0	80.88	2.79
Nitrobenzene	5.8	−8.1	211	5.24
Phenol	43	−7.27	181.8	3.56
Water	0.00	−1.86	100	0.512

19:3   Freezing Point Calculations

The freezing point of a solution can be calculated from the mass or the moles of the solute dissolved in a known mass of water. Or, if the

freezing point is known, the concentration of the solution can be calculated. The conversion ratio used is, $1m$ concentration per $1.86C°$:

$$\frac{1m \text{ concentration}}{1.86C°}$$

This constant relates the freezing point depression for water to the molal
concentration.

Example 8

Calculate the freezing point of a solution containing 5.70 grams of
sugar, $C_{12}H_{22}O_{11}$, in 50.0 grams of water.

Solving Process:

Convert grams of solute per gram of water to moles of solute per
kilogram of water (molality). Then multiply by the conversion ratio to
obtain the change in freezing point.

$$\frac{5.70 \text{ g } C_{12}H_{22}O_{11}}{50.0 \text{ g } H_2O} \left| \frac{1000 \text{ g } H_2O}{1 \text{ kg } H_2O} \right| \frac{1 \text{ mol } C_{12}H_{22}O_{11}}{342 \text{ g } C_{12}H_{22}O_{11}} \left| \frac{1.86C°}{1m} \right. = 0.62C°$$

To determine the freezing point of the solution, subtract the change in
freezing point from $0°$Celsius, the freezing point of water.

$$0°C - 0.620C° = -0.620°C$$

Example 9

How many grams of a molecular substance (molecular mass 50.0)
must be added to 500.0 grams of water to have a freezing point of
$-3.72°C$?

Solving Process:

Start with the change in the freezing point ($3.72C°$) and convert to
molal concentration.

$$\text{molality} = \frac{3.72C°}{} \left| \frac{1m \text{ concentration}}{1.86C°} \right. = 2.00m$$

Convert from the molality to the grams of solute by using the molecular
mass.

$$\text{grams solute} = \frac{500.0 \text{ g } H_2O}{} \left| \frac{2.00 \text{ mol}}{1000 \text{ g } H_2O} \right| \frac{50.0 \text{ g}}{1 \text{ mol}}$$

$$= 50.0 \text{ grams solute}$$

19:4 Boiling Point Calculations

These calculations are similar to the calculations involving the
freezing point of water solutions. The conversion ratio used is $1m$
concentration/$0.512C°$.

Example 10_____

Calculate the boiling point of a solution containing 5.70 grams of sugar, $C_{12}H_{22}O_{11}$, dissolved in 50.0 grams of water.

Solving Process:

Use the molal boiling point constant of 0.512C° to calculate the change in boiling point.

$$\frac{5.70 \text{ g } C_{12}H_{22}O_{11}}{50.0 \text{ g } H_2O} \left| \frac{1000 \text{ g } H_2O}{1 \text{ kg } H_2O} \right| \frac{1 \text{ mol } C_{12}H_{22}O_{11}}{342 \text{ g } C_{12}H_{22}O_{11}} \left| \frac{0.512C°}{1m} \right. = 0.171C°$$

Add the change in boiling point to the boiling point of water 100°C.

$$100°C + 0.171C° = 100.171°C$$

Example 11_____

How many grams of a molecular substance (molecular mass 50.0) must be added to 500.0 grams of water to have a boiling point of 101.56°C?

Solving Process:

This problem is similar to Example 9. Start with the change in boiling point (1.56C°) and convert to molal concentration.

$$\frac{1.56C°}{} \left| \frac{1m}{0.512C°} \right. = 3.05m$$

Convert to grams of solute.

$$\frac{500.0 \text{ g } H_2O}{} \left| \frac{3.05 \text{ mol}}{1000 \text{ g } H_2O} \right| \frac{50.0 \text{ g}}{1 \text{ mol}} = 76.3 \text{ grams}$$

19:5 Molecular Mass Calculations

The molecular mass of a solute can be determined by changes in the freezing point or boiling point. The freezing point method is more practical because of the greater temperature interval involved. It also can be more accurately measured since the boiling point is changed more by atmospheric pressure than the freezing point.

First, determine the molality of the solute from the freezing or boiling point data. Second, determine the grams per mole (molecular mass) from the calculated molality and the concentration given.

Example 12_____

If 3.25 grams of a molecular substance are dissolved in 125.0 grams of water, what is the molecular mass of the solute if the solution freezes at −0.93°C?

Solving Process:

Calculate the molality of the solution using the freezing point change.

$$\frac{0.930\cancel{\text{C}°}}{} \left| \frac{1\ m}{1.86\cancel{\text{C}°}} \right. = 0.500m$$

Convert from grams solute per grams water to grams per mole by using the concentration determined in the first step.

$$\frac{3.25\ \text{g solute}}{125.0\ \cancel{\text{g H}_2\text{O}}} \left| \frac{1000\ \cancel{\text{g H}_2\text{O}}}{0.500\ \text{mol solute}} \right. = \frac{52.0\ \text{g}}{\text{mol}}$$

Example 13_____

The freezing point of a solution is lowered to $-11.16°$C when 48.0 grams of a molecular substance are dissolved in 250.0 grams of water. What is the molecular mass of this compound?

Solving Process:

Calculate the molal concentration from the freezing point data.

$$\frac{11.16°\cancel{\text{C}}}{} \left| \frac{1\ m}{1.86\cancel{\text{C}°}} \right. = 6.00m$$

Convert from the grams solute per grams water to grams per mole using the conversion ratio involving molality.

$$\frac{48.0\ \text{g solute}}{250.0\ \cancel{\text{g H}_2\text{O}}} \left| \frac{1000\ \cancel{\text{g H}_2\text{O}}}{6.00\ \text{mol solute}} \right. = \frac{32.0\ \text{g}}{\text{mol}}$$

Example 14_____

When 72.0 grams of dextrose were dissolved in 100.0 grams of water, the boiling point of the solution was observed to be 102.05°C. What is the molecular mass of dextrose?

Solving Process:

Determine the molal concentration using the conversion ratio involving the molal boiling point elevation constant.

$$\frac{2.05\cancel{\text{C}°}}{} \left| \frac{1m}{0.512\cancel{\text{C}°}} \right. = 4.00m$$

Convert from grams solute per grams water to grams per mole using the conversion ratio involving molality.

$$\frac{72.0\ \text{g dextrose}}{100\ \cancel{\text{g H}_2\text{O}}} \left| \frac{1000\ \cancel{\text{g H}_2\text{O}}}{4.00\ \text{mol dextrose}} \right. = \frac{180\ \text{g}}{\text{mol}}$$

Problems

Unless otherwise stated, assume that the solvent is water.

7. Calculate the boiling point and freezing point of a solution which contains 30.0 grams of acetic acid, $HC_2H_3O_2$, dissolved in 250.0 grams of water.

8. Calculate the change in both boiling and freezing points if 46.0 grams of glycerol, $C_3H_5(OH)_3$, are dissolved in 500.0 grams of water.

9. How many grams of ethanol, C_2H_5OH, must be dissolved in 500.0 grams of water to lower the freezing point to $-6.51°C$?

10. Determine the freezing point and boiling point of the following solutions:
    a. 16.0 grams methanol, CH_3OH, dissolved in 250.0 grams H_2O
    b. 23.0 grams ethanol, C_2H_5OH, dissolved in 250.0 grams H_2O
    c. 30.0 grams propanol, C_3H_7OH, dissolved in 250.0 grams H_2O

11. How many grams of ethylene glycol, $C_2H_4(OH)_2$, must be dissolved in 2000.0 grams of water to lower the freezing point to $-29.75°C$? If the density of ethylene glycol is 1.12 g/mL, how many milliliters of ethylene glycol are required?

12. What is the molecular mass of glucose if 22.5 grams gives a freezing point of $-0.930°C$ when dissolved in 250.0 grams of water? If the simplest formula is CH_2O, what is the molecular formula?

13. If 23.0 grams ethanol are dissolved in 1000 grams of water, the freezing point is $-0.930°C$. What is the molecular mass of the solute?

14. When 92.0 grams of a molecular compound were dissolved in 1000.0 grams of water, the freezing point of the solution was lowered to $-3.72°C$. Determine the molecular mass of this compound.

Chapter Review Problems

15. Find the number of grams of NaCl required to make each of the following solutions:
    a. $0.250m$ solution containing 500.0 grams of water
    b. $0.500m$ solution containing 500.0 grams of water
    c. $0.750m$ solution containing 500.0 grams of water
    d. $1.00m$ solution containing 500.0 grams of water

16. Calculate the mass of water required to prepare each of the following:

a. a 1.00m solution containing 10.0 grams NaOH
b. a 1.00m solution containing 20.0 grams of NaOH
c. a 1.00m solution containing 40.0 grams of NaOH

17. Calculate the percentage by mass of the solute in the following solutions:
   a. $NaC_2H_3O_2$ in a 0.500m solution
   b. $NaNO_3$ in a 0.500m solution
   c. $NaClO_3$ in a 0.500m solution

18. Rank the following solutions in order of increasing molality:
   a. 49.0 grams H_2SO_4 in 500.0 grams of water
   b. 98.0 grams H_2SO_4 in 1250.0 grams of water
   c. 80.0 grams H_2SO_4 in 750.0 grams of water

19. What are the freezing and boiling points of a solution that contains 10.0 grams of naphthalene, $C_{10}H_8$, dissolved in 50.0 grams of benzene?

20. What are the freezing and boiling points of a solution that contains 23.0 grams ethanol dissolved in 250.0 grams of phenol?

21. How many grams of an organic compound (molecular mass 75.0) must be dissolved in 500.0 grams of acetic acid to lower the freezing point of the solution to 0.00°C?

22. Determine the grams of an organic compound (molecular mass 125) which must be dissolved in 750.0 grams of cyclohexane to raise the boiling point of the resulting solution to 88.46°C.

23. If the freezing point of a solution containing 0.258 grams of a substance dissolved in 40.0 grams of benzene is 5.20°C, what is the molecular mass of the substance?

24. What is the molecular mass of an organic compound if 16.0 grams of the compound when dissolved in 225.0 grams of nitrobenzene increased the boiling point by 8.56C°?

25. Chemical analysis of an organic compound gives the following results: C 69.50%, H 7.25%, O 23.25%. When 1.58 grams of this compound were dissolved in 30.0 grams of benzene, it gave a freezing point depression of 1.95C°. What is the molecular mass and the molecular formula of this compound?

26. Chemical analysis of an organic compound gave the following results: C 55.00%, H 2.75%, N 12.80%, O 29.40%. When 1.270 grams of this compound were dissolved in 35.00 grams cyclohexane the boiling point was elevated by 0.464C°. What is the molecular mass and the molecular formula of this compound?

Acid-Base Equilibrium ____ 20

20:1 Theories and Properties

Several definitions have been proposed for acids and bases. Depending upon the situation, each definition has its advantages and disadvantages. Three acid-base theories are: **Arrhenius, Brönsted-Lowry,** and **Lewis.**

The Arrhenius theory is the oldest approach to acid-base theory. It is adequate for most introductory chemistry concepts. The theory explains acids and bases by the concept of ion formation. An acid ionizes in solution to produce hydrogen ions, H^+, or more correctly hydronium ions, H_3O^+. Hydrochloric acid ionizes in one step.

$$HCl + H_2O \longrightarrow H_3O^+ + Cl^-$$

Sulfuric acid, a polyprotic compound, ionizes in two steps.

$$H_2SO_4 + H_2O \longrightarrow H_3O^+ + HSO_4^-$$
$$HSO_4^- + H_2O \longrightarrow H_3O^+ + SO_4^{2-}$$

A base ionizes or dissociates in solution to produce hydroxide ions, OH^-.

$$NaOH \longrightarrow Na^+ + OH^-$$

It is the Arrhenius theory applied to aqueous (water) solutions that accounts for the characteristic properties of acids and bases.

20:2 Reactions and Ionic Equations

Considering the Arrhenius theory, in a neutralization reaction an acid reacts with a base to form a salt. The reaction goes to completion since a molecular compound (water) is formed. The water is only slightly ionized. For practical purposes, the water does not react again.

$$H_2SO_4 + 2NaOH \longrightarrow Na_2SO_4 + 2H_2O$$

| Acid | Base | Salt | Water |

The other compound formed is called a salt. **Salts** are crystalline solids composed of metallic ions other than hydrogen bonded to nonmetallic ions or polyatomic ions other than hydroxide. A salt contains the positive ion of a base and the negative ion of an acid. In addition to common salts such as $NaCl$ and Na_2SO_4, another group of salts, termed acid salts, contain hydrogen, $NaHSO_4$, sodium hydrogen sulfate; K_2HPO_4, potassium monohydrogen phosphate; KH_2PO_4, potassium dihydrogen phosphate).

Salts may be soluble or insoluble in water. The common solubility rules are indicated in Table 20-1.

Table 20-1
Solubility Rules

You will be working with water solutions, and it is helpful to have a few rules concerning what substances are soluble in water. The most common rules are listed below.

1. All common salts of the Group IA elements and ammonium ion are soluble.
2. All common acetates and nitrates are soluble.
3. All binary compounds of Group VIIA elements (other than F) with metals are soluble except those of silver, mercury(I), and lead.
4. All sulfates are soluble except those of barium, strontium, lead, calcium, silver, and mercury(I).
5. Except for those in Rule 1, carbonates, hydroxides, oxides, and phosphates are insoluble.

Hydrolysis is the reaction of a salt with water. As the salt dissolves, an acidic, basic, or neutral solution forms. The type of solution formed depends upon the strength of the acid and base involved in the formation of the salt.

Strong acids	HCl, HNO_3, H_2SO_4, HBr, HI, $HClO_4$	completely ionized
Weak acids	$HC_2H_3O_2$, HF, H_2SO_3, HSO_4^-, H_3PO_4	slightly ionized
Strong bases	$NaOH$, KOH	completely ionized
Weak base	NH_3	slightly ionized

Due to hydrolysis, the solutions produced from the neutralization reactions may be acidic, basic or neutral as indicated:

Strong acid + Strong base $\longrightarrow$ neutral solution

Strong acid + Weak base $\longrightarrow$ acid solution

Weak acid + Strong base $\longrightarrow$ basic solution

Weak acid + Weak base $\longrightarrow$ Results depend upon the relative weaknesses the acid and base used.

   It is customary for reactions occurring in water to be written in ionic form. Only ions actually taking part in the reaction are written. The other ions present but not involved are termed **spectator ions** and are not written in the net ionic equation.

In writing ionic equations the following rules are observed:
1. Species occurring in molecular form are written as molecules. For example, H_2O, SO_2, CO_2, NH_3.
2. Weak electrolytes (partially ionized substances) are written in molecular 'form.
3. Strong electrolytes are written in ionic form.
4. Soluble salts are written in ionic form; insoluble salts in molecular form.

$$\text{Soluble} \quad Na^+ + Cl^-, Ca^{2+} + 2C_2H_3O_2^-$$
$$\text{Insoluble} \quad BaSO_4, Ag_2CrO_4$$

For example, note the steps in writing the following net ionic equations:

word   zinc + hydrochloric acid $\longrightarrow$ zinc chloride + hydrogen

balanced $Zn(c) + 2HCl(aq) \longrightarrow ZnCl_2(aq) + H_2(g)$

ionic $Zn + 2H^+ + 2Cl^- \longrightarrow Zn^{2+} + 2Cl^- + H_2$

net ionic $Zn + 2H^+ \longrightarrow Zn^{2+} + H_2$

word   aluminum nitrate + sodium hydroxide $\longrightarrow$ aluminum hydroxide + sodium nitrate

balanced $Al(NO_3)_3(aq) + 3NaOH(aq) \longrightarrow Al(OH)_3(c) + 3NaNO_3(aq)$

ionic $Al^{3+} + 3NO_3^- + 3Na^+ + 3OH^- \longrightarrow Al(OH)_3 + 3Na^+ + 3NO_3^-$

net ionic $Al^{3+} + 3OH^- \longrightarrow Al(OH)_3$

Problems

1. Write the net ionic equation for each word equation.
   a. sodium + water $\longrightarrow$ sodium hydroxide + hydrogen

   b. phosphoric acid + magnesium hydroxide ⟶
                  magnesium phosphate + water
   c. barium chloride + sodium sulfate ⟶
                  sodium chloride + barium sulfate
   d. magnesium hydroxide + ammonium phosphate ⟶
                  magnesium phosphate + ammonia + water
   e. iron(III) bromide + ammonium sulfide ⟶
                  iron(III) sulfide + ammonium bromide
   f. sodium carbonate + sulfuric acid ⟶
                  sodium sulfate + carbon dioxide + water
   g. aluminum + copper(II) chloride ⟶
                  aluminum chloride + copper
   h. aluminum chloride + sulfuric acid ⟶
                  aluminum sulfate + hydrogen chloride

20:3 Ionization Constant

When ionic compounds are dissolved in water the ions separate from each other in a process called **dissociation.** Many molecular compounds, when dissolved in water, react with the water to produce ions in a process called **ionization.**

It is assumed that strong electrolytes dissociate completely. A $0.1M$ solution of a strong acid, such as HCl, is a solution containing $0.1M$ hydronium ions. Similarly, a $0.5M$ solution of a strong base, such as NaOH, is a solution containing $0.5M$ hydroxide ions.

However, the ionization of weak electrolytes, such as the weak acids $HC_2H_3O_2$, HNO_2, H_2SO_3, and the only common weak base $NH_3(aq)$ is not complete.

Weak acids and weak bases ionize, in general, as follows (HA represents a weak acid and BOH represents a weak base):

$$HA + H_2O^+ \rightleftharpoons H_3O^+ + A^- \qquad B + H_2O \rightleftharpoons BH^+ + OH^-$$

The ionization of weak electrolytes occurs only to a small extent before equilibrium is established. An equation which allows you to determine the concentration of each substance at equilibrium is called an equilibrium expression.

The equilibrium expression for ionization involves the concentration of the products multiplied together and divided by the concentration of the reactants. All of these concentrations are in moles per liter and are thus placed in brackets [ ].

$$K = \frac{[\text{products}]}{[\text{reactants}]}$$

Assuming the reaction $A + 2B \rightleftharpoons C + 3D$, the constant K would be:

$$K = \frac{[C][D]^3}{[A][B]^2}$$

Note that the individual concentrations of B and D are raised to the second and third powers. The numbers 2 and 3 come from the coefficients in front of B and D, respectively, in the balanced equation. The equilibrium expression for the ionization equations of the weak acid and the weak base previously given would be:

$$K = \frac{[H_3O^+][A^-]}{[HA][H_2O]} \qquad K = \frac{[BH^+][OH^-]}{[B][H_2O]}$$

The concentration of the water is essentially constant. Multiplying both sides of the equation by $[H_2O]$ produces a new constant expression called an **ionization constant.**

The expression for the weak acid ionization constant is

$$K_a = \frac{[H_3O^+][A^-]}{[HA]}$$

The expression for the weak base ionization constant is

$$K_b = \frac{[BH^+][OH^-]}{[B]}$$

Example 1

Calculate the $[OH^-]$ of a $0.500\,M$ solution of aqueous ammonia. The K_b of NH_3 is 1.74×10^{-5}.

Solving Process:

From the ionization equation, $NH_3 + H_2O \rightleftharpoons NH_4^+ + OH^-$, write the ionization constant expression of ammonium hydroxide.

$$K_b = \frac{[NH_4^+][OH^-]}{[NH_3]}$$

Let $[NH_4^+] = [OH^-] = x$. $[NH_3]$ is slightly less than the $0.500\,M$ by the concentration of the $[NH_4^+]$. On substitution into the ionization constant expression:

$$1.74 \times 10^{-5} = \frac{x^2}{0.500 - x}$$

Assume that x is very small compared to 0.500. Thus, $0.500 - x \approx 0.500$.

$$1.74 \times 10^{-5} = \frac{x^2}{0.500}$$
$$x^2 = (1.74 \times 10^{-5})(0.500) = 8.70 \times 10^{-6}$$
$$x = \sqrt{8.70 \times 10^{-6}} = 2.95 \times 10^{-3}$$

Therefore, $x = [NH_4^+] = [OH^-] = 2.95 \times 10^{-3}M$

Example 2

Determine the experimental equilibrium constant of an acetic acid solution if 0.100 mole of acetic acid is dissolved in enough water to make 1.00 liter of solution which has a hydronium ion concentration of 0.00135 mole/liter.

Solving Process:

The ionization equation is

$$HC_2H_3O_2 + H_2O \rightleftharpoons H_3O^+ + C_2H_3O_2^-$$

The ionization constant, K_a, for the acetic acid is

$$K_a = \frac{[H_3O^+][C_2H_3O_2^-]}{[HC_2H_3O_2]}$$

The concentration of the hydronium ion and the acetate ion both equal 0.00135. Since 0.00135 is very small compared to 0.100, it is assumed that the molecular acetic acid has a concentration of 0.100. Substitute the value into the K_a expression and solve.

$$K_a = \frac{[0.00135][0.00135]}{[0.100]} = 1.82 \times 10^{-5}$$

20:4 Percent of Ionization

If the percent ionization of the weak electrolyte is known, the K_a or the K_b can be calculated if the concentration of the solution is given.

Example 3

If an acetic acid solution has a concentration of 0.0800M and is 1.50% ionized, determine the experimental K_a of the $HC_2H_3O_2$.

Solving Process:

If the initial $[HC_2H_3O_2]$ concentration is 0.0800, the $[H_3O^+]$ and the $[C_2H_3O_2^-]$ can be obtained by multiplying the concentration by the percent ionization.

$$[H_3O^+] = [C_2H_3O_2^-] = (0.0800)(0.0150) = 0.00120$$

At equilibrium $[HC_2H_3O_2] = 0.0800 - 0.00120 = 0.0788$

From the ionization equation $HC_2H_3O_2 + H_2O \rightleftharpoons H_3O^+ + C_2H_3O_2^-$ write the K_a expression. Substitute and solve for K_a.

$$K_a = \frac{[H_3O^+][C_2H_3O_2^-]}{[HC_2H_3O_2]} = \frac{[1.20 \times 10^{-3}]^2}{[7.88 \times 10^{-2}]} = \frac{1.44 \times 10^{-6}}{7.88 \times 10^{-2}} = 1.83 \times 10^{-5}$$

Example 4

If the K_a of hydrofluoric acid is 6.46×10^{-4} and the solution has a concentration of $0.150\,M$, calculate the degree and percent of ionization.

Solving Process:

In Example 3, the percent ionization was multiplied by the concentration to obtain the concentration of the ionic substance. If x is equal to the degree of ionization, then:

$$HF + H_2O \rightleftharpoons H_3O^+ + F^-$$

$$K_a = \frac{[H_3O^+][F^-]}{[HF]} = \frac{[0.150x][0.150x]}{[0.150]}$$

The [HF] is assumed to be 0.15 instead of $0.15 - x$, as x is a very small number. Substitute the K_a value and solve for x:

$$6.46 \times 10^{-4} = \frac{[0.150x][0.150x]}{[0.150]} = 0.150x^2$$

$$x^2 = \frac{6.46 \times 10^{-4}}{1.50 \times 10^{-1}} = 4.31 \times 10^{-3}$$

$$x = 6.56 \times 10^{-2} = 0.0656, \text{ the degree of ionization}$$

The percent ionization is $0.0656 \times 100\% = 6.56\%$.

Example 5

If the K_b of NH_3 is 1.74×10^{-5} and the percent ionization is 4.16%, determine the concentration of the solution in moles per liter.

Solving Process:

Let x be the molarity of the solution. Then $[NH_4^+] = [OH^-] = 0.0416x$. At equilibrium the $[NH_3] = x - 0.0416x$, but $0.0416x$ is extremely small. Assume that the $[NH_3] = x$. From the equation $NH_3 + H_2O \rightleftharpoons NH_4^+ + OH^-$, obtain the K_b expression. Then substitute and solve for x:

$$K_b = \frac{[NH_4^+][OH^-]}{[NH_3]}$$

$$1.74 \times 10^{-5} = \frac{[0.0416x][0.0416x]}{[x]} = (4.16 \times 10^{-2})^2 x$$

$$x = \frac{1.74 \times 10^{-5}}{1.73 \times 10^{-3}} = 1.01 \times 10^{-2}$$

The molarity of the ammonia solution is 0.0101M.

20:5 Common Ion

In the previous problems it was assumed that the ionization process occurred in pure water. If, however, a common ion provided by a electrolyte is present, the calculations are slightly different.

Consider the ionization of acetic acid in pure water:

$$HC_2H_3O_2 + H_2O \rightleftharpoons H_3O^+ + C_2H_3O_2^-$$

The concentrations of the $[H_3O^+]$ and the $[C_2H_3O_2^-]$ are the same, since both ions come from the same source which yields one ion of each when the acid ionizes.

If some sodium acetate is added, the concentration of the $[C_2H_3O_2^-]$ increases because there are two sources of acetate ion, and one of the sources (the $NaC_2H_3O_2$) is completely ionized. According to Le Chatelier's principle (an equilibrium reaction shifts so as to relieve a stress), the concentration of the $[H_3O^+]$ decreases sharply as the reverse reaction toward the molecular acid occurs. The K_a value remains constant. Thus, the acetic acid concentration increases.

The following table illustrates the common ion effect.

Table 20-2
Effect Due to Le Chatelier's Principle

Weak Electrolyte	Compound Added	Common Ion	Concentration Increased	Concentration Decreased
$HC_2H_3O_2$	$NaC_2H_3O_2$	$C_2H_3O_2^-$	$C_2H_3O_2^-$	H_3O^+
$HC_2H_3O_2$	HCl	H_3O^+	H_3O^+	$C_2H_3O_2^-$
NH_3	NH_4Br	NH_4^+	NH_4^+	OH^-
NH_3	NaOH	OH^-	OH^-	NH_4^+

Example 6

Determine the H_3O^+ in a solution of $HC_2H_3O_2$ which is 0.100M if enough $NaC_2H_3O_2$ is added to make the solution 2.00M with respect to the $C_2H_3O_2^-$. The K_a of $HC_2H_3O_2$ is 1.74×10^{-5}.

Solving Process:

$$HC_2H_3O_2 + H_2O \rightleftharpoons H_3O^+ + C_2H_3O_2^-$$

Let $[H_3O^+] = x$ and we know $[C_2H_3O_2^-] = 2.00$. Also $[HC_2H_3O_2] = 0.100 - x \cong 0.100$. Substitute into the K_a expression:

$$K_a = \frac{[H_3O^+][C_2H_3O_2^-]}{[HC_2H_3O_2]} \qquad \text{or} \qquad 1.74 \times 10^{-5} = \frac{x(2.00)}{(0.100)}$$

$$x = \frac{(1.74 \times 10^{-5})(0.100)}{(2.00)} = 8.70 \times 10^{-7} M$$

The $[H_3O^+]$ in a solution which is $2.00 M$ in acetate ion and $0.100 M$ in $HC_2H_3O_2$ is 8.70×10^{-7}. The $[H_3O^+]$ for a $0.100 M$ $HC_2H_3O_2$ solution is 1.32×10^{-3}.

20:6   Buffers

One use of the common ion effect is in buffering a solution. A solution is **buffered** if it resists change in its hydronium or hydroxide ion concentration when either of these ions is added.

A solution containing a weak acid or base and its completely ionized salt will act as a buffer. An example is a solution of acetic acid, $HC_2H_3O_2$, and sodium acetate, $NaC_2H_3O_2$. Another example is aqueous ammonia, $NH_3(aq)$ and ammonium chloride, NH_4Cl.

In a solution of $HC_2H_3O_2$ and $NaC_2H_3O_2$, there are a large quantity of $C_2H_3O_2^-$ ions, a large quantity of $HC_2H_3O_2$ molecules, and a small quantity of H_3O^+ ions. The Na^+ is a spectator ion and does not take part in the buffering. Any completely ionized acetate salt, such as $KC_2H_3O_2$, would work just as well.

If an acid were added to the buffer, the H_3O^+ of the acid, such as HNO_3, reacts with part of the $C_2H_3O_2^-$ to form more $HC_2H_3O_2$. The following equation indicates only those ions actually involved in the reaction.

$$\underset{\substack{\text{from the} \\ \text{acid}}}{H_3O^+} + \underset{\substack{\text{from the} \\ \text{salt}}}{C_2H_3O_2^-} \longrightarrow HC_2H_3O_2 + H_2O$$

The reaction tends to restore the original H_3O^+ concentration.

If a base, such as KOH, is added, the OH^- reacts with the $HC_2H_3O_2$ in a neutralization reaction.

$$\underset{\substack{\text{from acetic} \\ \text{acid}}}{HC_2H_3O_2} + \underset{\substack{\text{from the} \\ \text{base}}}{OH^-} \longrightarrow H_2O + C_2H_3O_2^-$$

If the concentrations of the weak acid and its salt or the weak base and its salt are varied, the H_3O^+ concentration of the solution can be fixed within broad limits. The calculations are the same as those illustrated under the common ion section.

20:7 Polyprotic Acids

A number of polyprotic (more than one proton) acids ionize to form one H_3O^+ ion in each step of the ionization. Thus a polyprotic acid has several ionization constants, with each constant relating to the ionization of that particular step. Two polyprotic acids, their ionization equations, and their K_a's are given.

Sulfurous acid (H_2SO_3) a diprotic acid:

$$H_2SO_3 + H_2O \rightleftharpoons H_3O^+ + HSO_3^-$$

$$K_1 = \frac{[H_3O^+][HSO_3^-]}{[H_2SO_3]}$$
$$= 1.26 \times 10^{-2}$$

$$HSO_3^- + H_2O \rightleftharpoons H_3O^+ + SO_3^{2-}$$

$$K_2 = \frac{[H_3O^+][SO_3^{2-}]}{[HSO_3^-]}$$
$$= 6.31 \times 10^{-8}$$

Phosphoric acid (H_3PO_4) a triprotic acid:

$$H_3PO_4 + H_2O \rightleftharpoons H_3O^+ + H_2PO_4^-$$

$$K_1 = \frac{[H_3O^+][H_2PO_4^-]}{[H_3PO_4]}$$
$$= 7.11 \times 10^{-3}$$

$$H_2PO_4^- + H_2O \rightleftharpoons H_3O^+ + HPO_4^{2-}$$

$$K_2 = \frac{[H_3O^+][HPO_4^{2-}]}{[H_2PO_4^-]}$$
$$= 7.99 \times 10^{-8}$$

$$HPO_4^{2-} + H_2O \rightleftharpoons H_3O^+ + PO_4^{3-}$$

$$K_3 = \frac{[H_3O^+][PO_4^{3-}]}{[HPO_4^{2-}]}$$
$$= 4.80 \times 10^{-13}$$

The smaller the value of K, the weaker the acid; thus H_3PO_4 is a weaker acid than H_2SO_3. The H_3PO_4 is less ionized than the H_2SO_3 at a given concentration. The H_2SO_3 is more ionized than the HSO_3^- and, therefore, the H_2SO_3 is a stronger acid. For any polyprotic acid, the first ionization constant is always considerably larger than the second; the second ionization constant is greater than the third. Each successive ionization leaves the negative polyatomic ion with greater attraction for the remaining hydrogen ion or ions and, therefore, each successive ionization is less likely to occur than the preceding ionizations.

For the previous problems in this chapter, it was assumed that the concentration of the ionized species was very small compared to the concentration of the molecular species. This assumption is correct for slightly ionized acids and bases in aqueous solution. However, for medium strength electrolytes, this simplifying assumption cannot be made. For these electrolytes, it is necessary to use the quadratic equation.

Example 7

Determine the hydronium ion concentration for a chlorous acid solution which is 0.0100M. The K_a of $HClO_2$ is 1.1×10^{-2}.

Solving Process:

From the equation, $HClO_2 + H_2O \rightleftarrows H_3O^+ + ClO_2^-$ obtain the expression for the equilibrium constant.

$$K_a = \frac{[H_3O^+][ClO_2^-]}{[HClO_2]}$$

Since $[H_3O^+] = [ClO_2^-]$, both can equal x. Also at equilibrium $[HClO_2] = 0.010 - x$. (In previous problems, $0.010 - x$ was assumed to be 0.010. This assumption cannot be made for medium strength electrolytes.) Substitute the values into the K_a expression.

$$1.1 \times 10^{-2} = \frac{[x][x]}{[0.010 - x]}$$

Rearrange and obtain

$$x^2 + 1.1 \times 10^{-2}x + (-1.1 \times 10^{-4}) = 0$$

The rearrangement has the form of the quadratic equation $ax^2 + bx + c = 0$. If a, b, and c are coefficients, the roots can be obtained by substituting into the quadratic equation.

$$x = \frac{-b \pm \sqrt{b^2 - 4ac}}{2a}$$

$a = 1$; $b = 1.1 \times 10^{-2}$; and $c = -1.1 \times 10^{-4}$. Or $a = 1$; $b = 0.011$, and $c = -0.00011$. Substituting the values into the quadratic equation gives

$$x = \frac{-0.011 \pm \sqrt{(0.011)^2 - 4(1)(-0.00011)}}{2(1)}$$

$$= \frac{-0.011 \pm 0.0237}{2}$$

$$= +0.0064 \text{ and } -0.017 \text{ mole/liter}$$

A negative concentration (-0.017) has no meaning in chemistry. The correct answer is $0.0064M$. Obviously $0.0064M$ is not negligible compared to the original concentration of $0.010M$.

Chapter Review Problems

2. Determine the ionization constant for each of the weak electrolytes:
   a. a $0.00100M$ acetic acid solution with $[H_3O^+] = 1.27 \times 10^{-4}$.
   b. a $0.0070M$ aqueous ammonia solution with $[OH^-] = 3.46 \times 10^{-4}$.
   c. a $0.100M$ hydrogen cyanide solution with $[H_3O^+] = 7.85 \times 10^{-6}$.

3. Determine the concentration of all substances in a bottle which contains $1.000M$ $HC_2H_3O_2$. The K_a is 1.74×10^{-5}.

4. What is the percent ionization in the $1.000M$ $HC_2H_3O_2$ in problem 3?

5. Find the ionization constants of the following weak electrolytes:
   a. $0.100M$ HF   8.50% ionized
   b. $0.0500N$ $HC_2H_3O_2$ 1.88% ionized
   c. $0.0130N$ $HC_2H_3O_2$ 3.70% ionized
   d. $0.200M$ $HAsO_2$ 0.00550% ionized

6. If the K_a of chlorous acid ($HClO_2$) is 1.1×10^{-2}, calculate the molarity of the solution if the degree of ionization is 0.14.

7. If it is necessary to reduce the concentration of the $[H_3O^+]$ to $2.00 \times 10^{-4}M$, what must be the concentration of the $[C_2H_3O_2^-]$ in a $0.400M$ solution of acetic acid? The K_a is 1.74×10^{-5}.

8. The medium strength electrolyte hydrofluoric acid has an ionization constant of $K_a = 6.46 \times 10^{-4}$. For a $0.0100M$ solution of HF calculate the hydronium ion concentration by:
   a. making the false assumption that x can be neglected compared to $0.0100M$
   b. solving by using the quadratic equation

Hydronium Ions in Solution and *pH* _____ 21

21:1 Ionization of Water; The *pH* Scale

Pure water ionizes slightly into hydronium and hydroxide ions:

$$H_2O(l) + H_2O(l) \longrightarrow H_3O^+(aq) + OH^-(aq)$$

It has been found by experiment that one liter of pure water contains only one ten millionth of a mole of hydronium ions and one ten millionth of a mole of hydroxide ions. A substance which contains more hydronium ions than hydroxide ions is acidic; a substance which contains more hydroxide ions than hydronium ions is basic; and a substance such as pure water which contains an equal number of hydronium ions and hydroxide ions is neutral. The ions are in equilibrium in pure water when the concentration of hydronium ions is 10^{-7} moles in each liter of water and the hydroxide ion concentration is also 10^{-7} moles per liter. In equation form:

$2H_2O$	$\rightleftharpoons$	H_3O^+	$+$	OH^-
1 liter of water (55.6 moles)	at equilibrium contains	10^{-7} moles of hydronium ions		10^{-7} moles of hydroxide ions

We can now write the equilibrium expression for water with the information just given and find an equilibrium constant for water. (Remember that the symbol [ ] means moles per liter.)

$$2H_2O \rightleftharpoons H_3O^+ + OH^-$$

$$K_{eq} = \frac{[H_3O^+][OH^-]}{[H_2O][H_2O]}$$

Since the ionization of water is very small in comparison with the total concentration of water (55.6 moles)*, the concentration of water can be assumed to remain constant. If the concentration of water is constant, we can multiply both sides of the equation by this constant without destroying the relationship.

$$[H_2O]^2 \times (K_{eq}) = [H_2O]^2 \times \left(\frac{[H_3O^+][OH^-]}{[H_2O]^2}\right)$$

Since both $[H_2O]$ and K_{eq} are constants, their product will also be constant. We call this constant the ion product constant of water and denote it by the symbol K_w. The ion product constant for water has been found to be 10^{-14} at room temperature.

$$K_w = [H_3O^+][OH^-] = 10^{-14}$$

Inspect this relationship and note that when:

$$[H_3O^+] = 10^{-1}, \qquad \text{the } [OH^-] = 10^{-13}$$
$$[H_3O^+] = 10^{-13}, \qquad \text{the } [OH^-] = 10^{-1}$$
$$[H_3O^+] = 10^{-7}, \qquad \text{the } [OH^-] = 10^{-7}$$

This simple relationship has been used to construct what is called the *pH* scale which is used to indicate how acidic or basic a solution is. The *pH* scale ranges from 0 to 14. A *pH* of 7 is neutral; a *pH* of 1 is acidic; and a *pH* of 14 is basic.

The *pH* scale indicates the hydronium ion concentration. Another related scale, the *pOH* scale, is used to indicate the hydroxide ion (OH^-) concentration. The relationship between the two can be seen in the chart. If you know the *pH*, simply subtract the *pH* value from 14 to change to the *pOH* scale.

$$pH + pOH = 14$$

	$[H_3O^+]$	pH	$[OH^-]$	pOH	$[H_3O^+][OH^-]$
Increasingly acidic ↑	10^{-1}	1	10^{-13}	13	10^{-14}
	10^{-2}	2	10^{-12}	12	10^{-14}
	10^{-3}	3	10^{-11}	11	10^{-14}
	10^{-4}	4	10^{-10}	10	10^{-14}
	10^{-5}	5	10^{-9}	9	10^{-14}
Least acidic	10^{-6}	6	10^{-8}	8	10^{-14}

*You may wonder where the 55.6 moles came from. We are working with one liter of water which has a mass of 1000 g. You know that one mole of water has a mass of 18 grams. Therefore, one liter of water must contain

$$\frac{1000 \text{ g}}{18 \text{ g/mol}} = 55.6 \text{ moles of water.}$$

Neutral	10^{-7}	7	10^{-7}	7	10^{-14}
Least basic	10^{-8}	8	10^{-6}	6	10^{-14}
	10^{-9}	9	10^{-5}	5	10^{-14}
	10^{-10}	10	10^{-4}	4	10^{-14}
	10^{-11}	11	10^{-3}	3	10^{-14}
Increasingly basic	10^{-12}	12	10^{-2}	2	10^{-14}
↓	10^{-13}	13	10^{-1}	1	10^{-14}

Note that as the *pH* increases, the *pOH* decreases and the product, $[H_3O^+] \times [OH^-]$, is always 10^{-14}.

Table 21-1
Approximate *pH* of Some Common Substances

	pH		pH
1.0*M* HCl	0	Milk	6.5
0.1*M* HCl	1.0	Pure water	7.0
Stomach acid	2.0	Human blood	7.4
Lemon	2.3	Seawater	8.5
Vinegar	2.8	Household bleach	9.0
Carbonated beverage	3.0	Household ammonia	11.0
Orange	3.5	0.1*M* NaOH	13.0
Tomato	4.2	1.0*M* NaOH	14.0
Rainwater	6.0		

K_w is a constant for all dilute aqueous solutions. Although the concentrations of H_3O^+ and OH^- may change when substances are added to water, the product of $[H_3O^+]$ and $[OH^-]$ remains the same.

$$K_w = [H_3O^+][OH^-] = 1.00 \times 10^{-14}$$

If an acid is added to a solution, the $[H_3O^+]$ increases and the $[OH^-]$ decreases. If a base is added, the $[OH^-]$ increases and H_3O^+ decreases. Even in solutions which are acidic and contain a very large number of hydronium ions, a very small number of hydroxide ions exist.

To work problems involving *pH* and *pOH*, you must translate from these two scales back to concentration of moles per liter. If you wish to prepare a solution of a specific *pH*, you must also know how many moles of hydronium ion must be present per liter. For the simpler problems, you will have no difficulty if you thoroughly understand the definitions of *pH*, *pOH*, $[H_3O^+]$ and $[OH^-]$. For the more complex problems, you must be able to manipulate logarithms and exponents.

We will use a neutral solution to show the relationship between the symbols and their relation to exponents and logarithms. A neutral solution contains 10^{-7} moles of hydronium ions per liter and 10^{-7} moles of hydroxide ions per liter.

$$[H_3O^+] = 10^{-7} \qquad pH = 7$$
$$[OH^-] = 10^{-7} \qquad pOH = 7$$

Note that the *pH* and *pOH* are simply the exponents of the ion concentrations without the negative signs. To translate into mathematical form, we must introduce logarithms because we are dealing with exponents.

$$pH = -\log[H_3O^+] \qquad pOH = -\log[OH^-]$$

Logs are used simply because they are exponents of ten and it is convenient to deal with hydronium ion concentrations in terms of powers of ten and scientific notation. (See the Appendix for a discussion on logs.)

Example 1

What is the *pH* and the *pOH* of a solution which contains 10^{-4} (the same as 1×10^{-4}) moles of H_3O^+ ions per liter?

Solving Process:

$$pH = -\log[H_3O^+]$$
$$= -\log(1 \times 10^{-4})$$
$$= -(\log 1 + \log 10^{-4})$$
$$pH = -[0 + (-4)] = 4$$

Since $pH + pOH = 14$; $pOH = 10$

Example 2

Calculate the *pOH* and *pH* of a solution which contains $0.001 M$ NaOH. Assume 100% ionization.

Solving Process:

One hundred percent ionization means there is 0.001 mole OH^- per liter or,

$$[OH^-] = \frac{0.001 \text{ moles } OH^-}{\text{liter solution}} = \frac{1 \times 10^{-3} \text{ moles } OH^-}{\text{liter solution}}$$

Substitute into the expression for *pOH*:

$$pOH = -\log[OH^-]$$
$$= -\log(1 \times 10^{-3})$$
$$= -(\log 1 + \log 10^{-3})$$
$$pOH = -[0 + (-3)] = 3$$

Thus, the *pOH* is 3. Since $pH + pOH = 14$, the *pH* of this solution is 11.

Example 3

What is the *pH* of a solution which contains 1×10^{-5} mole of OH^- per liter?

Solving Process:

Find the $[H_3O^+]$ from the expression $[H_3O^+] \times [OH^-] = 1 \times 10^{-14}$; then solve for the *pH*.

$$[H_3O^+] \times 1 \times 10^{-5} = 1 \times 10^{-14}$$

$$[H_3O^+] = \frac{1 \times 10^{-14}}{1 \times 10^{-5}} = 1 \times 10^{-9}$$

$$pH = -\log [H_3O^+] = -\log (1 \times 10^{-9})$$
$$= -(\log 1 + \log 10^{-9})$$
$$pH = -[0 + (-9)] = 9$$

Example 4

Determine the *pH* and *pOH* of a solution which contains 0.0035 mole of H_3O^+ per liter.

Solving Process:

$$pH = -\log [H_3O^+] = -\log (3.5 \times 10^{-3})$$
$$= -(\log 3.50 + \log 10^{-3})$$

The logarithm table in the Appendix shows that the log of 3.5 is equal to 0.54.

$$pH = -[0.54 + (-3)]$$
$$= 2.46$$

Solve for the *pOH*:

$$pH + pOH = 14.00$$
$$pOH = 14.00 - 2.46 = 11.54$$

Example 5

What is the *pOH* of a solution containing $0.042 M$ KOH? Assume 100% ionization.

Solving Process:

Assume 100% ionization gives 0.042 mole OH^- per liter. Therefore, the hydroxide ion concentration is $4.2 \times 10^{-2} M$.

$$pOH = -\log [OH^-] = -\log (4.2 \times 10^{-2})$$
$$= -(\log 4.2 + \log 10^{-2})$$

From the logarithm table, the log 4.2 is equal to 0.62.

$$pOH = -[0.62 + (-2)]$$
$$= 1.38$$

Example 6

What is the $[H_3O^+]$ in a solution which has a pH of 4.000?
Solving Process:

$$pH = -\log [H_3O^+]$$
$$4.000 = -\log [H_3O^+]$$
$$-4.000 = \log [H_3O^+]$$
$$\text{antilog } (-4.000) = [H_3O^+]$$
$$1.000 \times 10^{-4} = [H_3O^+]$$

Example 7

Calculate the $[H_3O^+]$ of a solution which has a pH of 3.70.
Solving Process:

$$pH = -\log [H_3O^+]$$
$$-3.70 = \log [H_3O^+]$$

Because the logarithm table does not give the mantissa for negative numbers, -3.70 is expressed as $0.30 - 4$. From the log table, the antilog 0.30 is 2.0.

$$0.300 - 4 = \log [H_3O^+]$$
$$2.0 \times 10^{-4} = [H_3O^+]$$

Example 8

What is the $[OH^-]$ and the $[H_3O^+]$ of a solution if the pOH is 4.40?
Solving Process:

$$pOH = -\log [OH^-]$$
$$-4.40 = \log [OH^-]$$

Because the logarithm table does not give the mantissa for negative numbers, -4.4 is expressed as $0.600 - 5$. From the log table, antilog $0.6 = 3.98$.

$$0.600 - 5 = \log [OH^-]$$
$$3.98 \times 10^{-5} = [OH^-]$$

To solve for the $[H_3O^+]$, substitute into the equation.

$$[H_3O^+] \times [OH^-] = 1.00 \times 10^{-14}$$

$$[H_3O^+] = \frac{1.00 \times 10^{-14}}{[OH^-]} = \frac{1.00 \times 10^{-14}}{3.98 \times 10^{-5}}$$

$$= 0.25 \times 10^{-9} = 2.5 \times 10^{-10}M$$

Problems

1. Calculate the *pH* and the *pOH* of solutions having the following concentration:
   a. 0.00010 mole H_3O^+ per liter
   b. 0.010 mole OH^- per liter
   c. 1.0×10^{-5} mole OH^- per liter
   d. 1.0×10^{-2} mole H_3O^+ per liter

2. Calculate the $[H_3O^+]$ of the following solutions:
   a. *pH* = 3.0   b. *pH* = 6.0   c. *pOH* = 12.0

3. Calculate the $[OH^-]$ of the following solutions:
   a. *pOH* = 11.0   b. *pH* = 4.0   c. *pOH* = 8.0

4. Calculate the *pH* and the *pOH* of solutions having the following concentrations. Assume 100% ionization. Remember that 1 mole of H_2SO_4 produces 2 moles of H_3O^+ ion.
   a. 0.0025*M* NaOH   d. 0.048*M* HCl
   b. 0.0025*M* H_2SO_4 e. 0.032*M* KOH
   c. 0.075*M* H_2SO_4 f. 0.00017*M* NaOH

21:2   Equilibrium Constants, Buffers, and *pH*

The acid – base equilibrium concepts (Chapter 20) can be used with the ideas discussed in this section. The constants K_a and K_b depend upon the temperature and are determined experimentally by measuring the *pH* of their solution.

Example 9

If the *pH* of a weak acid solution is 2.500 and the solution has a concentration of 0.1000*M*, what is the K_a of the weak acid HA?

Solving Process:
Determine the H_3O^+ concentration by substituting into the *pH* definition.

$$pH = -\log [H_3O^+]$$
$$-2.500 = \log [H_3O^+]$$

$$0.500 - 3 = \log [H_3O^+]$$
$$3.16 \times 10^{-3} = [H_3O^+]$$

From the equation $HA + H_2O \rightleftharpoons H_3O^+ + A^-$ and the calculation, $[H_3O^+] = [A^-] = 3.16 \times 10^{-3}$. Because each HA molecule that ionizes gives one H_3O^+ and one A^-, the original concentration of HA has decreased by the amount of H_3O^+ formed. Thus, the HA concentration is $0.1000 - 0.00316 = 0.0968 M$. On substituting into the K_a expression:

$$\frac{[H_3O^+][A^-]}{[HA]} = \frac{(3.16 \times 10^{-3})^2}{0.0968} = 1.03 \times 10^{-4}$$

If the K_a or the K_b is known, the concentration of the ionic species can be calculated if the concentration is given. Once the concentration of the H_3O^+ or the OH^- is known, the *pH* or the *pOH* can be calculated.

Example 10

Determine the *pH* of an aqueous ammonia solution, if the $[OH^-]$ is equal to 3.00×10^{-3}.

Solving Process:

Use the ion product expression for water and solve for the H_3O^+.

$$K_w = [H_3O^+][OH^-]$$
$$1.00 \times 10^{-14} = [H_3O^+]\,3.00 \times 10^{-3}$$

$$[H_3O^+] = \frac{1.00 \times 10^{-14}}{3.00 \times 10^{-3}} = 0.333 \times 10^{-11} = 3.33 \times 10^{-12}$$

Now use the definition of *pH*:

$$pH = -\log H_3O^+$$
$$= -\log (3.33 \times 10^{-12})$$
$$= -(\log 3.33 + \log 10^{-12})$$
$$= -[0.522 + (-12)]$$
$$pH = 11.478$$

Consider a buffer solution consisting of sodium acetate and acetic acid. Most of the acetate ion is furnished by the soluble salt. The K_a can be modified:

$$K_a = \frac{[H_3O^+][C_2H_3O_2^-]}{[HC_2H_3O_2]} = \frac{[H_3O^+][salt]}{[acid]}$$

$$[H_3O^+] = K_a \frac{[acid]}{[salt]}$$

Example 11

A buffer solution contains 0.500 mole per liter each of acetic acid and sodium acetate. Determine the pH of the solution. The K_a of the acetic acid is 1.74×10^{-5}.

Solving Process:

$$[H_3O^+] = K_a \frac{[acid]}{[salt]} = \frac{[1.74 \times 10^{-5}] \ [0.500]}{[0.500]} = 1.74 \times 10^{-5} M$$

$$pH = -\log H_3O^+ = -\log (1.74 \times 10^{-5})$$
$$= -(\log 1.74 + \log 10^{-5})$$
$$= -[0.241 + (-5)]$$
$$pH = 4.759$$

Chapter Review Problems

5. Calculate the $[H_3O^+]$ and $[OH^-]$ of the following solutions:
   a. $pH = 2.500$ c. $pOH = 3.200$ e. $pH = 9.600$
   b. $pOH = 5.800$ d. $pH = 4.700$ f. $pOH = 10.300$

6. The approximate pH of some common substances is listed. Calculate the pOH, the $[H_3O^+]$, and the $[OH^-]$:
   a. vinegar   2.8   e. soft drink   3.0
   b. orange   3.5   f. tomato   4.2
   c. rainwater   6.2   g. egg   7.8
   d. seawater   8.5   h. milk of magnesia 10.5

7. The approximate pH of some common chemical solutions is listed. Calculate the pOH, the $[H_3O^+]$, and the $[OH^-]$:
   a. $0.1 M$ HCl   1.00   d. $0.1 M$ H_2SO_4 1.20
   b. $0.1 M$ $HC_2H_3O_2$ 2.90   e. $0.1 M$ $NaHCO_3$ 8.40
   c. $0.1 M$ $NH_{3(aq)}$ 11.10   f. $0.1 M$ NaOH   13.00

8. Find the pH of the solutions:
   a. $0.100 M$ $NH_{3(aq)}$ K_b 1.74×10^{-5}
   b. $0.100 M$ $HC_2H_3O_2$ K_a 1.74×10^{-5}
   c. $0.0500 M$ $HC_2H_3O_2$ K_a 1.74×10^{-5}
   d. $0.750 M$ HNO_2 K_a 4.50×10^{-4}
   e. $0.0100 M$ H_3BO_3 K_{a1} 5.75×10^{-10}
   f. $0.00500 M$ $NH_{3(aq)}$ K_b 1.74×10^{-5}

9. Calculate the ionization constants of the following compounds:
   a. $0.05 M$ HCN pH 5.33   c. $0.10 M$ $NH_{3(aq)}$ pH 11.12
   b. $0.10 M$ $HC_2H_3O_2$ pH 2.87   d. $0.04 M$ $NH_{3(aq)}$ pOH 3.07

Titrations _____22

Titration is an experimental procedure in which the unknown concentration of a known volume of solution is determined by measuring the volume of a solution of known concentration required to react completely with it.

The most common titrations involve the reaction of an acid solution with a basic solution. In laboratory work, volumes used are measured and the concentration of either the acidic or basic solution is known. An indicator is used to detect the endpoint, that is, an equivalent amount of standard solution has been added to the titrated solution. The reaction of the acid and base is termed a **neutralization.** The products of this reaction are a salt and water.

$$\text{acid} + \text{base} \longrightarrow \text{salt} + \text{water}$$

22:1 Titrations

The three types of titration reactions are: (1) an acid with a base to give a soluble salt and water, (2) a soluble salt with a second soluble salt to give a precipitate, and (3) an oxidizing material with a reducing material.

The reaction between a strong acid (HCl or HNO_3) and a strong base ($NaOH$) gives salts ($NaCl$ and $NaNO_3$). Since these salts are products of strong acids and strong bases, the resulting solution is neutral.

For a strong acid/strong base titration, the pH at the endpoint is 7; but only a small amount of reagent causes a major pH change. The titration curve for the neutralization reaction is shown in Figure 22-1a. The indicator selected should change color in the pH range from about 4 to 10. Phenolphthalein is usually used since it is easy to detect visually a slight pink color from a colorless liquid. In the titration curves the letter E represents the endpoint.

Reaction between a strong acid (HCl, HNO_3, or H_2SO_4) and a weak base (NH_3) also produces salts (NH_4Cl, NH_4NO_3, and $(NH_4)_2SO_4$). These salts hydrolyze to form slightly acidic solutions.

For a strong acid/weak base titration, the pH at the endpoint is less than 7 due to the hydrolysis reaction. The titration curve for this reaction

193

is shown in Figure 22-1b. Methyl orange can be used as an indicator because of the low *pH* region in which it changes color.

The reaction between a weak acid ($HC_2H_3O_2$) and a strong base (NaOH) gives a salt ($NaC_2H_3O_2$). Such salts hydrolyze to give a slightly basic solution.

For a weak acid/strong base titration, the *pH* at the endpoint is greater than 7 due to the hydrolysis reaction. The titration curve for this reaction is shown in Figure 22-1c. Any indicator changing color in the higher *pH* ranges could be used but phenolphthalein is most frequently used.

The concentration of the acid solution and basic solution will change slightly the position of the curves (especially at the start and completion of the titration) in relation to the *pH*.

Example 1

If 20.0 mL of a 0.300*M* solution of NaOH is required to neutralize 30.0 mL of a sulfuric acid solution, what is the molarity of the H_2SO_4 solution?

Solving Process:

First write the balanced equation.

$$2NaOH + H_2SO_4 \longrightarrow Na_2SO_4 + 2H_2O$$

From the coefficients of the balanced equation, 2 moles of base are required for reaction with 1 mole of acid. From the problem, 20.0 mL of base are equivalent to 30.0 mL of acid.

$$M\ H_2SO_4 = \frac{20.0\ \text{mL NaOH}}{30.0\ \text{mL } H_2SO_4} \left| \frac{0.300\ \text{mol NaOH}}{1\ \text{L NaOH}} \right| \frac{1\ \text{mol } H_2SO_4}{2\ \text{mol NaOH}} = 0.100M$$

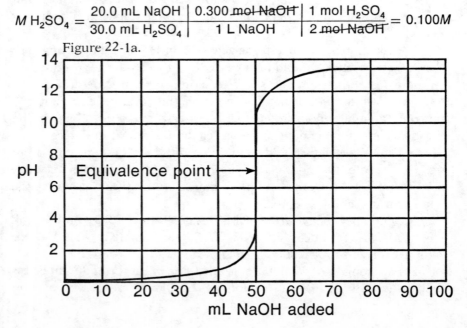

Figure 22-1a.

Figure 22-1b.

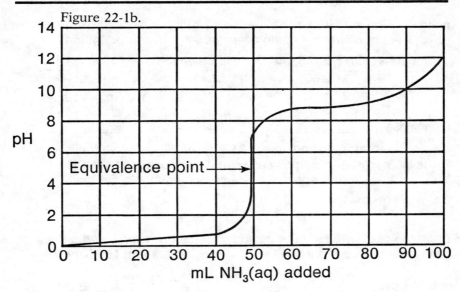

Figure 22-1c.

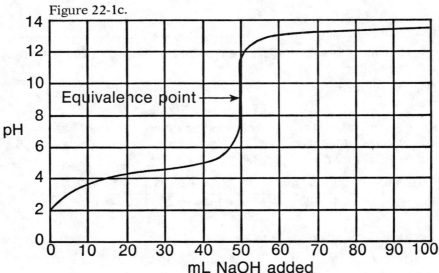

Example 2

What volume in milliliters of 0.500*M* HNO₃ is required to neutralize 25.0 mL of a 0.200*M* NaOH solution?

Solving Process:

The balanced equation is

$$HNO_3 + NaOH \longrightarrow NaNO_3 + H_2O$$

From the coefficients of the balanced equation, 1 mole of acid will react completely with 1 mole of base. Start with the 25.0 mL of NaOH solution. Convert the volume of base to moles using the concentration. Then convert to volume of acid using its concentration.

$$\frac{25.0 \text{ mL NaOH}}{} \left| \frac{0.200 \text{ mol NaOH}}{1000 \text{ mL NaOH}} \right| \frac{1 \text{ mol HNO}_3}{1 \text{ mol NaOH}} \left| \frac{1000 \text{ mL HNO}_3}{0.500 \text{ mol HNO}_3} \right.$$
$$= 10.0 \text{ mL HNO}_3 \text{ soln}$$

Example 3

In a laboratory experiment, 20.00 mL of $NH_3(aq)$ solution is titrated to the methyl orange endpoint using 15.65 mL of a 0.200M HCl solution. What is the concentration of the aqueous ammonia solution?

Solving Process:

$$NH_3 + HCl \longrightarrow NH_4Cl$$

From the coefficients of the balanced equation, 1 mole of base reacts with 1 mole of acid. Also 20.00 mL of NH_3 reacts with 15.65 mL of HCl.

$$M \text{ NH}_3(aq) = \frac{15.65 \text{ mL HCl}}{20.00 \text{ mL NH}_3} \left| \frac{0.200 \text{ mol HCl}}{1 \text{ L HCl}} \right| \frac{1 \text{ mol NH}_3}{1 \text{ mol HCl}} = 0.157M$$

Example 4

How many grams of KOH are required to neutralize 200.0 mL of a 4.00M solution of HNO_3?

Solving Process:

$$KOH + HNO_3 \longrightarrow KNO_3 + H_2O$$

From the coefficients of the balanced equation, 1 mole of base reacts completely with 1 mole of acid. From a formula mass calculation, 56.1 grams KOH equal 1 mole KOH.

$$\frac{200.0 \text{ mL HNO}_3}{} \left| \frac{4.00 \text{ mol HNO}_3}{1000 \text{ mL HNO}_3} \right| \frac{1 \text{ mol KOH}}{1 \text{ mol HNO}_3} \left| \frac{56.1 \text{ g KOH}}{1 \text{ mol KOH}} \right. = 44.9 \text{ g}$$

Example 5

How many liters of a 1.500M sulfuric acid solution are needed to neutralize completely 120.0 grams NaOH?

Solving Process:

$$2NaOH + H_2SO_4 \longrightarrow Na_2SO_4 + 2H_2O$$

From the coefficients of the balanced equation, 2 moles of NaOH react with 1 mole of H_2SO_4. Start with 120.0 grams NaOH.

$$\frac{120.0 \text{ g NaOH}}{} \left| \frac{1 \text{ mol NaOH}}{40.0 \text{ g NaOH}} \right| \frac{1 \text{ mol H}_2SO_4}{2 \text{ mol NaOH}} \left| \frac{1 \text{ L H}_2SO_4}{1.50 \text{ mol H}_2SO_4} \right. = 1.00 \text{ L}$$

Example 6

In a laboratory experiment, a student neutralizes a 15.00 mL sample of vinegar (acetic acid solution) with 31.85 mL of a 0.400M NaOH solution. Calculate the following:
(a)   the molarity of vinegar (acetic acid solution)
(b)   the grams of $HC_2H_3O_2$ in 1 L of vinegar
(c)   the percentage of acetic acid by mass in the vinegar (assume a density of 1.00 g/mL)

Solving Process:
(a)   molarity of vinegar

$$= \frac{31.85 \text{ mL NaOH}}{15.00 \text{ mL vinegar}} \left| \frac{0.400 \text{ mol NaOH}}{1 \text{ L NaOH}} \right| \frac{1 \text{ mol vinegar}}{1 \text{ mol NaOH}}$$

$$= 0.849M$$

(b)   grams $HC_2H_3O_2 = \dfrac{0.849 \text{ mol } HC_2H_3O_2}{1 \text{ L}} \left| \dfrac{60.1 \text{ g } HC_2H_3O_2}{1 \text{ mol } HC_2H_3O_2} \right.$

$$= \frac{51.0 \text{ g } HC_2H_3O_2}{1 \text{ L}}$$

(c)   The percent mass is the number of grams of acetic acid in 100 grams of vinegar. Convert 51.0 grams $HC_2H_3O_2$ per liter of vinegar to percent by using the density of vinegar.

percent mass $HC_2H_3O_2$

$$= \frac{51.0 \text{ g } HC_2H_3O_2}{1 \text{ L vinegar}} \left| \frac{1 \text{ L}}{1000 \text{ mL}} \right| \frac{1 \text{ mL}}{1.00 \text{ g}} \left| \frac{100\%}{1} \right. = 5.10\%$$

Example 7

What mass of barium chloride, $BaCl_2$, is required to completely precipitate the barium sulfate, $BaSO_4$, from 35.00 mL of 0.200M H_2SO_4?

Solving Process:
The balanced equation is

$$H_2SO_4 + BaCl_2 \longrightarrow BaSO_4 + 2HCl$$

$$\frac{35.00 \text{ mL } H_2SO_4}{} \left| \frac{0.200 \text{ mol } H_2SO_4}{1000 \text{ mL } H_2SO_4} \right| \frac{1 \text{ mol } BaCl_2}{1 \text{ mol } H_2SO_4} \left| \frac{208.0 \text{ g } BaCl_2}{1 \text{ mol } BaCl_2} \right.$$

$$= 1.46 \text{ g } BaCl_2$$

Problems

1.   Calculate the unknown quantity for the complete neutralization of the following:

	Acid		*Base*	
	concentration	*volume*	*concentration*	*volume*
a.	0.250*M* HCl	30.00 mL	? NaOH	25.00 mL
b.	0.500*M* H$_2$SO$_4$	?	0.750*M* KOH	20.00 mL
c.	? HNO$_3$	15.00 mL	1.50*M* NH$_3$	25.00 mL
d.	0.400*M* HNO$_3$	35.00 mL	0.800*M* NaOH	?

2. What is the molarity of a NaOH solution if 25.00 mL is required to completely neutralize 40.00 mL of a 1.50*M* solution of H$_2$SO$_4$?

3. Calculate the milliliters of a 0.600*M* solution of HNO$_3$ necessary to neutralize 28.55 mL of a 0.450*M* solution of KOH.

4. How many grams of calcium hydroxide, Ca(OH)$_2$, are required to neutralize 52.68 mL of a 0.750*M* H$_2$SO$_4$ solution?

5. How many milliliters of 0.500*M* NaOH are necessary to neutralize completely 20.00 mL of each of the following acids?
   a. 0.150*M* HNO$_3$ c. 0.220*M* HCl
   b. 0.250*M* H$_2$SO$_4$ d. 0.450*M* H$_3$PO$_4$

6. A titration of 15.00 mL of household ammonia NH$_3$(aq) required 38.57 mL of 0.780*M* HCl. Calculate:
   a. the molarity of the household ammonia
   b. the grams of NH$_3$(aq) per liter of solution
   c. the mass percentage of NH$_3$(aq) in the solution. Assume a density of 0.950 g/mL for the solution

7. Determine the mass of the precipitate lead(II) sulfate, PbSO$_4$, which is produced by the reaction of 30.00 mL of 0.750*M* Pb(NO$_3$)$_2$ with excess sulfuric acid.

8. How many milliliters of 1.50*M* HCl solution are required to react completely with a 0.500 gram sample of iron(II) sulfide ore if the ore contains 95.00% FeS?

22:2 Titrations with Normal Solutions

Titration problems can also be solved using the concentration expression normality and substituting into a mathematical equation.

Consider a reaction between a 1.00*N* HCl solution and a 1.00*N* NaOH solution. It is necessary to add equal volumes of the acid and base to have a complete reaction. An equal number of H$_3$O$^+$ ions and OH$^-$ ions react to produce water. The other product, NaCl, is a salt of a strong acid and a strong base. The resulting solution is neutral.

The equivalent mass of a substance is that mass of material that will produce one mole of charge. One equivalent mass of hydrogen ions will react with one equivalent mass of hydroxide ions. An equal number of equivalents of acid and equivalents of base will react completely to form a salt.

$$\text{normality} = \frac{\text{number of equivalents of solute}}{\text{1 L of solution}}$$

$$\frac{\text{eq acid}}{\text{1 L solution}} \Big| \text{liters of acid} = \frac{\text{eq base}}{\text{1 L solution}} \Big| \text{liters of base}$$

On substitution:

normality acid × volume acid = normality base × volume base

or

$$N_a \times V_a = N_b \times V_b$$

If any three values are known, the fourth value can be calculated. For the factors to be equivalent, both volume terms must be liters or both must be milliliters. Do not mix liters and milliliters.

Acids or bases with one reacting hydrogen ion or hydroxide ion per formula unit contain 1 equivalent per mole. Acids or bases with two reacting hydrogen ions or hydroxide ions contain 2 equivalents per mole. Examples of the relationship between molarity and normality are

| one reacting ion | HCl | 2.00M HCl | = 2.00N HCl |
| (1 eq = 1 mol) | NaOH | 0.300M NaOH | = 0.300N NaOH |

| two reacting ions | H_2SO_4 | 0.750M H_2SO_4 | = 1.50N H_2SO_4 |
| (2 eq = 1 mol) | | | |

Example 8

If 20.0 mL of a 3.00N solution of NaOH are required to neutralize 30.0 mL of a sulfuric acid solution, what is the normality of the H_2SO_4?
Solving Process:

$$\text{equivalents of acid} = \text{equivalents of base}$$
$$N_a \times V_a = N_b \times V_b$$

Change milliliters to liters and then substitute:

$$N_a = \frac{3.00N}{} \Big| \frac{0.0200\,\cancel{L}}{0.0300\,\cancel{L}} = 2.00N$$

Example 9

What volume in milliliters of 0.500N HNO_3 is required to neutralize 25.0 mL of a 2.00N NaOH solution?

Solving Process:

milligram-equivalents acid = milligram-equivalents base

$$N_a \times V_a = N_b \times V_b$$
$$0.500N \times V_a = 2.00N \times 25.0 \text{ mL}$$
$$V_a = \frac{2.00N}{0.500N} \, \Big| \, 25.00 \text{ mL} = 100 \text{ mL}$$

Example 10

How many grams of KOH are required to neutralize 200.0 mL of a 4.00N solution of HNO_3?

Solving Process:

For neutralization to be complete, the number of equivalents of acid must be equal to the number of equivalents of base. First, calculate the number of equivalents of acid. Then convert this answer to grams of KOH.

$$\text{equivalents } HNO_3 = \frac{4.00 \text{ eq } HNO_3}{1 \, L} \, \Big| \, 0.200 \, L = 0.800 \text{ eq}$$

equivalents acid = equivalents base

$$\frac{0.800 \text{ eq KOH}}{} \, \Big| \, \frac{1 \text{ mol KOH}}{1 \text{ eq KOH}} \, \Big| \, \frac{56.1 \text{ g KOH}}{1 \text{ mol KOH}} = 44.9 \text{ g KOH}$$

Problems

9. What is the normality and the molarity of a phosphoric acid solution if 25.00 mL of the solution is necessary to neutralize 30.00 mL of a 0.500N KOH solution?

10. In a laboratory experiment involving the neutralization of vinegar using 0.500N NaOH, the following data was collected:

	Volume of vinegar	Volume of base
Trial 1	10.00 mL	17.59 mL
Trial 2	15.27 mL	28.39 mL
Trial 3	20.14 mL	36.58 mL

Calculate:
a. the normality of the vinegar in each trial
b. the grams of acetic acid per liter of vinegar
c. the mass percentage of $HC_2H_3O_2$ in the vinegar. Assume a density of 1.00 g/mL
d. If the correct percentage is 5.40%, which trial gave the best results? What is the percent error of this trial?

Chapter Review Problems

11. Calculate the unknown quantity required for the complete neutralization of the following:

	Acid concentration	volume	Base concentration	volume
a.	$0.150M$ HNO_3	32.70 mL	? KOH	28.70 mL
b.	$0.350M$ H_2SO_4	26.50 mL	$0.450M$ NaOH	?
c.	$0.500M$ HCl	?	$1.00N$ KOH	15.00 mL
d.	? H_2SO_4	15.00 mL	$0.500M$ NaOH	20.00 mL
e.	$0.250M$ HNO_3	25.00 mL	$0.500N$ NH_3	?
f.	$0.500M$ H_3PO_4	30.00 mL	?	25.00 mL

12. Calculate the grams of $NH_3(aq)$ necessary to neutralize 30.00 mL of a $2.50M$ solution of HNO_3.

13. How many milliliters of $0.750M$ sulfuric acid are needed to neutralize completely 20.00 grams of NaOH?

14. What volume of $0.250N$ H_3PO_4 is required to neutralize 30.00 mL of a $0.0500M$ $Ba(OH)_2$ solution?

15. Determine the normality and the molarity of a sulfuric acid solution if 30.00 mL is used to neutralize 40.00 mL of a $0.500N$ KOH solution.

16. If 1.25 grams of pure $CaCO_3$ required 25.50 mL of a hydrochloric acid solution for complete reaction, calculate the normality of the acid.

17. How many milliliters of $0.250N$ $AgNO_3$ are required to precipitate all the chloride ion as AgCl in a solution made by dissolving a sample of rock salt which has a mass of 0.300 grams and is known to be 99.0% pure NaCl?

18. Hydrogen sulfide gas will react with a lead solution to give a precipitate of lead(II) sulfide, PbS. If H_2S is bubbled into 50.0 mL of a $0.250N$ $Pb(C_2H_3O_2)_2$ solution, calculate the following:
    a. the grams of H_2S required for complete reaction
    b. the volume of H_2S at STP required for complete reaction
    c. the grams of lead(II) sulfide produced

19. A common constituent of the "hardness" of water is often calcium carbonate. The amount of $CaCO_3$ is determined in the laboratory by titration with a standard acid such as HCl, producing water and CO_2. A laboratory technician has just titrated a 100.0 mL sample of water containing $CaCO_3$ with $0.100N$ HCl and finds that 15.20 mL of acid were needed to reach the endpoint. Calculate the mass of $CaCO_3$ contained in exactly one liter of the water.

20. Potassium hydrogen phthalate, $KHC_8H_4O_4$, is often used as a primary standard in the standardization of basic solutions. The potassium hydrogen phthalate, abbreviated KHP, reacts with a base to produce a salt and water. After preparing a solution of KOH which, you hope, is $0.100N$, you decide to check the concentration

with KHP. You dissolve 0.200 grams of KHP in water and titrate with the 0.100N base. If the base is exactly 0.100N, how much base solution will be required?

Solubility Product
Principle_____23

23:1 Solubility Product Constant

Most insoluble ionic solids are actually soluble in water to a limited extent. These solids dissociate slightly in water. The compound silver chloride dissociates slightly in water to give silver ions, Ag^+, and chloride ions, Cl^-. An equilibrium is established in the saturated solution between the solid and the ions in the solution. The equation for this equilibrium is

$$AgCl \rightleftharpoons Ag^+ + Cl^-$$

The above equation can be represented mathematically by a constant, K, called the **equilibrium constant.** By definition, this constant is equal to the concentration of the products in moles per liter divided by the concentration of the reactants in moles per liter. The concentration of each ion is raised to a power which is equal to the coefficient of the ion in the balanced equation. This constant can be expressed as follows:

$$K_{eq} = \frac{[products]}{[reactants]}$$

From the balanced equation:

$$K_{eq} = \frac{[Ag^+][Cl^-]}{[AgCl]}$$

The concentration of a pure solid such as AgCl is a constant. Since both terms, [AgCl] and K_{eq} are constants, they can be multiplied together to form a new constant which is termed the **solubility product constant, K_{sp}.**

$$[Ag^+][Cl^-] = K_{eq}[AgCl] = K_{sp}$$

The expression, $[Ag^+][Cl^-]$, is called the **solubility product.** The equation generally used in calculations is

$$[Ag^+][Cl^-] \quad = \qquad K_{sp}$$
$$\text{ion product} \quad \text{solubility product}$$
$$\text{constant}$$

The concentration of the ions in moles per liter (the solubility product) is equal to the K_{sp} when an equilibrium is established between the saturated solution and the solid particles. Note that there is no limit on the concentrations of the Ag^+ and Cl^- ions. In a solution containing only AgCl, the concentrations of Ag^+ and Cl^- are the same. However, if the solution contains AgCl and $AgNO_3$, the concentration of the Ag^+ is greater than the concentration of the Cl^-. Similarly, the Cl^- concentration can be larger than the Ag^+ concentration if the solution contains NaCl and AgCl. The only restriction is that the concentration of the Ag^+ multiplied by the concentration of the Cl^- must be equal to the K_{sp}.

The solubility product constant, K_{sp}, is the product of the concentrations of the ions in a saturated solution raised to the power of their coefficients in the balanced equation. For example, the expression of the solubility product for $PbCl_2$ would be

$$PbCl_2 \rightleftharpoons Pb^{2+} + 2Cl^-$$

$$K_{sp} = [Pb^{2+}][Cl^-]^2$$

Using the equation for K_{sp}, it is possible to calculate the solubility of a salt if its K_{sp} is known, or to calculate the K_{sp} from the solubility. The K_{sp} is an experimental value.

Example 1

A 1 liter saturated solution of AgCl is evaporated to dryness and the residue is equivalent to 1.34×10^{-5} mole. What is the experimental K_{sp} of the silver chloride?

Solving Process:

The equation for the system is $AgCl \rightleftharpoons Ag^+ + Cl^-$. Therefore, in a saturated solution of AgCl, 1.34×10^{-5} mole AgCl gives 1.34×10^{-5} mole Ag^+ and 1.34×10^{-5} mole Cl^-. The solubility product expression for AgCl is

$$K_{sp} = [Ag^+][Cl^-]$$

Since the concentration in moles per liter is given, substitute directly into the equation:

$$K_{sp} = [1.34 \times 10^{-5}][1.34 \times 10^{-5}] = 1.80 \times 10^{-10}$$

Example 2

What is the experimental K_{sp} of $CaCO_3$ if the residue after evaporation of a 1.00 liter saturated solution is found to have a mass of 6.90 milligrams?

Solving Process:

Since the expression for K_{sp} requires the concentration in moles per liter, convert the 6.90 mg/L to moles per liter:

$$\frac{\text{moles } CaCO_3}{\text{liter}} = \frac{6.90 \text{ mg } CaCO_3}{1 \text{ L}} \left| \frac{1 \text{ g } CaCO_3}{1000 \text{ mg } CaCO_3} \right| \frac{1 \text{ mol } CaCO_3}{100 \text{ g } CaCO_3}$$

The equation $CaCO_3 \rightleftarrows Ca^{2+} + CO_3^{2-}$ indicates that $[Ca^{2+}] = [CO_3^{2-}] = 6.90 \times 10^{-5}$ mol $CaCO_3$/L. Substituting into the K_{sp} expression:

$$K_{sp} = [Ca^{2+}][CO_3^{2-}] = [6.90 \times 10^{-5}][6.90 \times 10^{-5}] = 4.76 \times 10^{-9}$$

Example 3

A saturated solution of lead(II) chloride contains 4.50 grams of $PbCl_2$ per liter. What is the K_{sp} of the compound?

Solving Process:

Convert to the solubility in moles per liter.

$$\frac{4.50 \text{ g } PbCl_2}{1 \text{ L}} \left| \frac{1 \text{ mol } PbCl_2}{278 \text{ g } PbCl_2} \right. = 1.62 \times 10^{-2} \text{ mol } PbCl_2/L$$

The equation $PbCl_2 \rightleftarrows Pb^{2+} + 2Cl^-$ indicates that 1 mole $PbCl_2$ dissociates to give 1 mole Pb^{2+} and 2 moles Cl^-. Therefore, 1.62×10^{-2} mole $PbCl_2$ gives 1.62×10^{-2} mole Pb^{2+} and 3.24×10^{-2} mole Cl^-. By definition of the K_{sp}, the concentration of ions is raised to a power which is equal to the coefficient of the ion. Thus the Cl^- concentration is squared.

$$K_{sp} = [Pb^{2+}][Cl^-]^2 = [1.62 \times 10^{-2}][3.24 \times 10^{-2}]^2 = 1.70 \times 10^{-5}$$

Problems

1. From the solubilities, determine the experimental value of the K_{sp} for each compound:
   a. AgI 2.88×10^{-7} g/100 mL
   b. $BaCO_3$ 7.00×10^{-5} mol/L
   c. CaF_2 1.70 mg/100 mL

  d. $Pb(OH)_2$ 4.20×10^{-6} mol/L
  e. SrF_2 1.22×10^{-2} g/100 mL
  f. $Pb(IO_3)_2$ 2.30 mg/100 mL

Example 4

If the K_{sp} of AgCl is 1.81×10^{-10}, determine the solubility of AgCl in grams per liter.

Solving Process:

From the equation $AgCl \rightleftharpoons Ag^+ + Cl^-$, note that the concentration of Ag^+ is equal to the concentration of Cl^-. Let the Ag^+ concentration be equal to x:

$$[Ag^+] = [Cl^-] = x$$

Substitute into the K_{sp} equation:

$$[Ag^+][Cl^-] = [x][x] = K_{sp} = 1.81 \times 10^{-10}$$
$$x^2 = 1.81 \times 10^{-10}$$
$$x = \sqrt{1.81 \times 10^{-10}} = 1.35 \times 10^{-5}$$

The x, which is termed the **molar solubility,** is 1.35×10^{-5} mole per liter. In grams per liter it is

$$\frac{1.35 \times 10^{-5} \text{ mol AgCl}}{1 \text{ L}} \left| \frac{143 \text{ g AgCl}}{1 \text{ mol AgCl}} \right. = 1.93 \times 10^{-3} \text{ g AgCl/L}$$

Example 5

For a saturated silver chromate solution calculate the molar solubility, the molar concentration of Ag^+ and CrO_4^{2-}, and the solubility in grams per 100 mL of silver chromate. The K_{sp} of Ag_2CrO_4 is 1.12×10^{-12}.

Solving Process:

From the equation $Ag_2CrO_4 \rightleftharpoons 2Ag^+ + CrO_4^{2-}$ note that the concentration of the Ag^+ ion is twice the concentration of the CrO_4^{2-} ion. Let x equal the molar solubility:

$$[Ag^+] = 2x \qquad [CrO_4^{2-}] = x$$

Substitute into the K_{sp} expression:

$$[Ag^+]^2[CrO_4^{2-}] = K_{sp}$$
$$[2x]^2[x] = 4x^3 = 1.12 \times 10^{-12}$$
$$x^3 = \frac{1.12 \times 10^{-12}}{4} = 280 \times 10^{-15}$$
$$x = \sqrt[3]{280 \times 10^{-15}} = \sqrt[3]{280} \times 10^{-5}$$

$$x = 6.54 \times 10^{-5} = \text{molar solubility}$$

The concentrations of the ions are

$$[Ag^+] = 2x = 1.31 \times 10^{-4}$$
$$[CrO_4{}^{2-}] = x = 6.54 \times 10^{-5}$$

Solubility in grams per 10.0 mL is

$$\frac{6.54 \times 10^{-5}\ \cancel{\text{mol Ag}_2\text{CrO}_4}}{\cancel{1 \text{L}}} \left| \frac{332\ \text{g Ag}_2\text{CrO}_4}{1\ \cancel{\text{mol Ag}_2\text{CrO}_4}} \right| \frac{\cancel{1\text{L}}}{1000\ \cancel{\text{mL}}} \left| \frac{1000\ \cancel{\text{mL}}}{10(100\ \text{mL})} \right.$$

$$= 2.17 \times 10^{-3}\ \text{g/100 mL}$$

Problems

2. Calculate the molar solubility of the following compounds from their K_{sp} values:

a. CuS 6.31×10^{-36}
b. SrC_2O_4 1.58×10^{-7}
c. $Al(OH)_3$ 1.26×10^{-33}
d. PbI_2 1.66×10^{-8}

The following two Examples deal with the common ion effect.

Example 6

What is the molar solubility of $BaSO_4$ in a solution that contains $0.100M$ Na_2SO_4? The K_{sp} of $BaSO_4$ is 1.15×10^{-10}

Solving Process:
This solution contains Na_2SO_4 which is assumed to dissociate completely into Na^+ and $SO_4{}^{2-}$. There are two sources of $SO_4{}^{2-}$ from the barium sulfate and from the sodium sulfate.

$$Na_2SO_4 \longrightarrow 2Na^+ + SO_4{}^{2-}$$
$$BaSO_4 \rightleftharpoons Ba^{2+} + SO_4{}^{2-}$$

Let x equal the moles of $BaSO_4$ that dissolve per liter of $0.100M$ Na_2SO_4. The equation $BaSO_4 \rightleftharpoons Ba^{2+} + SO_4{}^{2-}$ indicates that the concentration of Ba^{2+} is equal to the concentration of $SO_4{}^{2-}$, for these two ions come from the barium sulfate. However, the solution already contains $0.100M$ $SO_4{}^{2-}$. The concentration of the ions in the solution is therefore

$$[Ba^{2+}] = x \qquad [SO_4{}^{2-}] = x + 0.100$$

Substitute into the K_{sp} expression:

$$[Ba^{2+}][SO_4{}^{2-}] = (x)(x + 0.100) = K_{sp} = 1.15 \times 10^{-10}$$

If the K_{sp} is small, very little $BaSO_4$ will dissolve. Some of the $BaSO_4$ will ionize but according to Le Chatelier's principle, a reaction shifts equilibrium in such a way as to relieve a stress. The additional SO_4^{2-} ions are removed from solution by uniting with Ba^{2+} to form $BaSO_4$. Then, assume that $x + 0.100 \cong 0.100$. (The symbol $\cong$ means approximately equal to.) Thus:

$$0.100x \cong 1.15 \times 10^{-10} \qquad x \cong \frac{1.15 \times 10^{-10}}{0.100} = 1.15 \times 10^{-9} M$$

Example 7

Determine the molar solubility of iron(II) hydroxide in $0.0500M$ NaOH. The K_{sp} of $Fe(OH)_2$ is 7.94×10^{-16}.

Solving Process:

Assume that the NaOH is completely dissociated and gives $0.0500M$ OH^- ions. There are two sources of OH^- ions — the NaOH and the $Fe(OH)_2$.

$$NaOH \longrightarrow Na^+ + OH^-$$
$$Fe(OH)_2 \rightleftarrows Fe^{2+} + 2OH^-$$

Let x equal the molar solubility or concentration in moles/liter. Using the equation $Fe(OH)_2 \rightleftarrows Fe^{2+} + 2OH^-$ we get the following:

$$[Fe^{2+}] = x \qquad [OH^-] = 2x + 0.0500$$

Substitute into the K_{sp} expression:

$$[Fe^{2+}][OH^-]^2 = (x)(2x + 0.0500)^2 = K_{sp} = 7.94 \times 10^{-16}$$

Assume that $2x + 0.0500 \cong 0.0500$.

$$(0.0500)^2 x \cong 7.94 \times 10^{-16}$$
$$x \cong \frac{7.94 \times 10^{-16}}{2.50 \times 10^{-3}} = 3.18 \times 10^{-13} M$$

Note that the OH^- concentration is squared without regard to the source of the OH^-. Since the x is small compared to the 0.0500, the assumption is valid. Thus, 3.18×10^{-13} mole $Fe(OH)_2$ can be dissolved in 1 liter of $0.0500M$ NaOH to give a saturated solution containing 3.18×10^{-13} mole Fe^{2+} and 0.0500 mole OH^-.

Problems

3. Determine the molar solubility or concentration of silver chloride when the compound is dissolved in:
   a. pure water   **b.** $0.1000M$ NaCl   **c.** $0.0100M$ NaCl
   The K_{sp} of AgCl is 1.81×10^{-10}

4. Determine the molar solubility or concentration of calcium hydroxide when the compound is dissolved in:
    a. pure water   **c.** $0.01 M$ NaOH
    b. $0.10 M$ NaOH   **d.** $0.10 M$ $Ca(NO_3)_2$
    The K_{sp} of $Ca(OH)_2$ is 5.50×10^{-6}

5. Find the molar solubility or concentration of silver chromate when the compound is dissolved in:
    a. pure water   **b.** $0.04 M$ $AgNO_3$ **c.** $0.25 M$ K_2CrO_4
    The K_{sp} of Ag_2CrO_4 is 1.12×10^{-12}

23:2 Predicting Precipitation

A useful application of the K_{sp} data is to determine if precipitation will occur when a salt and a solution or two solutions are mixed. Precipitation takes place only when the ion product exceeds the K_{sp}. If it exceeds the K_{sp}, precipitation will occur.

$$\left. \begin{array}{l} \text{ion product} < K_{sp} \\ \text{ion product} = K_{sp} \end{array} \right\} \quad \text{no precipitate will form}$$

$$\text{ion product} > K_{sp} \qquad \text{precipitate will form}$$

Remember, that if the final solution is formed by mixing two solutions it is necessary to consider dilution. Each solute is diluted when the other solution is added.

Example 8

Will precipitation occur in a solution containing a concentration of $2.00 \times 10^{-4} M$ Pb^{2+} ions when enough solid NaF is added to bring the fluoride ion concentration to $3.00 \times 10^{-2} M$? The K_{sp} of PbF_2 is 2.69×10^{-8}. (Ignore volume changes.)

Solving Process:
For precipitation to take place, the K_{sp} value must be exceeded. The value of the ion product must be calculated and then compared to the K_{sp} value. Since the dissociation equation is $PbF_2 \rightleftharpoons Pb^{2+} + 2F^-$, the ion product is $[Pb^{2+}][F^-]^2$.

$$[Pb^{2+}][F^-]^2 = [2.00 \times 10^{-4}][3.00 \times 10^{-2}]^2$$
$$= (2.00 \times 10^{-4})(9.00 \times 10^{-4})$$
$$= 1.80 \times 10^{-7}$$

Since 1.80×10^{-7} is larger than the K_{sp} value (2.69×10^{-8}), precipitation will occur.

Example 9

Will precipitation occur when 50.0 mL of a $3.00 \times 10^{-2}M$ $Pb(NO_3)_2$ solution is added to 50.0 mL of $2.00 \times 10^{-3}M$ KCl? The K_{sp} of $PbCl_2$ is 1.62×10^{-5}.

Solving Process:
Assume that no change in volume occurs when the two solutions are mixed and that the final volume will be 100.0 mL. First calculate the concentration of ions in the mixture as if they do not react. The Pb^{2+} concentration, because of a twofold dilution, is $1.50 \times 10^{-2}M$. The Cl^- concentration, because of a twofold dilution, is $1.00 \times 10^{-3}M$. Use these new concentrations of Pb^{2+} and Cl^- to calculate the ion product and determine if it exceeds the K_{sp}.

The equation for a saturated solution is $PbCl_2 \rightleftharpoons Pb^{2+} + 2Cl^-$. Therefore, on substitution the ion product becomes:

$$[Pb^{2+}][Cl^-]^2 = [1.50 \times 10^{-2}][1.00 \times 10^{-3}]^2 = 1.50 \times 10^{-8}$$

Since 1.50×10^{-8} is smaller than the K_{sp} of $PbCl_2$ (1.62×10^{-5}), precipitation does not occur. The 100 mL solution is unsaturated.

Example 10

What concentration of carbonate should be added to a silver solution to reduce the concentration of Ag^+ ion to 2.00×10^{-6} mole? The K_{sp} of Ag_2CO_3 is 7.07×10^{-12}.

Solving Process:
From the equation $Ag_2CO_3 \rightleftharpoons 2Ag^+ + CO_3^{2-}$, obtain the K_{sp} expression.

$$K_{sp} = [Ag^+]^2[CO_3^{2-}]$$

Solve for CO_3^{2-} concentration.

$$[CO_3^{2-}] = \frac{K_{sp}}{[Ag^+]^2} = \frac{7.07 \times 10^{-12}}{[2.00 \times 10^{-6}]^2} = \frac{7.07 \times 10^{-12}}{4.00 \times 10^{-12}} = 1.77 \text{ mol/L}$$

Example 11

Calculate the $[OH^-]$ from iron(III) hydroxide in a water solution saturated with $Fe(OH)_3$. The K_{sp} of $Fe(OH)_3$ is 3.98×10^{-38}. Determine the *pH* of the solution.

Solving Process:
From the equation, write the K_{sp} expression.

$$Fe(OH)_3 \rightleftharpoons Fe^{3+} + 3OH^-$$

Let $x = [Fe^{3+}]$ and $3x = [OH^-]$.

$$K_{sp} = [Fe^{3+}][OH^-]^3 = 3.98 \times 10^{-38}$$
$$[x][3x]^3 = 3.98 \times 10^{-38}$$
$$x^4 = \frac{3.98 \times 10^{-38}}{27}$$
$$x = 1.96 \times 10^{-10} M$$

$$[OH^-] \text{ from } Fe(OH)_3 = 3(1.96 \times 10^{-10}) = 5.88 \times 10^{-10}$$

Because of the small quantity of $[OH^-]$ from $Fe(OH)_3$ the $pH \cong 7$ since the water will provide $[OH^-] = 10^{-7}$ mol/L.

Chapter Review Problems

6. Given the following solubilities, determine the K_{sp} for each compound:
   a. Ag_2S 1.60×10^{-16} g/100 mL
   b. As_2S_3 5.17×10^{-5} g/100 mL
   c. Ag_3PO_4 8.50×10^{-4} g/100 mL
   d. Bi_2S_3 1.70×10^{-15} mol/L
   e. $Mn(OH)_2$ 2.10×10^{-4} g/100 mL
   f. $Ca_3(PO_4)_2$ 3.92×10^{-6} mol/L

7. Calculate the molar solubility for each using the following K_{sp} values:
   a. Ag_2S 6.31×10^{-50}
   b. $BaCrO_4$ 1.17×10^{-10}
   c. $Fe(OH)_2$ 7.94×10^{-16}
   d. $Pb_3(PO_4)_2$ 7.94×10^{-43}

8. Determine the molar concentration of the metallic ions from the K_{sp} values of the following compounds:
   a. $BaSO_3$ 7.94×10^{-7} e. $Ba(OH)_2$ 4.01×10^{-3}
   b. MgF_2 6.46×10^{-9} f. Hg_2Cl_2 1.32×10^{-18}
   c. Ag_2SO_4 1.45×10^{-5} g. Ag_3PO_4 1.45×10^{-16}
   d. $Ca_3(PO_4)_2$ 2.00×10^{-29}

9. From the K_{sp} values, calculate the solubility in milligrams per 100 milliliters for the following compounds:
   a. $CdCO_3$ 5.25×10^{-12} d. $CaSO_4$ 9.12×10^{-6}
   b. $Cu(OH)_2$ 2.19×10^{-20} e. $AgCl$ 1.81×10^{-10}
   c. $Fe(OH)_3$ 3.98×10^{-38} f. Ag_2CO_3 7.07×10^{-12}

10. If a solution contains $1.00 \times 10^{-2} M$ chloride ions and $1.00 \times 10^{-3} M$ iodide ions, which will precipitate first, AgCl or AgI, if a solution of $AgNO_3$ is added one drop at a time? The K_{sp} of AgCl is 1.81×10^{-10}; K_{sp} of AgI is 8.32×10^{-17}.

11. If a solution contains $2.00 \times 10^{-3}M$ lead ions and $1.00 \times 10^{-2}M$ silver ions, which will precipitate first, $PbSO_4$ or Ag_2SO_4, when a solution of Na_2SO_4 is added one drop at a time? The K_{sp} of $PbSO_4$ is 1.62×10^{-8}; the K_{sp} of Ag_2SO_4 is 1.45×10^{-5}.

12. Would it be possible to separate a solution containing $0.00200M$ Pb^{2+} and $0.0300M$ Ag^+ by adding drops of Na_2CO_3 solution? If so, which compound, $PbCO_3$ or Ag_2CO_3, would precipitate first? The K_{sp} of $PbCO_3$ is 7.41×10^{-14}; the K_{sp} of Ag_2CO_3 is 7.07×10^{-12}.

13. What concentration of hydroxide ion would be required to bring about precipitation of the following metallic ions?
    a. Al^{3+} $2.00 \times 10^{-5}M$ $K_{sp}\ Al(OH)_3 = 1.26 \times 10^{-33}$
    b. Ba^{2+} $4.00 \times 10^{-4}M$ $K_{sp}\ Ba(OH)_2 = 5.01 \times 10^{-3}$
    c. Co^{2+} $1.50 \times 10^{-3}M$ $K_{sp}\ Co(OH)_2 = 1.58 \times 10^{-15}$

14. Determine if precipitation would occur in the following cases:
    a. $100.0\ mL$ of a $5.00 \times 10^{-3}M\ Ba(NO_3)_2$ is mixed with $100.0\ L$ of $2.00 \times 10^{-2}M\ NaF$. K_{sp} of BaF_2 is 1.05×10^{-6}.
    b. $50.0\ mL$ of $6.0 \times 10^{-4}M\ AgNO_3$ is mixed with $50.0\ mL$ of $5.0 \times 10^{-4}M\ K_2CrO_4$. K_{sp} of Ag_2CrO_4 is 1.12×10^{-12}.
    c. $25.0\ mL$ of $6.0 \times 10^{-6}M\ Sr(NO_3)_2$ is mixed with $25.0\ mL$ of $4.0 \times 10^{-7}M\ H_3PO_4$. K_{sp} of $Sr_3(PO_4)_2$ is 4.07×10^{-28}.

15. The solubility product of barium sulfate is 1.15×10^{-10}. Find the solubility of $BaSO_4$ in $0.0100M\ BaCl_2$.

16. Determine the mass of calcium fluoride, CaF_2, that will dissolve in $200.0\ mL$ of water. Assume that there is no volume change. K_{sp} of CaF_2 is 2.69×10^{-11}.

17. Determine if a precipitate of silver chromate, Ag_2CrO_4, will form when $100.0\ mL$ of $0.100M\ AgNO_3$ are added to $100.0\ mL$ of $0.350M\ K_2CrO_4$. K_{sp} of Ag_2CrO_4 is 1.12×10^{-12}.

18. Pure silver sulfate, Ag_2SO_4, is dissolved in enough water to make $800.0\ mL$ of a saturated solution. Determine the grams of Ag_2SO_4 that dissolve if the K_{sp} is 1.45×10^{-5}.

19. Determine the mass in grams of Fe^{3+} in exactly $1.000\ mL$ of a saturated solution of iron(III) hydroxide. The K_{sp} is 3.98×10^{-38}.

20. A solution containing $0.100M\ HF$ also contains $0.0100M\ Ca(NO_3)_2$. Hydrochloric acid is added slowly till the solution has a pH of 2.00. Will a precipitate of calcium fluoride, CaF_2, occur? For the HF, $K_a = 6.46 \times 10^{-4}$; and for the CaF_2, $K_{sp} = 2.69 \times 10^{-11}$.

21. Iron(II) hydroxide, $Fe(OH)_2$, has a K_{sp} of 7.94×10^{-16}. If a solution has a pH of 10.00, what is the solubility of the metallic hydroxide?

22. Solid silver nitrate, $AgNO_3$, is slowly added to a solution containing $0.100M$ chloride ion and $0.100M$ chromate ion. Assume that the addition of the solid causes no volume change. Which will precipitate first, the silver chloride or the silver chromate? For AgCl, $K_{sp} = 1.81 \times 10^{-10}$; for Ag_2CrO_4, $K_{sp} = 1.12 \times 10^{-12}$.

23. Using the information in problem 22, determine the chloride ion concentration when the red silver chromate just begins to precipitate. What percent of the chloride ion originally present ($0.100M$) remains in solution when precipitation begins?

Oxidation-Reduction Reactions _____ 24

In most of the equations considered in previous chapters one species displaces another species which is similarly charged. Double displacement reactions such as the neutralizations are common examples. The species are ionic and retain the same charge as reactants and products.

$$2NaOH(aq) + H_2SO_4(aq) \longrightarrow Na_2SO_4(aq) + 2HOH(l)$$

$$2Na^+(aq) + 2OH^-(aq) + 2H^+(aq) + SO_4{}^{2-}(aq) \longrightarrow 2Na^+(aq)^+$$
$$SO_4{}^{2-}(aq) + 2H^+(aq) + 2OH^-(aq)$$

This reaction is not an oxidation-reduction reaction as there is no change in the charges of the ions. Reactions such as synthesis and single displacement are oxidation-reduction reactions since there have been changes in the charges.

24:1 Oxidation Numbers

Oxidation number is defined as the charge that an atom *appears* to have when both electrons in a bond are assigned to the more electronegative atom. Without knowledge of electron bond formulas, the oxidation states of an atom may be assigned from the following arbitrary rules.

1. All free elements are assigned an oxidation number of zero without regard to the molecule. Thus, hydrogen in H_2, oxygen in O_2, and phosphorus in P_4, all have an oxidation number of zero.

2. The oxidation number of a monatomic ion is equal to the charge on the ion.
    a. Group I elements form only 1+ ions.
    b. Group II elements form only 2+ ions.
    c. Halogen elements in binary compounds have a 1− oxidation number except in interhalogen compounds.
    d. The oxidation number of oxygen in compounds is generally 2−. The exceptions are the peroxides, in which the oxidation number is 1−, and in oxygen difluoride, OF_2, where oxygen has an oxidation number of 2+.
    e. In practically all hydrogen-containing compounds, the oxidation number of hydrogen is 1+. The exception occurs with the metal hydrides, in which the oxidation number of hydrogen is 1−.

3. All oxidation numbers that are assigned must be consistent with the conservation of charge. For neutral particles, the oxidation numbers of all atoms must add up to zero. For a polyatomic ion, the oxidation numbers of the atoms must add up to the charge on the polyatomic ion. Review the following examples.

	hydrogen	oxygen	sulfur	Total Charge
sulfuric acid H_2SO_4	2(1+) +	4(2−) +	?	= 0
	oxidation number of S = 6+			
disulfurous acid $H_2S_2O_5$	2(1+) +	5(2−) +	?	= 0
	oxidation number of S = 4+			
sulfite ion $SO_3{}^{2-}$		3(2−) +	?	= 2−
	oxidation number of S = 4+			
thiosulfate ion $S_2O_3{}^{2-}$		3(2−) +	?	= 2−
	oxidation number of S = 2+			

Oxidation is the process by which electrons are removed from atoms or ions. **Reduction** is the process by which electrons are added to atoms or ions. Oxidation and reduction must occur at the same time in a reaction, and the number of electrons lost must equal the number gained. This idea can be illustrated by the reaction of magnesium with oxygen to form magnesium oxide.

$$2Mg(c) + O_2(g) \longrightarrow 2MgO(c)$$

Magnesium metal and oxygen gas have an oxidation state of zero. In MgO the magnesium ion has a charge of 2+ and the oxygen ion has a charge of 2−. Remember: In every reaction in which oxidation occurs, reduction also occurs.

24:2 Half-Reactions

A redox equation can be separated into an oxidation half-reaction and a reduction half-reaction. Notice that only electrons are transferred. For the magnesium-oxygen reaction the half reactions are

Oxidation half-reaction $\quad\quad Mg \longrightarrow Mg^{2+} + 2e^-$ $\quad$ (Loss of electrons)

Reduction half-reaction $\quad\quad O_2 + 4e^- \longrightarrow 2O^{2-}$ $\quad$ (Gain of electrons)

An oxidation half-reaction (electron loss) must always be paired with a reduction (electron gain). The loss and gain of electrons must be equal as electrons are not created or destroyed in these reactions.

For the two half-reactions given, multiply the oxidation half-reaction by 2, and then add all reactants and products. The electrons then subtract out.

$$2Mg \longrightarrow 2Mg^{2+} + 4e^-$$
$$O_2 + 4e^- \longrightarrow 2O^{2-}$$
$$2Mg + O_2 \longrightarrow 2Mg^{2+} + 2O^{2-}$$
or
$$2Mg + O_2 \longrightarrow 2MgO$$

The method of balancing oxidation-reduction equations is to balance separately the oxidation half-reaction and the reduction half-reaction. The number of electrons gained in one half-reaction and lost in the other half-reaction must be the same. The two half-reactions are added to obtain the balanced equation for the total reaction.

A general approach to balancing redox reactions is as follows:
1. Write the separate half-reactions.
2. Balance the electrons using oxidation numbers.
3. Balance the atoms in each half-reaction as follows:
   a. Balance all atoms with the use of coefficients, except hydrogen and oxygen atoms.
   b. Add enough water (H_2O) to the side deficient in oxygen to balance the oxygen.

c. Add sufficient hydrogen ion (H$^+$) to the side deficient in hydrogen to balance the hydrogen.

4. Multiply the half-reactions by small whole numbers to balance the electrons.

5. Add the two half-reactions and subtract any duplications on either side of the equation.

Example 1

Write a balanced oxidation-reduction equation for the following reaction:

$$H_3AsO_4 + Zn \longrightarrow AsH_3 + Zn^{2+}$$

Solving Process:

Separate the reaction into two half-reactions. Balance the half-reactions separately. The reduction half-reaction is

$$H_3AsO_4 \longrightarrow AsH_3$$

The first step in balancing the half-reaction is to indicate the number of electrons gained or lost. In the reduction half-reaction being considered here, the arsenic has an oxidation number 5+ before the reaction and 3− after the reaction. Thus arsenic must gain 8 electrons.

$$H_3AsO_4 + 8e^- \longrightarrow AsH_3$$

The next step is to balance all elements other than oxygen and hydrogen. In the reaction above, one arsenic atom appears on each side of the equation. The equation is balanced with respect to arsenic atoms, the only element present in addition to oxygen and hydrogen. No change is needed to balance the arsenic. Next oxygen should be balanced. You may assume that all the oxidation-reduction reactions in this book take place in water solution. Thus, oxygen atoms are always available in the form of water molecules.

$$H_3AsO_4 + 8e^- \longrightarrow AsH_3 + 4H_2O$$

Finally the hydrogen atoms must be balanced. Hydrogen is available in water molecules, of course, but using water to balance hydrogen atoms would throw the oxygen atoms out of balance. If you note that the solution is acidic (H_3AsO_4 is one of the reactants) then you will realize that H$^+$ ions will be abundant in the solution and can be used to balance the hydrogen atoms.

$$H_3AsO_4 + 8H^+ + 8e^- \longrightarrow AsH_3 + 4H_2O$$

The reduction half-reaction is now balanced. The oxidation half-reaction must now be balanced. The zinc atoms change oxidation number from 0 to 2+, and they lose two electrons each.

$$Zn \longrightarrow Zn^{2+} + 2e^-$$

The half-reaction is also balanced with respect to all atoms, there being one zinc atom on each side and no other elements present. Before the two half-reactions can be combined to give the overall equation, the coefficients of the electrons must be adjusted so that the same number of electrons are lost as are gained. The arsenic half-reaction requires eight electrons while the zinc half-reaction produces two. The least common multiple of eight and two is eight, so the reduction half-reaction is multiplied by one and the oxidation half-reaction by four.

Reduction half-reaction × 1

$$H_3AsO_4 + 8H^+ + 8e^- \longrightarrow AsH_3 + 4H_2O$$

Oxidation half-reaction × 4

$$4Zn \longrightarrow 4Zn^{2+} + 8e^-$$

Adding the two half-reactions and eliminating the electrons which appear in equal numbers on both sides gives

$$H_3AsO_4 + 8H^+ + 4Zn \longrightarrow AsH_3 + 4H_2O + 4Zn^{2+}$$

Example 2

Write a balanced oxidation-reduction equation for the following reaction:

$$MnO_4^- + H_2SO_3 \longrightarrow Mn^{2+} + HSO_4^- + H_2O$$

Solving Process:

Separate into two half-reactions. Balance the separate half-reactions.

Reduction		Oxidation
	Skeleton	
$MnO_4^- \longrightarrow Mn^{2+}$		$H_2SO_3 \longrightarrow HSO_4^-$
	Electron balance	
$MnO_4^- + 5e^- \longrightarrow Mn^{2+}$		$H_2SO_3 \longrightarrow HSO_4^- + 2e^-$
	Atom balance	
$8H^+ + MnO_4^- + 5e^- \longrightarrow Mn^{2+} + 4H_2O$		$H_2O + H_2SO_3 \longrightarrow HSO_4^- + 2e^- + 3H^+$

The number of electrons needed for the reduction half-reaction is five since the manganese atom changes oxidation number from $7+$ to $2+$. The number of electrons produced by the oxidation half-reaction is two since the sulfur atom changes oxidation number from $4+$ to $6+$. The least common multiple of five and two is ten. Thus the reduction half-reaction must be multiplied by two and the oxidation half-reaction by five to obtain the same number of electrons given up as are taken up.

Oxidation half-reaction × 5

$$5H_2O + 5H_2SO_3 \longrightarrow 5HSO_4^- + 10e^- + 15 H^+$$

Reduction half-reaction × 2

$$16H^+ + 2MnO_4^- + 10e^- \longrightarrow 2Mn^{2+} + 8H_2O$$

Adding the half-reactions and subtracting out those species appearing on both sides produces the completed, balanced equation:

$$H^+ + 2MnO_4^- + 5H_2SO_3 \longrightarrow 2Mn^{2+} + 3H_2O + 5HSO_4^-$$

Example 3

Reactions of the oxidation-reduction type can also take place in basic solution. Balance these just as you would an acidic reaction and then add sufficient hydroxide ions (OH^-) to each side to change all H^+ ions to H_2O molecules. Remember that the same number of hydroxide ions must be added to each side of the reaction. Write a balanced oxidation-reduction equation for the following reaction:

$$NO_2 + OH^- \longrightarrow NO_2^- + NO_3^-$$

Solving Process:

Note that nitrogen is both oxidized and reduced in this reaction.

Reduction	*Oxidation*
	Skeleton
$NO_2 \longrightarrow NO_2^-$	$NO_2 \longrightarrow NO_3^-$
	Electron balance
$NO_2 + e^- \longrightarrow NO_2^-$	$NO_2 \longrightarrow NO_3^- + e^-$
	Nitrogen atoms are balanced
	Oxygen balance
$NO_2 + e^- \longrightarrow NO_2^-$	$H_2O + NO_2 \longrightarrow NO_3^- + e^-$
	Hydrogen balance
(same)	$H_2O + NO_2 \longrightarrow NO_3^- + 2H^+ + e^-$
	Convert to basic solution
(same)	$H_2O + NO_2 + 2OH^- \longrightarrow NO_3^- + 2H_2O + e^-$
	Eliminate the water molecules on both sides
	$NO_2 + 2OH^- \longrightarrow NO_3^- + H_2O + e^-$

The number of electrons in each half-reaction is the same, so they may be added directly. The nitrogen dioxide molecules appearing in each half-reaction are combined in the final equation just as the electrons appearing on each side are eliminated.

$$2NO_2 + 2OH^- \longrightarrow NO_2^- + NO_3^- + H_2O$$

Problems

Balance the following oxidation-reduction equations. All reactions take place in an acidic solution unless otherwise indicated.

1. $Cr(c) + Sn^{4+}(aq) \rightarrow Cr^{3+}(aq) + Sn^{2+}(aq)$
2. $Al(c) + H^{+}(aq) \rightarrow Al^{3+}(aq) + H_2(g)$
3. $Zn(c) + Ag^{+}(aq) \rightarrow Zn^{2+}(aq) + Ag(c)$
4. $NO_3^{-}(aq) + S(c) \rightarrow NO_2(g) + H_2SO_4(aq)$
5. $Br_2(l) + SO_3^{2-}(aq) \rightarrow Br^{-}(aq) + SO_4^{2-}(aq)$
6. $Fe^{2+}(aq) + MnO_4^{-}(aq) \rightarrow Mn^{2+}(aq) + Fe^{3+}(aq)$
7. $Cu(c) + SO_4^{2-}(aq) \rightarrow Cu^{2+}(aq) + SO_2(g)$
8. $Cu(c) + NO_3^{-}(aq) \rightarrow Cu^{2+}(aq) + NO(g)$
9. $MnO_4^{-}(aq) + S^{2-}(aq) \rightarrow Mn^{2+}(aq) + S(c)$
10. $CuS(c) + NO_3^{-}(aq) \rightarrow Cu^{2+}(aq) + NO_2(g) + S(c)$
11. $NO_2(g) + ClO^{-}(aq) \rightarrow NO_3^{-}(aq) + Cl^{-}(aq)$
12. $Fe^{2+}(aq) + Cr_2O_7^{2-}(aq) \rightarrow Fe^{3+}(aq) + Cr^{3+}(aq)$
13. $MnO_4^{-}(aq) + Cl^{-}(aq) \rightarrow Mn^{2+}(aq) + Cl_2(g)$
14. $IO_3^{-}(aq) + H_2S(g) \rightarrow I_2(g) + SO_3^{2-}(aq)$
15. $H_2SeO_3(aq) + Br^{-}(aq) \rightarrow Se(c) + Br_2(g)$
16. $BrO_3^{-}(aq) + MnO_2(c) \rightarrow Br^{-}(aq) + MnO_4^{-}(aq)$
17. $H_2S(g) + NO_3^{-}(aq) \rightarrow S(c) + NO(g)$

24:3   Reduction Potential and Reaction Prediction

Oxidation is the loss of electrons. A substance which acquires electrons from other substances easily is called an **oxidizing agent.** It is an oxidizing agent because it causes other substances to be oxidized. By convention, a series of half reactions, termed the standard reduction potential table, is set up with the best oxidizing agent at the bottom left position. Each half-reaction has a characteristic reduction potential ($\varepsilon°$) which is compared to a standard reference half-reaction:

$$2H^{+}(aq) \longrightarrow H_2(g) + 2e^{-}$$

This reaction is assumed to have a reduction potential of 0.000 volt (V) at 25°C, 1.01325 bars pressure and 1 molar H^{+}. Fluorine, F_2, is at the bottom of the list because it shows the greatest tendency to acquire electrons and become the fluoride ion. The fluoride ion is a very weak reducing agent since F^{-} does not readily give up its electrons.

Table 24-1
Standard Reduction Potentials for Half-Reactions
(Ionic concentrations, $1\,M$ in water at 25°C)

	Half-Reaction	Volts	
Weak	$Li^+ + e^- \longrightarrow Li$	−3.05	*Strong*
oxidizing	$\frac{1}{2}Ca^{2+} + e^- \longrightarrow \frac{1}{2}Ca$	−2.87	*reducing*
agents	$\frac{1}{2}Mg^{2+} + e^- \longrightarrow \frac{1}{2}Mg$	−2.37	*agents*
	$\frac{1}{3}Al^{3+} + e^- \longrightarrow \frac{1}{3}Al$	−1.66	
	$\frac{1}{2}Mn^{2+} + e^- \longrightarrow \frac{1}{2}Mn$	−1.18	
	$\frac{1}{2}Cr^{2+} + e^- \longrightarrow \frac{1}{2}Cr$	−0.91	
	$\frac{1}{2}Zn^{2+} + e^- \longrightarrow \frac{1}{2}Zn$	−0.76	
	$U^{4+} + e^- \longrightarrow U^{3+}$	−0.61	
	$CO_2 + H^+ + e^- \longrightarrow \frac{1}{2}H_2C_2O_4$	−0.49	
	$\frac{1}{2}Fe^{2+} + e^- \longrightarrow \frac{1}{2}Fe$	−0.44	
	$\frac{1}{2}Cd^{2+} + e^- \longrightarrow \frac{1}{2}Cd$	−0.40	
	$\frac{1}{2}Co^{2+} + e^- \longrightarrow \frac{1}{2}Co$	−0.28	
	$\frac{1}{2}Ni^{2+} + e^- \longrightarrow \frac{1}{2}Ni$	−0.25	
	$\frac{1}{2}Sn^{2+} + e^- \longrightarrow \frac{1}{2}Sn$	−0.14	
	$\frac{1}{2}Pb^{2+} + e^- \longrightarrow \frac{1}{2}Pb$	−0.13	
	$H^+ + e^- \longrightarrow \frac{1}{2}H_2(g)$	0.00	
	$\frac{1}{2}S + H^+ + e^- \longrightarrow \frac{1}{2}H_2S(g)$	0.14	
	$\frac{1}{2}Sn^{4+} + e^- \longrightarrow \frac{1}{2}Sn^{2+}$	0.15	
	$Cu^{2+} + e^- \longrightarrow Cu^+$	0.16	
	$\frac{1}{2}SO_4^{2-} + 2H^+ + e^- \longrightarrow \frac{1}{2}SO_2(aq) + H_2O$	0.17	
	$\frac{1}{2}Cu^{2+} + e^- \longrightarrow \frac{1}{2}Cu$	0.34	
	$Cu^+ + e^- \longrightarrow Cu$	0.52	
	$\frac{1}{2}I_2(c) + e^- \longrightarrow I^-$	0.53	
	$HgCl_2 + e^- \longrightarrow \frac{1}{2}Hg_2Cl_2 + Cl^-$	0.63	
	$Fe^{3+} + e^- \longrightarrow Fe^{2+}$	0.77	
	$\frac{1}{2}Hg_2^{2+} + e^- \longrightarrow Hg(l)$	0.79	
	$Ag^+ + e^- \longrightarrow Ag$	0.80	
	$NO_3^- + 2H^+ + e^- \longrightarrow NO_2 + H_2O$	0.80	
	$\frac{1}{2}Hg^{2+} + e^- \longrightarrow \frac{1}{2}Hg$	0.85	
	$Hg^{2+} + e^- \longrightarrow Hg^+$	0.92	
	$\frac{1}{3}NO_3^- + \frac{4}{3}H^+ + e^- \longrightarrow \frac{1}{3}NO(g) + \frac{2}{3}H_2O$	0.96	
	$\frac{1}{2}Br_2(l) + e^- \longrightarrow Br^-$	1.07	
	$\frac{1}{4}O_2 + H^+ + e^- \longrightarrow \frac{1}{2}H_2O$	1.23	
	$\frac{1}{6}Cr_2O_7^{2-} + \frac{7}{3}H^+ + e^- \longrightarrow \frac{1}{3}Cr^{3+} + \frac{7}{6}H_2O$	1.33	
	$\frac{1}{2}Cl_2(g) + e^- \longrightarrow Cl^-$	1.36	
Strong	$\frac{1}{5}MnO_4^- + \frac{8}{5}H^+ + e^- \longrightarrow \frac{1}{5}Mn^{2+} + \frac{4}{5}H_2O$	1.51	*Weak*
oxidizing	$\frac{1}{2}H_2O_2 + H^+ + e^- \longrightarrow H_2O$	1.77	*reducing*
agents	$\frac{1}{2}F_2(g) + e^- \longrightarrow F^-$	2.87	*agents*

Remember H^+ stands for H_3O^+ in solution.

The lithium ion, Li^+, is a weak oxidizing agent as it does not readily gain electrons. However, the lithium atom easily gives up electrons so it is a strong reducing agent.

A large positive potential indicates a great tendency for the reaction to occur. Fluorine gas will proceed readily to fluoride ion, since the potential is +2.87 volts. For all practical purposes, fluoride ion will not go to fluorine gas. Lithium ion will not proceed to lithium metal since the potential is negative, −3.05 volts.

The potentials given in Table 24-1 apply when the half-reaction takes place in the forward direction. In the reverse direction, the sign of the voltage is reversed. The $\varepsilon°$ values do not indicate the number of electrons transferred. The potential difference is not an indication of the quantity of electricity.

Use the table to see if two half-reactions will react by adding the half-reaction potentials. It is necessary to balance the chemical quantities and the number of electrons, but no adjustment need be made in potential values. The potential is the ease with which certain electrons per atom or ion are lost, and does not depend on the total number of atoms or ions present. Keep in mind that the given potential applies to the forward reaction. For the reverse direction, the sign of the potential is reversed.

Example 4

The following equation represents copper metal placed in a colorless silver ion solution.

$$Cu(c) + Ag^+(aq) \longrightarrow Cu^{2+}(aq) + Ag(c)$$

Solving Process:
Write the half-reactions and obtain each voltage from the reduction potential table. Remember that the sign of the voltage may be reversed. Balance the electrons and add.

$$
\begin{array}{ll}
Cu \longrightarrow Cu^{2+} + 2e^- & -0.34 \text{ V} \\
2Ag^+ + 2e^- \longrightarrow 2Ag & +0.80 \text{ V} \\
\hline
Cu + 2Ag^+ \longrightarrow Cu^{2+} + 2Ag & +0.46 \text{ V}
\end{array}
$$

Since the voltage is positive, this reaction should occur spontaneously. Spontaneous does not mean instantaneous. A reaction occurs spontaneously when it occurs without additional energy such as heat or light.

Note that the reverse reaction does not take place:

$$
\begin{array}{ll}
Cu^{2+} + 2e^- \longrightarrow Cu & +0.34 \text{ V} \\
2Ag \longrightarrow 2Ag^+ + 2e^- & -0.80 \text{ V} \\
\hline
\text{No reaction} & -0.46 \text{ V}
\end{array}
$$

This reaction does not occur spontaneously since the voltage is negative.

Example 5

The following equation represents zinc metal placed in a copper ion solution.

$$Zn(c) + Cu^{2+}(aq) \longrightarrow Zn^{2+}(aq) + Cu(c)$$

Solving Process:

Write the half-reaction which actually occurs and obtain the appropriate voltage values. Then balance the electrons and add.

$$
\begin{array}{ll}
Zn \longrightarrow Zn^{2+} + 2e^- & +0.76 \text{ V} \\
\underline{Cu^{2+} + 2e^- \longrightarrow Cu} & \underline{+0.34 \text{ V}} \\
Zn + Cu^{2+} \longrightarrow Zn^{2+} + Cu & +1.10 \text{ V}
\end{array}
$$

Since the potential is positive, the reaction will occur spontaneously.

Problems

18. Calculate the potential in volts for each of the following reactions:
   a. $Cr(c) + Ni^{2+}(aq) \rightarrow Cr^{2+}(aq) + Ni(c)$
   b. $Al(c) + H^+(aq) \rightarrow Al^{3+}(aq) + H_2(g)$
   c. $Br_2(l) + I^-(aq) \rightarrow Br^-(aq) + I_2(c)$
   d. $Fe^{2+}(aq) + MnO_4^-(aq) \rightarrow Fe^{3+}(aq) + Mn^{2+}(aq)$
   e. $Cl_2(g) + Sn^{2+}(aq) \rightarrow Cl^-(aq) + Sn^{4+}(aq)$
   f. $Hg(l) + Hg^{2+}(aq) \rightarrow Hg_2^{2+}(aq)$

Chapter Review Problems

Balance the following oxidation-reduction equations. All reactions take place in an acidic solution unless otherwise indicated.

19. $AsH_3(g) + ClO_3^-(aq) \rightarrow H_3AsO_4(aq) + Cl^-(aq)$

20. $HNO_2(aq) + I^-(aq) \rightarrow NO(g) + I_2(g)$

21. $MnO_4^-(aq) + H_2O_2(aq) \rightarrow Mn^{2+}(aq) + O_2(g)$

22. $MnO_2(c) + ClO_3^-(aq) \rightarrow MnO_4^{2-}(aq) + Cl^-(aq)$ (basic solution)

23. $Br_2(l) \rightarrow Br^-(aq) + BrO_3^-(aq)$ (basic solution)

24. $N_2O_4(aq) + Br^-(aq) \rightarrow NO_2^-(aq) + BrO_3^-(aq)$ (basic solution)

25. $H_2PO_2^-(aq) + SbO_2^-(aq) \rightarrow HPO_3^{2-}(aq) + Sb(c)$ (basic solution)

26. $CrO_2^-(aq) + ClO^-(aq) \rightarrow CrO_4^{2-}(aq) + Cl^-(aq)$ (basic solution)

27. $Cu(OH)_2(c) + HPO_3^{2-}(aq) \rightarrow Cu_2O(c) + PO_4^{3-}(aq)$

28. $HS^-(aq) + IO_3^-(aq) \rightarrow I^-(aq) + S(c)$

29. $N_2O(g) + ClO^-(aq) \rightarrow Cl^-(aq) + NO_2^-(aq)$ (basic solution)

30. $H_2SO_3(aq) + MnO_2(c) \rightarrow SO_4^{2-}(aq) + Mn^{2+}(aq)$

31. $IO_4^-(aq) + I^-(aq) \rightarrow I_2(g)$

32. $CrO_4^{2-}(aq) + I^-(aq) \rightarrow Cr^{3+}(aq) + I_2(g)$

33. $Cr^{2+}(aq) + O_2(g) \rightarrow Cr^{3+}(aq) + H_2O(l)$
34. $H_3PO_3(aq) + NO_3^-(aq) \rightarrow PO_4^{3-}(aq) + N_2O_4(g)$
35. $Cr_2O_7^{2-}(aq) + HNO_2(aq) \rightarrow Cr^{3+}(aq) + NO_3^-(aq)$
36. $Sb_2O_5(c) + I^-(aq) \rightarrow Sb^{3+}(aq) + I_2(g)$
37. $H_2SO_3(aq) + IO_3^-(aq) \rightarrow SO_4^{2-}(aq) + I^-(aq)$
38. $NO_3^-(aq) + SO_2(g) \rightarrow N_2O_3(g) + SO_4^{2-}(aq)$
39. $SbO^+(aq) + HClO(aq) \rightarrow Sb_2O_5(c) + Cl^-(aq)$
40. $NO_3^-(aq) + H_2S(g) \rightarrow NO(g) + S(c)$
41. $TeO_2(c) + BrO_3^-(aq) \rightarrow H_6TeO_6(aq) + Br_2(g)$
42. $I^-(aq) + HClO_2(aq) \rightarrow IO_3^-(aq) + Cl_2(g)$
43. $Bi_2S_3(c) + NO_3^-(aq) \rightarrow Bi^{3+}(aq) + NO(g) + S(c)$
44. $S(c) + HNO_2(aq) \rightarrow H_2SO_3(aq) + N_2O(g)$
45. $NO(g) + H_5IO_6(aq) \rightarrow NO_3^-(aq) + IO_3^-(aq)$
46. Some of the following reactions will occur and others will not. Determine the positive or negative potential for each equation. For reactions that will not occur, rewrite them so they will react.
   a. $Ni(c) + Cu^{2+}(aq) \rightarrow Ni^{2+}(aq) + Cu(c)$
   b. $Cl^-(aq) + Br_2(l) \rightarrow Cl_2(g) + Br^-(aq)$
   c. $Cu(c) + H^+(aq) \rightarrow Cu^{2+}(aq) + H_2(g)$
   d. $Mn(c) + Co^{2+}(aq) \rightarrow Mn^{2+}(aq) + Co(c)$
   e. $Zn^{2+}(aq) + Pb(c) \rightarrow Zn(c) + Pb^{2+}(aq)$

Electrochemistry _____ 25

25:1 Faraday's Laws

Electrochemistry is the study of the relationship between chemical change and electric energy. Michael Faraday experimented extensively to determine the relationship between electric charge and chemical energy. Faraday's laws state:

1. The mass of an element released at the electrode during electrolysis varies directly as the quantity of electricity which is passed through a solution.

2. The mass of different elements deposited by the same quantity of electricity varies directly as the equivalent mass of the element which is under consideration. Chemists measure the quantity of electrons in moles. Electricians measure electricity in coulombs. One coulomb is the quantity of electricity in one ampere flowing for one second. The relationship of all these quantities is

$$1 \text{ mole } e^- = 96\,500 \text{ coulomb} = 1 \text{ ampere} \cdot \text{second}$$

Thus 96 500 coulombs passing through molten NaCl will liberate one equivalent mass of sodium (23.0 g) and one equivalent mass of chlorine (35.5 g).

$$96\,500 \text{ coulombs} = 23.0 \text{ grams Na} = 1 \text{ mole Na} = 6.02 \times 10^{23} \text{ electrons}$$

$$96\,500 \text{ coulombs} = 35.5 \text{ grams Cl} = 1 \text{ mole Cl} = 6.02 \times 10^{23} \text{ electrons}$$

The following shows the grams liberated (or deposited) from a solution (or molten salt) during the liberation of one mole of electrons. (Atomic masses are rounded off.)

Ion	Solution or Molten Salt	Oxidation Number	Equivalents per Mole	Grams of Element Released
Na^+	$NaCl(l)$	1	1	23
H^+	$HCl(aq)$	1	1	1
Cl^-	$HCl(aq)$	1	1	35.5
Mg^{2+}	$MgCl_2$	2	2	12.2 (24.3/2)
Ni^{2+}	$NiSO_4(aq)$	2	2	29.4 (58.7/2)
Al^{3+}	$AlCl_3$	3	3	9 (27/3)
Al^{3+}	$Al_2(SO_4)_3(aq)$	3	3	9 (27/3)
Fe^{2+}	$FeCl_2(aq)$	2	2	27.9 (55.8/2)
Fe^{3+}	$FeCl_3$	3	3	18.6 (55.8/3)

Example 1

A single electron has a charge of 1.60219×10^{-19} coulomb. Determine Avogadro's number from the relationship between moles of electrons and coulombs, which is

$$96\ 500 \text{ coulomb} = 1 \text{ mole of electrons.}$$

Solving Process:

$$\text{number of electrons} = \frac{96\ 500 \text{ coulombs}}{} \left| \frac{1 \text{ electron}}{1.60219 \times 10^{-19} \text{ coulombs}} \right.$$

$$= 6.02 \times 10^{23} \text{ electrons}$$

Example 2

If 3.00 moles of electrons are required to electrolyze an iron(II) bromide solution, how many grams of iron metal will be deposited?

Solving Process:

Write the balanced equation and determine the conversions involving moles of iron and electrons. Convert from moles of electrons, to moles, to grams.

$FeBr_2 \longrightarrow Fe^{2+} + 2Br^-$ $\qquad\qquad$ $Fe^{2+} + 2e^- \longrightarrow Fe$

1 mole $\longrightarrow$ 1 mole $\qquad\qquad$ 2 moles of electrons $\longrightarrow$ 1 mole of iron

One mole of $FeBr_2$ yields one mole of Fe^{2+} ions and uses two moles of electrons. Use the factor-label method to change 3.00 moles of electrons to grams of iron deposited.

$$\text{grams Fe} = \frac{3.00 \text{ mole } e^-}{} \left| \frac{1 \text{ mol Fe}}{2 \text{ mol } e^-} \right| \frac{55.8 \text{ g Fe}}{1 \text{ mol Fe}} = 83.7 \text{ g Fe}$$

Example 3

How many grams of aluminum can be deposited if 31 500 coulombs of electricity pass through an aluminum nitrate solution?

Solving Process:

Begin with the balanced equation for the reaction.

$$Al^{3+} + 3e^- \longrightarrow Al$$

Convert coulombs to moles of electrons, to moles, to grams.

$$\text{grams Al} = \frac{31\ 500\ \cancel{C}}{} \left| \frac{1\ \cancel{\text{mole}^-}}{96\ 500\ \cancel{C}} \right| \frac{1\ \cancel{\text{mol Al}}}{3\ \cancel{\text{mole}^-}} \left| \frac{27.0\ \text{g Al}}{1\ \cancel{\text{mol Al}}} \right.$$

$$= 2.94\ \text{g Al}$$

Example 4

If 10.0 amperes of current flow for 20.0 minutes through a solution of copper(II) nitrate, how many moles of copper are deposited?

Solving Process:

$$Cu^{2+} + 2e^- \longrightarrow Cu$$

$$\frac{10.0\ \cancel{A}}{} \left| \frac{20.0\ \cancel{\text{min}}}{1\ \cancel{\text{min}}} \right| \frac{60\ \cancel{s}}{\cancel{A} \cdot \cancel{s}} \left| \frac{1\ \cancel{C}}{96\ 500\ \cancel{C}} \right| \frac{1\ \cancel{\text{mole}^-}}{2\ \cancel{\text{mole}^-}} \left| \frac{1\ \text{mol Cu}}{} \right.$$

$$= 0.0622\ \text{mol Cu}$$

Example 5

Calculate the mass of silver metal which can be deposited if a 5.12 ampere current is passed through a silver nitrate solution for 2.00 hours. The equation for the reaction is $Ag^+ + e^- \longrightarrow Ag$.

Solving Process:

Obtain ampere · seconds by converting hours to seconds and multiplying by the number of amperes given. Convert ampere · seconds to coulombs. Finally change to moles of electrons, to moles, to grams.

$$\frac{5.12\ \cancel{A}}{} \left| \frac{2.00\ \cancel{h}}{1\ \cancel{h}} \right| \frac{60\ \cancel{\text{min}}}{1\ \cancel{\text{min}}} \left| \frac{60\ \cancel{s}}{\cancel{A} \cdot \cancel{s}} \right| \frac{1\ \cancel{C}}{96\ 500\ \cancel{C}} \left| \frac{1\ \cancel{\text{mole}^-}}{1\ \cancel{\text{mole}^-}} \right| \frac{1\ \cancel{\text{mol Ag}}}{1\ \cancel{\text{mol Ag}}} \left| \frac{108\ \text{g Ag}}{} \right.$$

$$= 41.3\ \text{g Ag}$$

Example 6

How many seconds are required to deposit 2.51 grams of iron metal on an object using 15.4 amperes of current passing through an iron(III) nitrate solution? The equation for the reaction is $Fe^{3+} + 3e^- \longrightarrow Fe$.

Solving Process:

Since 2.51 grams of iron are deposited with 15.4 amperes, we know the rate at which electricity is flowing. The time required will be the quantity (2.51 g Fe) divided by the rate (15.4 A). The following conversions are made: grams, to moles, to moles of electrons, and to coulombs. All units will divide out except seconds.

$$\frac{2.51 \text{ g Fe}}{15.4 \text{ A}} \left| \frac{1 \text{ mol Fe}}{55.8 \text{ g Fe}} \right| \frac{3 \text{ mole}^-}{1 \text{ mol Fe}} \left| \frac{96\,500\,C}{1 \text{ mole}^-} \right| \frac{A \cdot s}{1\,C} = 846 \text{ seconds}$$

Example 7

How many amperes are required to deposit 0.504 grams of iron in 40.0 minutes by passing a current through a solution of iron(II) acetate?

Solving Process:

This problem is similar to Example 6, except rate is calculated instead of time. The equation for this reaction is $Fe^{2+} + 2e^- \longrightarrow Fe$. The rate will be the quantity divided by time.

$$\frac{0.504 \text{ g Fe}}{40.0 \text{ min}} \left| \frac{1 \text{ min}}{60 \text{ s}} \right| \frac{1 \text{ mol Fe}}{55.8 \text{ g Fe}} \left| \frac{2 \text{ mole}^-}{1 \text{ mol Fe}} \right| \frac{96\,500\,C}{1 \text{ mole}^-} \left| \frac{A \cdot s}{1\,C} \right. = 0.726 \text{ A}$$

Example 8

How many cubic decimeters of chlorine gas measured at STP are released by the passage of 8.12 amperes for 2.00 hours through molten magnesium chloride?

Solving Process:

The equation would be $2Cl^- \longrightarrow Cl_2 + 2e^-$.

$$8.12 \cancel{A} \left| 2.00 \cancel{h} \right| \frac{60 \cancel{min}}{1 \cancel{h}} \left| \frac{60 \cancel{s}}{1 \cancel{min}} \right| \frac{1 \cancel{C}}{\cancel{A} \cdot \cancel{s}} \left| \frac{1 \cancel{mole}}{96\,500 \cancel{C}} \right| \frac{1 \cancel{mol\,Cl_2}}{2 \cancel{mole}} \right|$$

$$\frac{22.4 \text{ dm}^3 \text{ Cl}_2}{1 \cancel{mol\,Cl_2}} = 6.79 \text{ dm}^3 \text{ Cl}_2$$

Example 9

Calculate the current required to liberate 5.60 cubic decimeters of chlorine at STP in 2.00 hours in the electrolysis of molten sodium chloride.

Solving Process:

The equation for the reaction is $2Cl^- \longrightarrow Cl_2 + 2e^-$.

$$\frac{5.60 \cancel{dm^3\,Cl_2}}{2 \cancel{h}} \left| \frac{1 \cancel{h}}{60 \cancel{min}} \right| \frac{1 \cancel{min}}{60 \cancel{s}} \left| \frac{1 \cancel{mol\,Cl_2}}{22.4 \cancel{dm^3\,Cl_2}} \right| \frac{2 \cancel{mole}}{1 \cancel{mol\,Cl_2}} \left| \frac{96\,500 \cancel{C}}{1 \cancel{mole}} \right| \frac{A \cdot \cancel{s}}{1 \cancel{C}}$$

$$= 6.70 \text{ A}$$

Example 10

How many amperes are required to liberate 2.18 cubic decimeters of oxygen gas measured at 99.5 kPa and 15°C if the current flows for 30.0 minutes in the electrolysis of iron(II) nitrate?

Solving Process:

Start with the volume of O_2 at the conditions given and convert to the volume of O_2 at STP. Then solve as in Example 9.

$$2H_2O \longrightarrow 4H^+ + 4e^- + O_2$$

$$\frac{2.18 \cancel{dm^3\,O_2}}{30.0 \cancel{min}} \left| \frac{99.5 \cancel{kPa}}{101.3 \cancel{kPa}} \right| \frac{273 \cancel{K}}{288 \cancel{K}} \left| \frac{1 \cancel{min}}{60 \cancel{s}} \right| \frac{1 \cancel{mol\,O_2}}{22.4 \cancel{dm^3\,O_2}} \right|$$

$$\frac{4 \cancel{mole}}{1 \cancel{mol\,O_2}} \left| \frac{96\,500 \cancel{C}}{1 \cancel{mole}} \right| \frac{A \cdot \cancel{s}}{1 \cancel{C}} = 19.4 \text{ A}$$

Example 11

During the operation of a lead storage battery, the reaction at the two electrodes is as follows:

cathode $PbO_2 + 4H^+ + SO_4^{2-} + 2e^- \longrightarrow PbSO_4 + 2H_2O$

anode $Pb + SO_4^{2-} \longrightarrow PbSO_4 + 2e^-$

How much PbO_2 (in grams) is used when a current of 50.0 amperes in 1 hour is withdrawn from the battery?

Solving Process:

Convert from ampere · hours to coulombs, to moles, and to grams of PbO_2.

$$\frac{50.0 \,\cancel{A} \mid 1\,\cancel{h} \mid 60\,\cancel{min} \mid 60\,\cancel{s} \mid 1\,\cancel{C} \mid 1\,\cancel{mole^-} \mid 1\,\cancel{mol\,PbO_2} \mid 239 \text{ g } PbO_2}{ \mid \mid 1\,\cancel{h} \mid 1\,\cancel{min} \mid \cancel{A}\cdot\cancel{s} \mid 96\,500\,\cancel{C} \mid 2\,\cancel{mole^-} \mid 1\,\cancel{mol\,PbO_2}}$$

$= 223 \text{ g } PbO_2$

Example 12 —————————————————————

A current of 3.75 amperes is used for 40.0 minutes in the electrolysis of copper(II) sulfate solution. The two reactions are

$$\text{anode} \qquad 2H_2O \longrightarrow 4H^+ + O_2 + 4e^-$$
$$\text{cathode} \qquad 2Cu^{2+} + 4e^- \longrightarrow 2Cu$$

a. Calculate the volume of oxygen gas liberated in the electrolysis at STP.
b. Convert the volume of oxygen formed at STP to the actual conditions of the dry gas at 23°C and 99.2 kPa.
c. Determine the concentration of the H^+, if 150.0 cm³ of $CuSO_4$ are used.

Solving Process:

(a) Start with the data given in the problem and convert to moles of electrons. Then change moles of electrons to cubic decimeters.

$$\frac{3.75 \,\cancel{A} \mid 40.0\,\cancel{min} \mid 60\,\cancel{s} \mid 1\,\cancel{C} \mid 1\,\cancel{mole^-}}{ \mid 1\,\cancel{min} \mid \cancel{A}\cdot\cancel{s} \mid 96\,500\,\cancel{C}}$$

$$\frac{1\,\cancel{mol\,O_2} \mid 22.4 \text{ dm}^3\,O_2 \text{ (STP)}}{4\,\cancel{mole^-} \mid 1\,\cancel{mol\,O_2}} = 0.522 \text{ dm}^3\,O_2$$

(b) Change the 0.522 dm³ O_2 (STP) to the actual conditions.

$$\frac{0.522 \text{ dm}^3\,O_2 \mid 101.3 \,\cancel{kPa} \mid 296\,\cancel{K}}{ \mid 99.2 \,\cancel{kPa} \mid 273\,\cancel{K}} = 0.578 \text{ dm}^3\,O_2$$

(c) Ignore the hydronium ion from the ionization of water and assume that there is no volume change in the solution. From the equation, 4 moles of H_3O^+ are produced.

$$\text{molarity} = \frac{3.75 \cancel{A}}{150 \cancel{cm^3}} \left| \frac{40.0 \cancel{min}}{} \right| \frac{60 \cancel{s}}{1 \cancel{min}} \left| \frac{1 \cancel{C}}{\cancel{A} \cdot \cancel{s}} \right| \frac{1 \cancel{mole}}{96\,500 \cancel{C}} \left| \frac{4 \text{ mol } H^+}{4 \cancel{mole}} \right.$$

$$\left| \frac{1000 \cancel{cm^3}}{1 \text{ dm}^3} = 0.622M \text{ } H_3O^+ \right.$$

Chapter Review Problems

1. How many moles of electrons are required to produce a 5.00-ampere current for 2.00 hours?

2. If 3.00 moles of electrons are required in producing 10.0 amperes of current, how many seconds are required?

3. What mass of copper is produced if 10 000.0 ampere · seconds pass through a copper(II) nitrate solution?

4. Calculate the grams of zinc deposited if 5.00 moles of electrons pass through a zinc acetate solution.

5. Using 2.50 moles of electrons how many grams of cadmium metal will be deposited from a cadmium sulfate solution?

6. If 193 000 coulombs of electricity pass through a silver nitrate solution, how many grams of silver metal are produced?

7. In the electrolysis of molten sodium chloride, how many moles of sodium metal are produced if 20.0 amperes of current flowing for 8.00 hours are used?

8. If it is necessary to deposit 1.50 grams of silver on an object, how many seconds must 5.00 amperes of electricity flow through a solution of silver nitrate?

9. How many amperes of electricity flowing for 30.0 minutes are required to deposit 0.250 grams of iron metal from an iron(III) nitrate solution?

10. Calculate the cubic decimeters of oxygen and of hydrogen (both at STP) which are liberated in the electrolysis of water if a current of 5.00 amperes flows for 30.0 minutes.

11. Calculate the grams of magnesium deposited and the cubic decimeters chlorine (STP) liberated in the electrolysis of molten magnesium chloride if 15.0 amperes of electricity flow for 8.00 hours.

12. If 10.0 amperes flow for 1.00 hour through the following molten salts, calculate the moles of metal and the cubic decimeters of chlorine gas (STP) which are produced.
    a. NaCl   b. $CaCl_2$ c. $AlCl_3$

13. To produce 44.8 cubic decimeters of oxygen (STP), how many minutes are required if 10.0 amperes are used?

14. How long will it take to deposit all of the cadmium from 300.0 cm^3 of a 0.300M CdSO$_4$ solution using a current of 1.50 amperes?

15. Using a current of 8.00 amperes, how long will it take to produce 30.0 dm^3 of dry oxygen at 98.0 kPa and 20°C by the electrolysis of a copper(II) sulfate solution?

16. How many amperes are required to produce 15.0 dm^3 of dry hydrogen measured at 98.7 kPa and 25°C if the current is passed through water for 5.00 hours?

17. In the following pairs of solutions, determine which solution will produce the most metal (or gas at STP) if 10.0 amperes of electricity flow for 2.00 hours through each solution.
    a. Co in CoCl$_2$ or Co in CoCl$_3$
    b. Fe in Fe(NO$_2$)$_2$ · 6H$_2$O or Fe in Fe(NO$_3$)$_3$ · 6H$_2$O
    c. Cl$_2$ in LiCl or Cl$_2$ in MgCl$_2$

18. An electric current was passed through a silver solution and deposited 0.500 gram of silver metal. How many grams of magnesium would the same quantity of electricity deposit?

19. A certain quantity of electricity is passed through the following separate solutions, which connected in series, and 1.25 grams of silver metal is deposited from the first solution.

    Solutions: 1. silver nitrate   3. zinc acetate
               2. iron(III) chloride   4. cobalt(II) nitrate

    Determine the following:
    a. How many grams of zinc and moles of iron are deposited from solutions 2 and 3, respectively?
    b. For solution 2, how many cubic decimeters of oxygen gas at STP are produced?
    c. In solution 4, how many cubic decimeters of oxygen gas are produced at 98.7 kPa and 15°C? How many grams of cobalt are deposited?
    d. How many coulombs of electricity are used?
    e. How many moles of electrons are required?

Nuclear Chemistry_____26

The reactions studied in preceding chapters have been reactions involving alterations in the electronic structure of atoms. In chemical reactions, the atom's nucleus remains unchanged.

In contrast, nuclear reactions result in important changes in the nucleus of an atom. The numbers of protons and/or neutrons in the nucleus may increase or decrease. One element may be converted into another element. Nuclear reactions are accompanied by a change in energy. The amount of energy involved is many times greater than that associated with chemical reactions. Nuclear chemists study applications of this energy and the changes that produce it.

26:1 Types of Radiation

Radioactive elements such as uranium, radium, and polonium have unstable nuclei. Particles are emitted from unstable nuclei as they undergo a process called **radioactive decay.** The decay process continues until a stable element is formed. Stable nuclei do not give off particles of radiation.

Radioactive elements may occur naturally in the earth, as in the case of uranium, radium, and polonium. Normally stable elements can be made radioactive in the laboratory by bombarding them with high speed neutrons or charged particles.

Naturally occurring radioactive material produces three types of radiation. Alpha and beta rays are made up of particles. Gamma rays are quanta of energy.

Alpha rays (α) are streams of positively charged helium nuclei, each consisting of 2 protons and 2 neutrons. Each particle can be represented by the symbol $^4_2$He, in which the 2 represents the number of protons and the 4 represents the mass number.

Beta rays (β) are streams of electrons represented by the symbol $_{-1}^{0}e$. The atomic number of each particle is -1 and the mass number is zero. Electrons do not exist in the nucleus as such but are produced when a neutron decays to form a proton.

$$^1_0\text{n} \longrightarrow \, ^1_1\text{H} + \, _{-1}^{0}e$$

When beta rays are emitted, the mass number of the nucleus remains the same, but the neutron/proton ratio is reduced.

Gamma rays (γ) possess neither mass nor charge but are quanta of energy similar to highly energetic X rays. Gamma rays are emitted when changes in the nucleus produce an excess of energy. Gamma radiation does not change the mass number or atomic number of the nucleus. The emission of excess energy brings the nucleus to a less excited, more stable state. Gamma rays travel at the speed of light.

Other types of radiation particles can be emitted when nuclei are bombarded with charged particles or high-speed neutrons and made artificially radioactive. Examples of these particles include the following:

^1_1H is a proton or hydrogen atom with mass number 1 and atomic number 1

^2_1H is a deuteron or hydrogen atom with mass number 2 and atomic number 1

^1_0n is a neutron with mass number 1 and an atomic number of 0 (no electric charge)

$_{+1}^{0}e$ is a positron with mass number 0 and atomic number of 1

^0_0v is a neutrino with mass number 0 and atomic number 0

26:2 Isotopic Abundance

It is known that most elements exist as two or more isotopes. A number of elements have five or more isotopes. Examples of these elements are nickel, selenium, palladium, cadmium, and barium. For elements with two or more isotopes, the natural relative abundance of each isotope varies considerably as shown in Table 26-1.

26:3 Balancing Nuclear Equations

In balancing nuclear equations, two rules must be followed:

1. The sum of the mass numbers on the left side of the equation must be equal to the sum of the mass numbers on the right side.
2. The sum of the electric charges on the left side and the right side of the equation must be equal.

Radiation particles given off during nuclear reactions are included in these equations in order to balance them. For example, the balanced nuclear equation for the decay of uranium-238 to thorium is

$$^{238}_{92}U \longrightarrow {}^{234}_{90}Th + {}^{4}_{2}He$$

Examples of balanced nuclear equations showing bombardment reactions are

$$^{14}_{7}N + {}^{4}_{2}He \longrightarrow {}^{17}_{8}O + {}^{1}_{1}H$$
$$^{10}_{5}B + {}^{4}_{2}He \longrightarrow {}^{13}_{7}N + {}^{1}_{0}n$$

Table 26-1
Some Naturally Occurring Isotopes

Element	Atomic Number	Mass Number	Natural Occurrence
lithium	3	6	7.42%
		7	92.58%
carbon	6	12	98.89%
		13	1.11%
		14* *Radioactive	trace
magnesium	12	24	78.70%
		25	10.13%
		26	11.17%
chlorine	17	35	75.53%
		37	24.47%
copper	29	63	69.09%
		65	30.91%
silver	47	107	51.82%
		109	48.18%

26:4 Half-Life

In a nuclear reaction, one element may be changed into another element. This process results in a change in the number of protons in the nucleus. This process is called **transmutation** and can be natural or artificial. Transmutation continues until a stable element, whose nucleus is not radioactive, is produced. The time required for half of a sample of a radioactive isotope to decay is termed its **half-life.** Half-lives of some isotopes are only a fraction of a second. For others, the half-life may be millions or billions of years.

The half-life of one isotope of zinc, $^{71}_{30}$Zn, is 2.4 minutes. Suppose we begin with 10.0 grams of this isotope. At the end of 2.4 minutes, 5.0 grams of $^{71}_{30}$Zn would remain. The rest of the 10.0 gram sample would have decayed to gallium. At the end of another 2.4 minutes, 2.5 grams of $^{71}_{30}$Zn would remain. After the third 2.4 minutes, the original 10.0 gram sample would contain 1.25 grams of the zinc isotope. The other 8.75 grams of $^{71}_{30}$Zn would have decayed to gallium.

Table 26-2
Half-Life and Decay Mode of Some Selected Nuclides

Nuclide	Half-Life	Decay Mode
$^{3}_{1}$H	12.3 years	β^-
$^{14}_{6}$C	5730 years	β^-
$^{19}_{8}$O	29.1 seconds	β^- and γ
$^{20}_{9}$F	11.6 seconds	β^- and γ
$^{26}_{14}$Si	2.1 seconds	β^+ and γ
$^{39}_{17}$Cl	55.5 minutes	β^- and γ
$^{71}_{30}$Zn	2.4 minutes	β^- and γ
$^{87}_{37}$Rb	4.8×10^{10} years	β^-
$^{91}_{42}$Mo	15.5 minutes	β^+ and γ
$^{100}_{46}$Pd	4.0 days	K-capture and γ
$^{129}_{55}$Cs	32.1 hours	K-capture and γ
$^{149}_{61}$Pm	53.1 hours	β^- and γ
$^{183}_{76}$Os	12.0 hours	K-capture and γ
$^{212}_{82}$Pb	10.6 hours	β^- and γ
$^{194}_{84}$Po	0.5 seconds	α
$^{210}_{84}$Po	138 days	α
$^{227}_{92}$U	1.3 minutes	α and γ
$^{235}_{92}$U	7.1×10^{8} years	α and γ
$^{238}_{92}$U	4.51×10^{9} years	α and γ
$^{236}_{94}$Pu	2.85 years	α and γ
$^{242}_{94}$Pu	3.79×10^{5} years	α

Chapter Review Problems

1. Using the periodic table, write nuclear symbols for the following isotopes:

    a. lead-208   **e.** helium-5

    b. lead-210   **f.** potassium-40

    c. uranium-235   **g.** lithium-8

    d. carbon-14   **h.** uranium-238

2. Complete and balance the following nuclear equations:

    a. $^{7}_{3}Li + ^{1}_{1}H \longrightarrow ^{4}_{2}He$

    b. $^{3}_{1}H + ^{2}_{1}H \longrightarrow ? + ^{1}_{0}n$

    c. $^{14}_{6}C \longrightarrow ^{14}_{7}C + ?$

    d. $^{9}_{4}Be + ^{4}_{2}He \longrightarrow ^{12}_{6}C + ?$

    e. $^{14}_{7}N + ^{4}_{2}He \longrightarrow ? + ^{0}_{+1}e$

    f. $^{26}_{12}Mg + ^{1}_{0}n \longrightarrow ? + ^{0}_{+1}e$

    g. $^{59}_{27}Co + ^{2}_{1}H \longrightarrow ? + ^{0}_{+1}e$

3. In a portion of the uranium decay series, lead-214 decays to bismuth-214 by beta emission. The bismuth-214 decays to polonium-214 by beta emission. The polonium-214 decays to lead-210 by alpha emission. Write balanced nuclear equations to represent these three steps.

4. Complete the following nuclear equations. Indicate the new element formed during these reactions. Name the type of nuclear particle emitted.

    a. $^{22}_{11}Na \longrightarrow ? + ^{0}_{-1}e$

    b. $^{66}_{29}Cu \longrightarrow ? + ^{0}_{-1}e$

    c. $^{208}_{84}Po \longrightarrow ? + ^{4}_{2}He$

    d. $^{27}_{14}Si \longrightarrow ? + ^{0}_{+1}e$

Organic Chemistry _____ 27

Organic compounds are compounds which contain carbon atoms linked together in chains or rings. **Hydrocarbons** are compounds which contain carbon and hydrogen.

27:1 Hydrocarbons

Hydrocarbons are the simplest organic compounds. They may be grouped into families. In some of these families, all the carbon-carbon bonds are single bonds. These compounds are said to be **saturated.** In other families, the compounds contain multiple bonds and are **unsaturated.**

27:2 Alkanes

Alkanes are saturated hydrocarbons conforming to the general formula C_nH_{2n+2}, where n is a whole number equal to the number of carbon atoms. The alkane series is also termed the methane or paraffin series. The simplest alkanes are

$$CH_4 \quad H-\underset{\underset{H}{|}}{\overset{\overset{H}{|}}{C}}-H \qquad CH_3CH_3 \quad H-\underset{\underset{H}{|}}{\overset{\overset{H}{|}}{C}}-\underset{\underset{H}{|}}{\overset{\overset{H}{|}}{C}}-H$$

methane   ethane

$$CH_3CH_2CH_3 \quad H-\underset{\underset{H}{|}}{\overset{\overset{H}{|}}{C}}-\underset{\underset{H}{|}}{\overset{\overset{H}{|}}{C}}-\underset{\underset{H}{|}}{\overset{\overset{H}{|}}{C}}-H$$

propane

The first formula is a condensed structural formula. The second formula is an expanded structural formula. With C_4H_{10}, the carbon atoms may be connected to give two different structural formulas. These two arrangements are **isomers.** Isomers have the same chemical formula but different structural formulas.

$$CH_3CH_2CH_2CH_3 \qquad \begin{array}{c} H \;\; H \;\; H \;\; H \\ | \;\;\; | \;\;\; | \;\;\; | \\ H-C-C-C-C-H \\ | \;\;\; | \;\;\; | \;\;\; | \\ H \;\; H \;\; H \;\; H \end{array}$$

$$CH_3CH(CH_3)CH_3 \qquad \begin{array}{c} CH_3 \\ | \\ CH_3CHCH_3 \end{array} \qquad \begin{array}{c} H \\ H-C-H \\ H \quad\;\; H \\ | \qquad | \\ H-C-C-C-H \\ | \quad\; | \quad\; | \\ H \;\; H \;\; H \end{array}$$

Table 27-1 lists the stem name for each number of carbon atoms in a continuous chain or ring. It also gives some information about the alkanes of low molecular mass.

Table 27-1
Alkanes—Saturated Hydrocarbons

Stem Name	Alkane Name	Condensed Structural Formula (unbranched)	Chemical Formula	Number of Isomers
meth-	methane	CH_4	CH_4	1
eth-	ethane	CH_3CH_3	C_2H_6	1
prop-	propane	$CH_3CH_2CH_3$	C_3H_8	1
but-	butane	$CH_3(CH_2)_2CH_3$	C_4H_{10}	2
pent-	pentane	$CH_3(CH_2)_3CH_3$	C_5H_{12}	3
hex-	hexane	$CH_3(CH_2)_4CH_3$	C_6H_{14}	5
hept-	heptane	$CH_3(CH_2)_5CH_3$	C_7H_{16}	9
oct-	octane	$CH_3(CH_2)_6CH_3$	C_8H_{18}	18
non-	nonane	$CH_3(CH_2)_7CH_3$	C_9H_{20}	35
dec-	decane	$CH_3(CH_2)_8CH_3$	$C_{10}H_{22}$	75

27:3 Rules for Naming Hydrocarbons

1. Pick the longest continuous chain of carbon atoms and obtain its name.
2. Number the carbon atoms in the chain beginning at the end which will give the lowest possible numbers for the different attached hydrocarbon groups.

3. Name the hydrocarbon groups attached to the longest chain by adding *-yl* to the stem name. Indicate the point of attachment by the number of the carbon atom to which the group is attached. Common group names are meth*yl*, —CH_3, and eth*yl*, —CH_2CH_3.

For example, consider the following compound:

$$\boxed{CH_3-CH_2-\underset{\underset{CH_3}{|}}{CH}-CH_2-CH_2-CH_3}$$

The longest chain, which consists of six carbon atoms, is enclosed in a box. Consider this compound:

$$CH_3-\boxed{\begin{array}{l}CH-CH_2-CH_2-CH_3\\ |\\ CH_2\\ |\\ CH_3\end{array}}$$

The longest chain in this compound also contains six carbon atoms. A chain of six carbon atoms is termed *hexane*. The carbon atoms in the longest chain are numbered in such a way as to give the lowest number possible to the attached group. At position 3 the attached group is termed *methyl*. The name of the compound is 3-methylhexane. Note that position numbers are separated from the name by hyphens.

The C_4H_{10} isomers we discussed previously (page 239) are named butane and 2-methyl propane. The following are the isomers of pentane:

$$CH_3CH_2CH_2CH_2CH_3 \quad \text{pentane}$$

$$\underset{\underset{CH_3}{|}}{CH_3CHCH_2CH_3} \quad \text{2-methylbutane}$$

$$\underset{\underset{CH_3}{|}}{\overset{\overset{CH_3}{|}}{CH_3CCH_3}} \quad \text{2,2-dimethylpropane}$$

Note that the position numbers are separated from each other by commas. The following are the isomers of hexane:

$$CH_3CH_2CH_2CH_2CH_2CH_3 \quad \text{hexane}$$

$$\underset{\underset{CH_3}{|}}{CH_3CHCH_2CH_2CH_3} \quad \text{2-methylpentane}$$

$$\underset{\underset{CH_3}{|}}{CH_3CH_2CHCH_2CH_3} \quad \text{3-methylpentane}$$

$$\underset{\displaystyle CH_3}{\overset{\displaystyle CH_3 \quad CH_3}{CH_3CH-CHCH_3}}$$ 2,3-dimethylbutane

$$\underset{\displaystyle CH_3}{\overset{\displaystyle CH_3}{CH_3CCH_2CH_3}}$$ 2,2-dimethylbutane

When two or more groups are attached to a compound, the groups are named in alphabetical order. Consider the following example:

$$\underset{\displaystyle \underset{\displaystyle CH_3}{\overset{\displaystyle |}{CH_2}}}{\overset{\displaystyle \overset{\displaystyle CH_3}{\overset{\displaystyle |}{}}}{CH_3-CH-CH-CH_2-\overset{\displaystyle \overset{\displaystyle CH_3}{\overset{\displaystyle |}{}}}{CH}-CH_2-CH_3}}$$ 3-ethyl-2,5-dimethylheptane

The longest continuous chain of carbon atoms is named heptane. The branched groups are ethyl and methyl. Since there are two methyl groups the prefix *di* is used to indicate this number.

Problems

1. Find the longest carbon chain in each formula and number the carbons. Use your rules to name these hydrocarbons.

a. $$\underset{\displaystyle \underset{\displaystyle CH_3}{\overset{\displaystyle |}{CH_2}}}{CH_3-CH_2-\overset{\displaystyle \overset{\displaystyle CH_3}{\overset{\displaystyle |}{}}}{CH}-CH-CH_3}$$

b. $$CH_3-\overset{\displaystyle \overset{\displaystyle CH_3}{\overset{\displaystyle |}{}}}{CH}-\underset{\displaystyle CH_3}{CH}-\overset{\displaystyle \overset{\displaystyle CH_3}{\overset{\displaystyle |}{CH_2}}}{CH}-CH_3$$

c. $$CH_3-\underset{\displaystyle CH_3}{\overset{\displaystyle CH_3}{C}}\!-\!-\!\overset{\displaystyle \overset{\displaystyle CH_3}{\overset{\displaystyle |}{CH_2}}}{CH}-CH_3$$

d.
$$CH_3-CH_2-\overset{\overset{\displaystyle CH_3}{|}}{CH}-\overset{\overset{\displaystyle CH_2-CH_3 \;(stacked)}{|}}{CH}-\overset{\overset{\displaystyle CH_2 \;(with\;CH_3\;above)}{|}}{CH}-CH_3$$

d.
$$CH_3-CH_2-\underset{\underset{CH_3}{|}}{\overset{\overset{CH_3}{|}}{CH}}-CH-\overset{\overset{CH_2-CH_3}{\overset{CH_3}{|}}}{CH}-CH_3$$

e.
$$CH_3-\underset{\underset{\underset{CH_3}{|}}{\overset{CH_2}{|}}}{\overset{\overset{CH_3}{|}}{C}}-CH_3$$

f.
$$CH_3-\underset{\underset{\underset{CH_3}{|}}{\overset{CH-CH_2-CH_3}{|}}}{\overset{\overset{\overset{CH_3}{|}}{CH_2}}{CH}}-CH-CH_3$$

g.
$$CH_3-CH_2-\underset{\underset{CH_2-CH_3}{|}}{\overset{\overset{CH_2-CH_2-CH_3}{|}}{C}}-CH_2-CH_3$$

h.
$$CH_3-\underset{\underset{CH_3-CH-CH_3}{|}}{\overset{\overset{CH_2-CH_3}{|}}{CH}}-CH-CH_3$$

2. Name the following organic compounds:

a. $CH_3CH_2CH_2\underset{\underset{CH_3}{|}}{CH}CH_3$

b. $CH_3\underset{\underset{CH_3}{|}}{CH}CH_2CH_3$

c. $CH_3\underset{\underset{CH_2CH_3}{|}}{CH}CHCH_3$

d. $CH_3CH_2\underset{\underset{\underset{CH_3}{|}}{CH_2}}{CH}CH_2CH_3$

e. $CH_3\underset{\underset{CH_3}{|}}{CH}CH_2\underset{\underset{CH_3}{|}}{CH}CH_3$

f. $CH_3\underset{\underset{CH_3}{|}}{CH}\overset{\overset{CH_3}{|}}{CH}CH_2CH_3$

g. $CH_3\underset{\underset{\underset{CH_3}{|}}{CH_2}}{CH}CH_2CH_3$

h. $CH_3\underset{\underset{CH_3}{|}}{CH}\overset{\overset{\overset{CH_3}{|}}{CH_2}}{CH}CH_3$

3. Listed below are the condensed structural formulas or names of the nine isomers of heptane, C_7H_{16}. Write either the formula or name for each.

a. $CH_3CH_2CH_2CH_2CH_2CH_2CH_3$

f. $CH_3CH_2\overset{\overset{\displaystyle CH_3}{|}}{C}HCH_2CH_2CH_3$

b. $CH_3\overset{\overset{\displaystyle CH_3}{|}}{C}HCH_2\overset{\overset{\displaystyle CH_3}{|}}{C}HCH_3$

g. $CH_3\overset{\overset{\displaystyle CH_3}{|}}{\underset{\underset{\displaystyle CH_3}{|}}{C}}CH_2CH_2CH_3$

c. $CH_3\overset{\overset{\displaystyle CH_3}{|}}{\underset{\underset{\displaystyle CH_3}{|}}{C}}\text{———}\overset{\overset{\displaystyle CH_3}{|}}{C}HCH_3$

h. 2-methylhexane

i. 3-ethylpentane

d. 2,3-dimethylpentane

e. 3,3-dimethylpentane

27:4 Cycloalkanes

The cycloalkanes are saturated ring compounds having the general formula C_nH_{2n}. The following are some examples of cycloalkanes:

C_3H_6

$\begin{array}{c} CH_2\text{—}CH_2 \\ \diagdown\;\diagup \\ CH_2 \end{array}$ cyclopropane

C_4H_8

$\begin{array}{c} CH_2\text{—}CH_2 \\ |\qquad| \\ CH_2\text{—}CH_2 \end{array}$ cyclobutane

$\begin{array}{c} CH_3 \\ | \\ CH \\ \diagup\;\diagdown \\ CH_2\text{—}CH_2 \end{array}$ methylcyclopropane

C_5H_{10}

$\begin{array}{c} CH_2 \\ \diagup\quad\diagdown \\ CH_2\quad CH_2 \\ |\qquad| \\ CH_2\text{—}CH_2 \end{array}$ cyclopentane

$\begin{array}{c} CH_2\text{—}CH\text{—}CH_3 \\ |\qquad| \\ CH_2\text{—}CH_2 \end{array}$ methylcyclobutane

$\begin{array}{c} CH_2\text{—}CH_2 \\ \diagdown\;\diagup \\ C \\ \diagup\;\diagdown \\ CH_3\quad CH_3 \end{array}$ 1,1-dimethylcyclopropane

27:5 Alkenes

Alkenes are unsaturated compounds containing one double bond and having the general formula C_nH_{2n}. The *-ene* ending indicates a double bond. The position of the double bond is indicated by using the lower number of the two carbon atoms which the double bond joins. In compounds containing branched groups, the numbering of the double bond takes precedence. Note the following examples:

$$CH_2{=}CH_2 \qquad \text{ethene}$$

$$CH_3CH{=}CH_2 \qquad \text{propene}$$

$$CH_2{=}CHCH_2CH_3 \qquad \text{1-butene}$$

$$CH_3CH{=}CHCH_3 \qquad \text{2-butene}$$

$$\overset{\displaystyle CH_3}{\underset{\displaystyle |}{CH_3CH_2C}}{=}CH_2 \qquad \text{2-methyl-1-butene}$$

$$\underset{\displaystyle CH_3}{\underset{\displaystyle |}{CH_3CHCH}}{=}CH_2 \qquad \text{3-methyl-1-butene}$$

If a compound contains more than one double bond, the numbers of double bonds are noted with a Greek prefix preceding the *-ene* ending. For example,

$$CH_2{=}CHCH_2CH{=}CH_2 \qquad \text{1,4-pentadiene}$$

$$CH_2{=}CHCH{=}CH_2 \qquad \text{1,3-butadiene}$$

$$CH_2{=}C{=}CHCH_2CH_3 \qquad \text{1,2-pentadiene}$$

27:6 Alkynes

Alkynes contain a triple bond and have the general formula C_nH_{2n-2}. They are named by replacing the *-ane* of the corresponding saturated hydrocarbon with *-yne*, except for the first compound in the series, for which the common name is used.

$$HC{\equiv}CH \qquad \text{acetylene}$$

$$HC{\equiv}C{-}CH_3 \qquad \text{propyne}$$

Table 27-2
Hydrocarbon Summary

Family	Unit	Formula	Prefix or Suffix	Type of Compound
alkanes	CH_2	C_nH_{2n+2}	-ane	unbranched chain, saturated, single bonds
cycloalkanes	CH_2	C_nH_{2n}	cyclo-	ring structure, saturated
alkenes	CH_2	C_nH_{2n}	-ene	double bond, unsaturated
alkynes	CH	C_nH_{2n-2}	-yne	triple bond, unsaturated

27:7 Aromatic Hydrocarbons

All aromatic hydrocarbons contain one or more rings of carbon atoms held together by delocalized electrons. The compounds are named as derivatives of basic ring systems. Consider the ring structure of benzene. All positions on the benzene ring are equivalent.

benzene

Thus, only one monosubstituted compound is possible. For two substituents on the benzene ring three positions are possible. These positions may be designated by numbers or names, although the use of numbers is more correct.

position number	name
1,2	ortho (*o*-)
1,3	meta (*m*-)
1,4	para (*p*-)

The following are some examples of monosubstituted aromatic hydrocarbons:

CH₃ ⟨ring⟩   ⟨ring⟩—CH₂CH₃   ⟨ring⟩—CH₂CH₂CH₃

toluene   ethylbenzene   propylbenzene

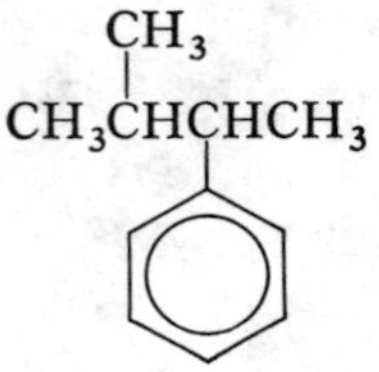

CH3
CH3CHCHCH3

2-methyl-3-phenylbutane

Disubstituted aromatic hydrocarbons:

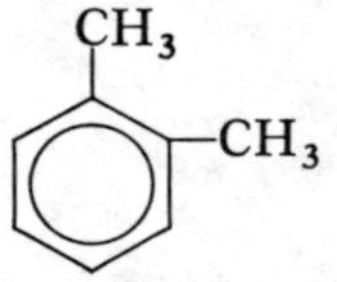

CH3
CH3

1,2-dimethylbenzene

CH3
CH3

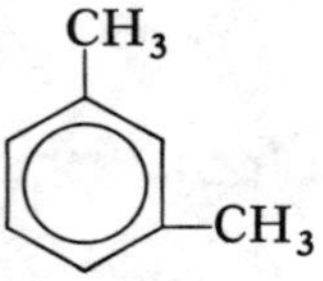

1,3-dimethylbenzene

CH3
CH3

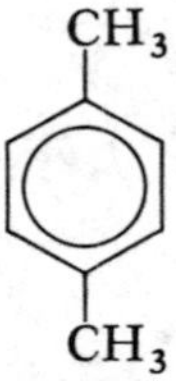

1,4-dimethylbenzene

Thousands of compounds are derived from benzene or other ring systems. These other rings may be considered to be fused benzene rings. Two examples of fused rings are naphthalene, $C_{10}H_8$, and anthracene, $C_{14}H_{10}$. The structural formulas show exactly how the atoms are arranged in the compounds.

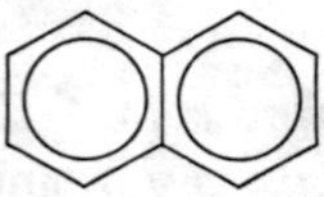

naphthalene

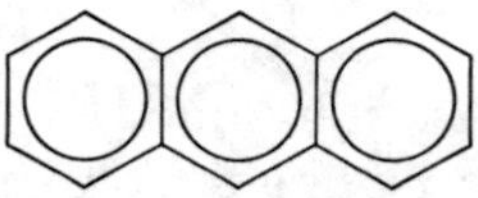

anthracene

The radical —C_6H_5 which is the benzene ring with one less hydrogen is termed the **phenyl radical.** Note the following examples:

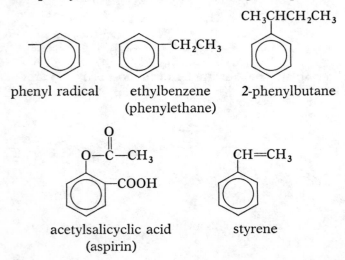

phenyl radical

CH2CH3

ethylbenzene
(phenylethane)

CH3CHCH2CH3

2-phenylbutane

O
O—C—CH3
COOH

acetylsalicyclic acid
(aspirin)

CH=CH3

styrene

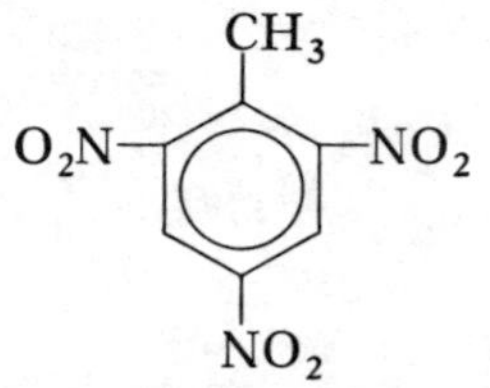

2,4,6-trinitrotoluene
(TNT)

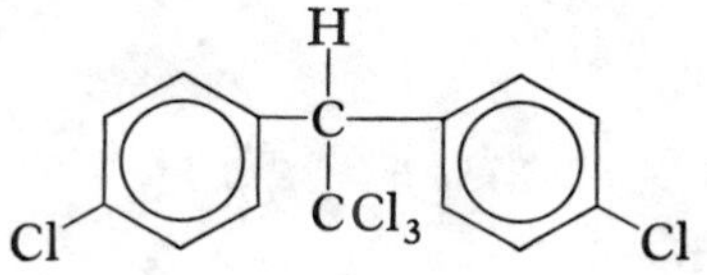

dichlorodiphenyltrichloroethane
(DDT)

Problems

4. Name the compounds represented by the following formulas:

a. $CH_3CH=CHCH_2CH_3$ **c.** 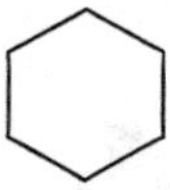   **e.**

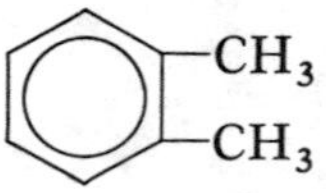

b.   **d.**

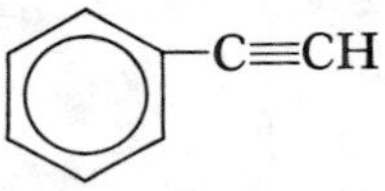

5. Draw the structural formulas for the following:
   a. 3-heptyne   **d.** 1,3-butadiene
   b. cyclopentene   **e.** 1-ethyl-2-methylbenzene
   c. 3-phenyl-2,2-dimethylhexane

27:8 Halogen Derivatives of Hydrocarbons

By replacing a hydrogen atom with a halogen atom (—Cl, *chloro;* —Br, *bromo;* and —I, *iodo*) on a hydrocarbon, additional isomers are possible. For these alkyl halides, the longest chain must contain the halogen-bearing carbon which is given the lowest possible number. For example,

$CH_3CH_2CH_2Cl$ 1-chloropropane

$CH_3\overset{\text{Cl}}{\underset{}{C}}HCH_3$ 2-chloropropane

$CH_3CH_2\overset{\text{Cl}}{\underset{}{C}}H\overset{\text{CH}_3}{\underset{}{C}}HCH_2CH_3$ 3-chloro-4-methylhexane

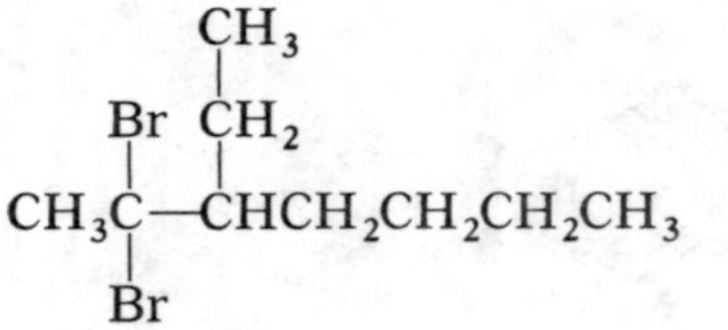

$$
\begin{array}{c}
CH_3 \\
| \\
Br \quad CH_2 \\
| \quad \quad | \\
CH_3C{-\!\!-}CHCH_2CH_2CH_2CH_3 \\
| \\
Br
\end{array}
$$
2,2-dibromo-3-ethylheptane

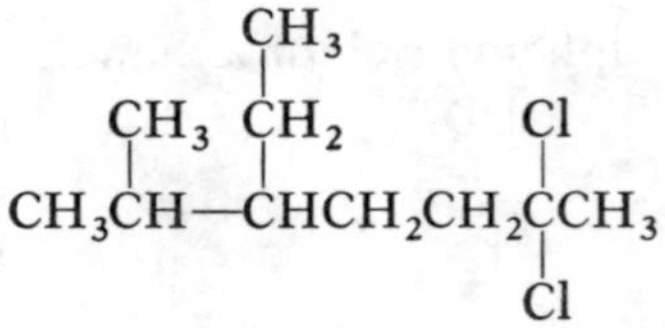

$$
\begin{array}{c}
CH_3 \\
| \\
CH_3 \quad CH_2 \quad \quad \quad Cl \\
| \quad \quad \quad | \quad \quad \quad \quad | \\
CH_3CH{-\!\!-}CHCH_2CH_2CCH_3 \\
| \\
Cl
\end{array}
$$
2,2-dichloro-5-ethyl-6-methylheptane

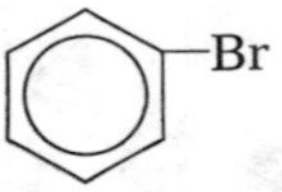

bromobenzene

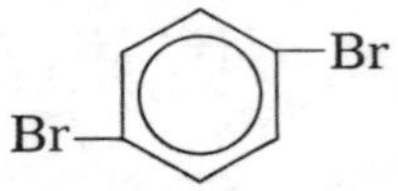

1,4-dibromobenzene

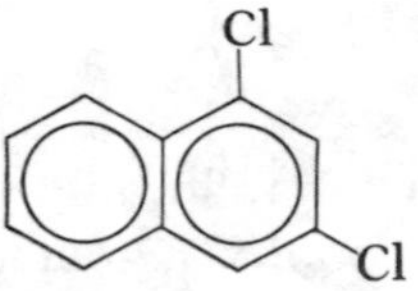

1,3-dichloronaphthalene

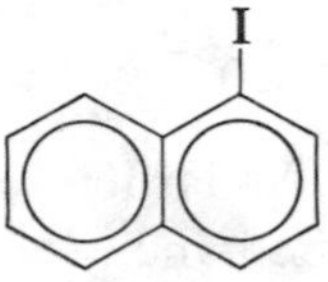

1-iodonaphthalene

Problems

6. Listed below are the condensed structural formulas or the names of the eight isomers of $C_5H_{11}Cl$. Write either the formula or the name for each.

   a. $CH_3CH_2CH_2CH_2CH_2Cl$

   b. 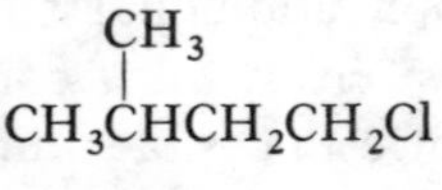 $\begin{array}{c} CH_3 \\ | \\ CH_3CHCH_2CH_2Cl \end{array}$

   c. 2-chloropentane

   d. 2-chloro-2-methylbutane

   e. 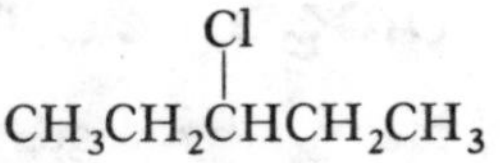 $\begin{array}{c} Cl \\ | \\ CH_3CH_2CHCH_2CH_3 \end{array}$

   f. 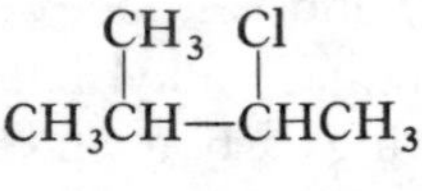 $\begin{array}{c} CH_3 \quad Cl \\ | \quad \quad | \\ CH_3CH{-\!\!-}CHCH_3 \end{array}$

   g. 1-chloro-2-methylbutane

   h. 1-chloro-2,2-dimethylpropane

7. Name the following compounds:

   a. 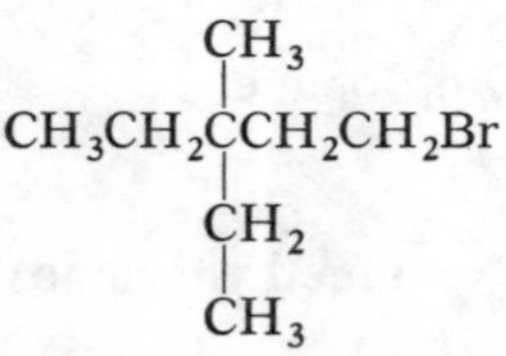 $\begin{array}{c} CH_3 \\ | \\ CH_3CH_2CCH_2CH_2Br \\ | \\ CH_2 \\ | \\ CH_3 \end{array}$

   b. $CH_3CH_2CH{=\!\!=}CH_2$

   c. 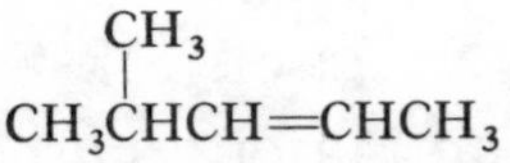 $\begin{array}{c} CH_3 \\ | \\ CH_3CHCH{=\!\!=}CHCH_3 \end{array}$

d. 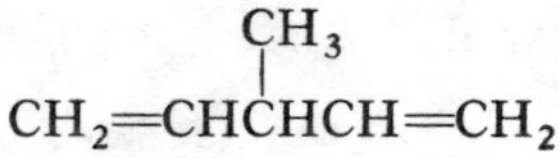 $CH_2{=}CHCHCH{=}CH_2$ (with CH_3 substituent)

e. 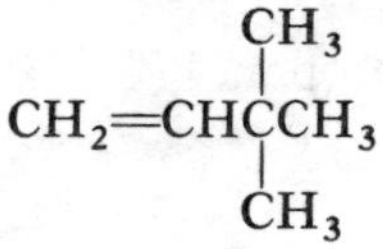 $CH_2{=}CHCCH_3$ (with CH_3 substituents above and below)

f. C_6H_5Cl

g. $CH_3CH{=}CHCH_2CH_3$

h. 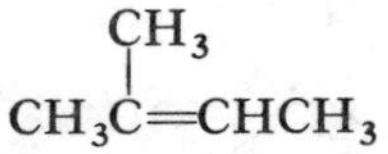 $CH_3C{=}CHCH_3$ (with CH_3 substituent)

i. 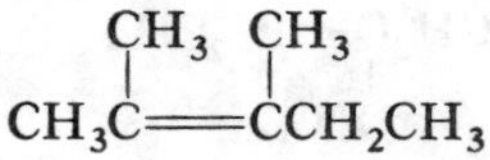 $CH_3C{=}CCH_2CH_3$ (with CH_3, CH_3 substituents)

j. 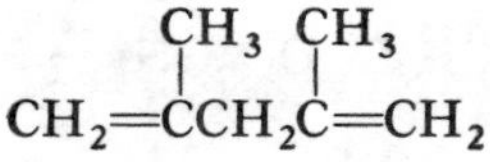 $CH_2{=}CCH_2C{=}CH_2$ (with CH_3, CH_3 substituents)

k. 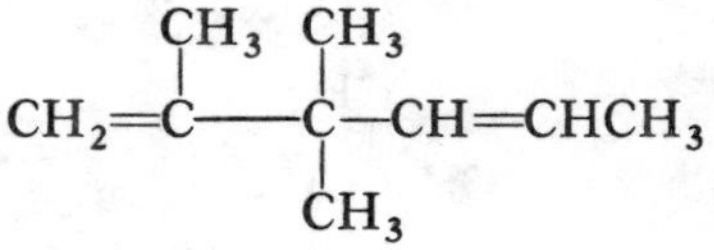 $CH_2{=}C\,{-}\,C{-}CH{=}CHCH_3$ (with CH_3, CH_3, CH_3 substituents)

l.

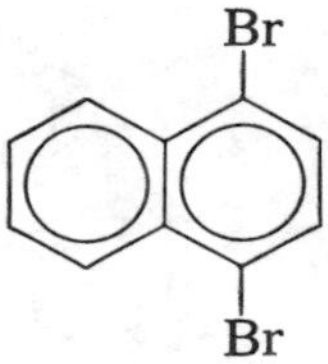

8. Draw structural formulas for the following:
   a. 3-heptene
   b. 2-methylnaphthalene
   c. trichloromethane
   d. 2-chloro-3-phenylhexane
   e. 1,3-cyclopentadiene
   f. toluene
   g. 1,4-dibromobenzene
   h. 2-bromo-3-methyl-2-butene

27:9 Hydroxy Compounds

The hydroxy compounds or alcohols, have a **hydroxyl group,** —OH, attached to the alkyl group. They are named by dropping the -e of the alkane series and adding -ol. If the hydroxyl group is attached to an aromatic group, the compound is called a **phenol.** Note the following examples:

CH_3OH methanol

CH_3CH_2OH ethanol

$CH_3CH_2CH_2OH$ 1-propanol

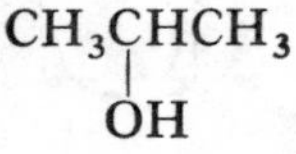

CH_3CHCH_3 (with OH below)   2-propanol

$CH_3CH_2CH_2CH_2OH$ 1-butanol

$$CH_3CHCH_2CH_3 \atop \quad\ OH$$ 2-butanol

$$CH_3CHCH_2OH \atop \quad\ CH_3$$ 2-methyl-1-propanol

$$CH_3\underset{OH}{\overset{CH_3}{\underset{|}{\overset{|}{C}}}}CH_3$$ 2-methyl-2-propanol

phenol   3-bromophenol   2-hydroxynaphthalene
(2-naphthol)

27:10 Carboxylic Acids

All organic acids have the functional group

which is called the **carboxyl group.** The carboxylic acid group is usually written as —COOH. This group is given the number 1 in naming compounds. The -e in the chain name is dropped and -oic plus the word *acid* is added. Common names are given in parenthesis.

HCOOH   CH$_3$COOH   CH$_3$CH$_2$COOH
methanoic acid   ethanoic acid   propanoic acid
(formic acid)   (acetic acid)

CH$_3$CH$_2$CH$_2$COOH   (CH$_3$)$_2$CHCOOH   CH$_3$CH$_2$CH$_2$CH$_2$COOH
butanoic acid   2-methylpropanoic acid   pentanoic acid

benzoic acid   4-bromobenzoic acid   2-hydroxybenzoic acid

27:11 Aldehydes

The functional group characteristic of aldehydes is

$$-\overset{\displaystyle O}{\underset{\displaystyle H}{C}}$$

These compounds are named by dropping the -e and adding -al to the chain name. The aldehyde carbon is given the number 1 in naming.

$$\begin{array}{ccc}
\text{HCHO} & \text{CH}_3\text{CHO} & \text{CH}_3\text{CH}_2\text{CHO} \\
\text{methanal} & \text{ethanal} & \text{propanal} \\
\text{(formaldehyde)} & &
\end{array}$$

CH$_3$CH$_2$CH$_2$CHO   (CH$_3$)$_2$CHCHO   [benzene ring]—CHO

butanal   2-methylpropanal   benzaldehyde

27:12 Ketones

Ketones contain the functional group

$$\rangle C=O$$

These compounds have the ending -one. The functional group is given the lowest possible number.

$$\begin{array}{ccc}
\overset{\displaystyle O}{\overset{\|}{\text{CH}_3\text{CCH}_3}} & \overset{\displaystyle O}{\overset{\|}{\text{CH}_3\text{CH}_2\text{CCH}_3}} & \overset{\displaystyle O}{\overset{\|}{\text{CH}_3\text{CH}_2\text{CCH}_2\text{CH}_3}} \\
\text{propanone} & \text{2-butanone} & \text{3-pentanone} \\
\text{(acetone)} & &
\end{array}$$

$$\overset{\displaystyle O}{\overset{\|}{\text{CH}_3\text{CCH}_2\text{CH}_2\text{CH}_3}} \qquad \underset{\underset{\displaystyle \text{CH}_3}{|}}{\overset{\displaystyle O}{\overset{\|}{\text{CH}_3\text{CCHCH}_3}}} \qquad \text{[benzene ring]}-\overset{\displaystyle O}{\overset{\|}{\text{C}}}-\text{CH}_3$$

2-pentanone   3-methyl-2-butanone   1-phenylethanone

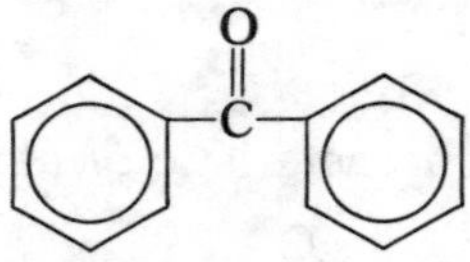

diphenylmethanone

27:13 Esters

Esters contain the group

$$-\overset{\overset{\textstyle O}{\|}}{C}-O-$$

and are formed from organic acids. The *-ic* of the acid name is dropped and the ending *-ate* is added. The alkyl group replacing the hydrogen atom in the carboxyl group is named first as a separate word.

$$CH_3CH_2\overset{\overset{\textstyle O}{\|}}{C}-OCH_2CH_3$$
ethylpropanoate

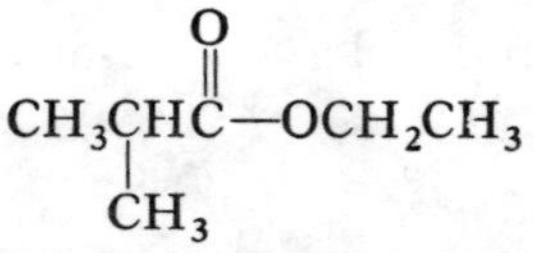

$$CH_3\underset{\underset{\textstyle CH_3}{|}}{CH}\overset{\overset{\textstyle O}{\|}}{C}-OCH_2CH_3$$
ethyl 2-methylpropanoate

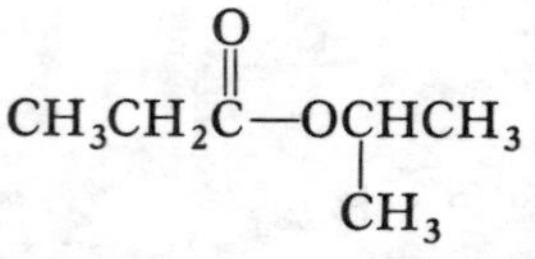

$$CH_3CH_2\overset{\overset{\textstyle O}{\|}}{C}-O\underset{\underset{\textstyle CH_3}{|}}{C}HCH_3$$
1-methylethyl propanoate

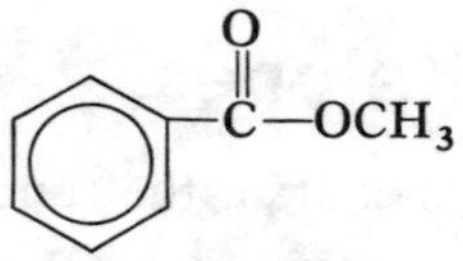

$$\overset{\overset{\textstyle O}{\|}}{C}-OCH_3$$
methyl benzoate

27:14 Ethers

Ethers have the general formula R—O—R in which an oxygen atom is joined to two separate hydrocarbon groups. Ethers are named as *oxy* derivatives of hydrocarbons.

$CH_3—O—CH_3$ $CH_3—O—CH_2CH_3$ $CH_3CH_2CH_2—O—CH_2CH_3$
methoxymethane   methoxyethane   1-ethoxypropane

$$CH_3—O—C_6H_5$$
methoxybenzene

Table 27-3
Organic Compounds Containing Oxygen

Compound	General Formula*	Characteristic Group	Naming	Example
Alcohol	R—OH	—OH	-ol	$CH_3CH_2CH_2OH$ 1-propanol
Carboxylic Acid	R—C(=O)—OH	—C(=O)—OH	-oic acid	CH_3C(=O)—OH ethanoic acid
Aldehyde	R—C(=O)—H	—C(=O)—H	-al	CH_3C(=O)—H ethanal
Ketone	R—C(=O)—R	—C(=O)—	-one	$CH_3\overset{O}{\overset{\|}{C}}CH_3$ propanone
Ester	R—C(=O)—O—R	—C(=O)—O—	-ate	CH_3CH_2C(=O)—OCH_2CH_3 ethyl propanoate
Ether	R—O—R	—O—	-oxy-	CH_3CH_2—O—CH_2CH_3 ethoxyethane

*R represents any alkyl group such as CH_3, methyl; CH_3CH_2, ethyl; etc.

27:15 Nitrogen Containing Compounds

Amines are organic compounds containing nitrogen. Amines are derivatives of ammonia. One, two, or three of the hydrogens in ammonia can be replaced with an alkyl group. General formulas for amines are

$$H-\underset{H}{N}-H \qquad H-\underset{H}{N}-R \qquad R-\underset{H}{N}-R \qquad R-\underset{R}{N}-R$$

| ammonia | primary amine | secondary amine | tertiary amine |

The following table lists other classes of nitrogen containing organic compounds.

Table 27-4
Organic Compounds Containing Nitrogen

Compound	General Formula	Example	
Amines	R—NH$_2$	CH$_3$CH$_2$NH$_2$	ethylamine
Amides	$R-\overset{\overset{\displaystyle O}{\|\|}}{C}-NH_2$	CH$_3$CONH$_2$	ethanamide
Amino acids	$G-\overset{\overset{\displaystyle NH_2}{\|}}{C}H-COOH$	CH$_3$CH(NH$_2$)COOH alanine (2-aminopropanoic acid)	
Nitriles	R—C≡N	CH$_3$CH$_2$CH$_2$CN	butanenitrile
Nitro compounds	R—NO$_2$	C$_6$H$_5$NO$_2$	nitrobenzene

*R represents any alkyl group such as —CH$_3$, methyl; CH$_3$CH$_2$⁻, ethyl and so on. G can represent a group made up of elements other than just carbon and hydrogen.

Chapter Review Problems

9. Write structural formulas for the following compounds:
    a. 2-chlorobutane
    b. 2-butene
    c. 2-ethyl-3-methyl-1-butanol
    d. 3,3-dimethylbutanoic acid
    e. 2,5,5-trimethyl-4-heptone
    f. 2,5-nonadiyne
    g. 1,3-diiodobenzene
    h. ethoxybenzene
    i. 1-butanol
    j. 3-methyl-2-pentene
    k. 2-ethyl-4-methylpentanal
    l. 3-ethyl-2,4-dimethyl-3-hexanol
    m. 5-chloro-3-ethyl-2-methylheptanoic acid
    n. 2-phenylbutane
    o. 7-bromo-2-naphthol
    p. 4-bromobenzoic acid

10. Name the following organic compounds:

    a. 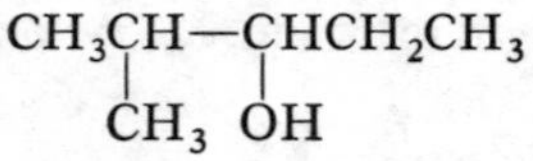 $CH_3CH-CHCH_2CH_3$
            $\quad\ \ \ |\quad\ \ \ |$
            $\quad\ \ \ CH_3\ \ OH$

    d. 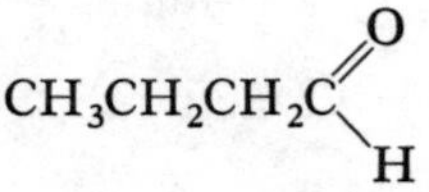 $CH_3CH_2CH_2C\overset{\displaystyle O}{\underset{\displaystyle H}{\diagup}}$

b. $\overset{\overset{\displaystyle O}{\|}}{CH_3CH_2C}\underset{\underset{\displaystyle CH_3}{|}}{CHCH_3}$

e. $CH_3\underset{\underset{\displaystyle CH_3}{|}}{\overset{\overset{\displaystyle CH_3}{|}}{C}}CH_2CH_2CH_2OH$

c. $CH_3\underset{\underset{\displaystyle CH_3}{|}}{CH}CH{=}CH_2$

f. $CH_2{=}CHC\underset{\underset{\displaystyle OH}{|}}{\overset{\overset{\displaystyle CH_3}{|}}{C}}H{=}CHCH_3$

11. Name the following organic compounds:

a. $CH_3CH_2\underset{\underset{\displaystyle CH_3}{|}}{CH}CH_2Cl$

d. $CH_3CH_2\underset{\underset{\displaystyle Cl}{|}}{CH}CH_2CH_3$

b. $CH_3\underset{\underset{\displaystyle CH_3}{|}}{\overset{\overset{\displaystyle CH_3}{|}}{C}}{-}\underset{\underset{\displaystyle CH_3}{|}}{CH}CH_2Br$

e. $CH_3\underset{\underset{\displaystyle OH}{|}}{\overset{\overset{\displaystyle CH_3}{|}}{C}}CH_2CH_3$

c.

f. $CH_3CH_2\underset{\underset{\displaystyle Br}{|}}{C}{=}CHCH_3$

12. Each of the following formulas can be written as two compounds with different functional groups. Write the structural formulas, name the compounds, and identify the functional groups.

a. C_2H_6O b. C_3H_6O c. C_5H_{10}

Appendix A

Table A-1
Major Formal Oxidation States of Some Elements and Polyatomic Ions

1+

ammonium	NH_4^+
cesium	Cs^+
copper(I)	Cu^+
gold(I)	Au^+
hydrogen	H^+
lithium	Li^+
mercury(I)	Hg_2^{2+}
potassium	K^+
rubidium	Rb^+
sodium	Na^+
silver	Ag^+
thallium(I)	Tl^+

2+

barium	Ba^{2+}
cadmium	Cd^{2+}
calcium	Ca^{2+}
cerium(II)	Ce^{2+}
chromium(II)	Cr^{2+}
cobalt(II)	Co^{2+}
copper(II)	Cu^{2+}
iron(II)	Fe^{2+}
lead(II)	Pb^{2+}
magnesium	Mg^{2+}
mercury(II)	Hg^{2+}
nickel(II)	Ni^{2+}
strontium	Sr^{2+}
tin(II)	Sn^{2+}
zinc	Zn^{2+}

3+

aluminum	Al^{3+}
antimony(III)	Sb^{3+}
arsenic(III)	As^{3+}
bismuth	Bi^{3+}
boron	B^{3+}
cerium(III)	Ce^{3+}
cobalt(III)	Co^{3+}
gold(III)	Au^{3+}
iron(III)	Fe^{3+}
manganese(III)	Mn^{3+}
thallium(III)	Tl^{3+}
titanium(III)	Ti^{3+}
tungsten(III)	W^{3+}
vanadium	V^{3+}
zirconium(III)	Zr^{3+}

4+

carbon	C^{4+}
cerium(IV)	Ce^{4+}
lead(IV)	Pb^{4+}
manganese(IV)	Mn^{4+}
tin(IV)	Sn^{4+}
titanium(IV)	Ti^{4+}

5+

antimony(V)	Sb^{5+}
arsenic(V)	As^{5+}
bismuth(V)	Bi^{5+}
tungsten(V)	W^{5+}
uranium(V)	U^{5+}
vanadium(V)	V^{5+}

6+

chromium(VI)	Cr^{6+}
manganese(VI)	Mn^{6+}
tungsten(VI)	W^{6+}
uranium(VI)	U^{6+}

1−

acetate	$C_2H_3O_2^-$
amide	NH_2^-
azide	N_3^-
chlorate	ClO_3^-
chlorite	ClO_2^-
bromate	BrO_3^-
cyanate	OCN^-
cyanide	CN^-
hydrogen carbonate	HCO_3^-
hypochlorite	ClO^-
hydroxide	OH^-
iodate	IO_3^-
nitrate	NO_3^-
nitrite	NO_2^-
permanganate	MnO_4^-
thiocyanate	SCN^-

2−

benzoate	$C_7H_6O_2^{2-}$
carbonate	CO_3^{2-}
chromate	CrO_4^{2-}
dichromate	$Cr_2O_7^{2-}$
disulfate	$S_2O_7^{2-}$
manganate	MnO_4^{2-}
oxalate	$C_2O_4^{2-}$
oxide	O^{2-}
peroxide	O_2^{2-}
sulfate	SO_4^{2-}
sulfide	S^{2-}
sulfite	SO_3^{2-}
thiosulfate	$S_2O_3^{2-}$

3−

arsenate	AsO_4^{3-}
arsenite	AsO_3^{3-}
borate	BO_3^{3-}
phosphate	PO_4^{3-}

Table A-2
Molar Heats of Fusion and Vaporization for Some Substances

Fusion (H_f)		Vaporization (H_v)	
aluminum	10.8 kJ/mol	aluminum	284 kJ/mol
arsenic	93.7 kJ/mol	benzene	30.8 kJ/mol
gold	12.4 kJ/mol	helium	0.0182 kJ/mol
indium	3.27 kJ/mol	selenium	86.2 kJ/mol
iron	15.4 kJ/mol	water	40.7 kJ/mol
steel	15.4 kJ/mol		
titanium	18.8 kJ/mol		
water	6.02 kJ/mol		

Table A-3
Specific Heat Capacities of Some Substances

acetic acid	2.05 J/g·C°	steel(c)	0.450 J/g·C°
aluminum	0.903 J/g·C°	steel(l)	0.719 J/g·C°
chalk	0.920 J/g·C°	tin	0.222 J/g·C°
glass	0.753 J/g·C°	toluene	1.615 J/g·C°
indium(c)	0.238 J/g·C°	water(c)	2.06 J/g·C°
indium(l)	0.216 J/g·C°	water(l)	4.18 J/g·C°
kerosene	2.09 J/g·C°	water(g)	2.02 J/g·C°
methylbenzene	1.80 J/g·C°		

Table A-4
Thermodynamic Properties

	$\Delta G°$	$\Delta H°$	$S°$
Ag(c)	0	0	42.6
Ag_2SO_4(aq)	−590	−698	33.1
Br_2(l)	0	0	152
CO_2(g)	−394	−394	214
Cl_2(g)	0	0	223
$CaCl_2$(aq)	−815	−878	54.8
$Ca(OH)_2$(c)	−897	−987	76.1
Cu(c)	0	0	33.1
$Cu(NO_3)_2$(aq)	−157	−350	193
$CuSO_4$(aq)	−679	−844	109
H_2(g)	0	0	131
HBr(g)	−36.4	−53.4	199
HCl(g)	−95.3	−92.3	187
HCl(aq)	−131	−167	56.5
HI(g)	26.5	1.72	206
HNO_2(aq)	−55.6	−119	46.1
HNO_3(aq)	−111	−207	53.3
H_2O(l)	−237	−286	69.9
H_2SO_4(l)	−690	−814	139
I_2(c)	0	0	116
ICl(l)	−13.6	−23.9	135
KBr(c)	−379	−392	96.4

KCl(aq)	−413	−419	158
K$_2$SO$_4$(aq)		−1409	
Mg(c)	0	0	32.5
Mg$_3$N$_2$(c)	−422	−461	
Mg(NO$_3$)$_2$(aq)	−677	−875	175
Mg(OH)$_2$(c)	−834	−925	63.1
N$_2$(g)	0	0	192
NH$_3$(g)	−16.5	−46.1	192
NH$_4$Cl(aq)	−211	−300	170
NH$_4$NO$_2$(c)		−256	
NH$_4$NO$_3$(c)	−184	−366	151
N$_2$O(g)	104	82.0	220
NO(g)	86.6	90.2	211
NO$_2$(g)	51.3	33.2	240
N$_2$O$_5$(g)	115	11.3	356
NaCl(c)	−384	−411	72.4
NaCl(aq)	−393	−407	115
NaNO$_3$(aq)	−372	−446	207
NaOH(aq)	−419	−470	11.9
Na$_2$SO$_4$(aq)	−1266	−1387	138
O$_2$(g)	0	0	205
SiO$_2$(c)	−857	−511	41.8
Sn(c)	0	0	51.5
SnO$_2$(c)	−520	−581	52.3
Zn(c)	0	0	41.6
Zn(OH)$_2$(c)	−554	−642	81.2
Zn(NO$_3$)$_2$(aq)	−370	−569	181

Appendix B

Using Logarithms

A log or logarithm is an exponent. In our work, the log or exponent of a number will always be given in terms of the base 10. Read the following discussion carefully if you do not understand logarithms. The mathematical equation defining a log is

N   = b^a exponent or log   log of N to the base b equals a
number   base $\log_b N = a$

Logs are simply exponents and they can be added to multiply the numbers they represent and subtracted to divide the numbers they represent. If we define pH to be the negative log of the hydronium ion concentration, we get the following:

if [H$_3$O$^+$] = 10^{-7} mol/L;   then log [H$_3$O$^+$] = −7
and if pH = −log [H$_3$O$^+$];   then pH = 7

The pOH is defined as the negative log of the hydroxide ion concentration. The concentrations of the H$_3$O$^+$ and OH$^-$ must be expressed in moles per liter which is indicated by the brackets.

$$pH = -\log [H_3O^+] \qquad pOH = -\log [OH^-]$$

Table B-1
Logarithms of Numbers

N	0	1	2	3	4	5	6	7	8	9
10	0000	0043	0086	0128	0170	0212	0253	0294	0334	0374
11	0414	0453	0492	0531	0569	0607	0645	0682	0719	0775
12	0792	0828	0864	0899	0934	0969	1004	1038	1072	1106
13	1139	1173	1206	1239	1271	1303	1335	1367	1399	1430
14	1461	1492	1523	1553	1584	1614	1644	1673	1703	1732
15	1761	1790	1818	1847	1875	1903	1931	1959	1987	2014
16	2041	2068	2095	2122	2148	2175	2201	2227	2253	2279
17	2304	2330	2355	2380	2405	2430	2455	2480	2504	2529
18	2553	2577	2601	2625	2648	2672	2695	2718	2742	2765
19	2788	2810	2833	2856	2878	2900	2923	2945	2967	2989
20	3010	3032	3054	3075	3096	3118	3139	3160	3181	3201
21	3222	3243	3263	3284	3304	3324	3345	3365	3385	3404
22	3424	3444	3464	3483	3502	3522	3541	3560	3579	3598
23	3617	3636	3655	3674	3692	3711	3729	3747	3766	3784
24	3802	3820	3838	3856	3874	3892	3909	3927	3945	3962
25	3979	3997	4014	4031	4048	4065	4082	4099	4116	4133
26	4150	4166	4183	4200	4216	4232	4249	4265	4281	4298
27	4314	4330	4346	4362	4378	4393	4409	4425	4440	4456
28	4472	4487	4502	4518	4533	4548	4564	4579	4594	4609
29	4624	4639	4654	4669	4683	4698	4713	4728	4742	4757
30	4771	4786	4800	4814	4829	4843	4857	4871	4886	4900
31	4914	4928	4942	4955	4969	4983	4997	5011	5024	5038
32	5051	5065	5079	5092	5105	5119	5132	5145	5159	5172
33	5185	5198	5211	5224	5237	5250	5263	5276	5289	5302
34	5315	5328	5340	5353	5366	5378	5391	5403	5416	5428
35	5441	5453	5465	5478	5490	5502	5514	5527	5539	5551
36	5563	5575	5587	5599	5611	5623	5635	5647	5658	5670
37	5682	5694	5705	5717	5729	5740	5752	5763	5775	5786
38	5798	5809	5821	5832	5843	5855	5866	5877	5888	5899
39	5911	5922	5933	5944	5955	5966	5977	5988	5999	6010
40	6021	6031	6042	6053	6064	6075	6085	6096	6107	6117
41	6128	6138	6149	6160	6170	6180	6191	6201	6212	6222
42	6232	6243	6253	6263	6274	6284	6294	6304	6314	6325
43	6335	6345	6355	6365	6375	6385	6395	6405	6415	6425
44	6435	6444	6454	6464	6474	6484	6493	6503	6513	6522
45	6352	6542	6551	6561	6571	6580	6590	6599	6609	6618
46	6628	6637	6646	6656	6665	6675	6684	6693	6702	6712
47	6721	6730	6739	6749	6758	6767	6776	6785	6794	6803
48	6812	6821	6830	6839	6848	6857	6866	6875	6884	6893
49	6902	6911	6920	6928	6937	6946	6955	6964	6972	6981
50	6990	6998	7007	7016	7024	7033	7042	7050	7059	7067
51	7076	7084	7093	7101	7110	7118	7126	7135	7143	7152
52	7160	7168	7177	7185	7193	7202	7210	7218	7226	7235
53	7243	7251	7259	7267	7275	7284	7292	7300	7308	7316
54	7324	7332	7340	7348	7356	7364	7372	7380	7388	7396

N	0	1	2	3	4	5	6	7	8	9
55	7404	7412	7419	7427	7435	7443	7451	7459	7466	7474
56	7482	7490	7497	7505	7513	7520	7528	7536	7543	7551
57	7559	7566	7574	7582	7589	7597	7604	7612	7619	7627
58	7634	7642	7649	7657	7664	7672	7679	7686	7694	7701
59	7709	7716	7723	7731	7738	7745	7752	7760	7767	7774
60	7782	7789	7796	7803	7810	7818	7825	7832	7839	7846
61	7853	7860	7868	7875	7882	7889	7896	7903	7910	7917
62	7924	7931	7938	7945	7952	7959	7966	7973	7980	7987
63	7993	8000	8007	8014	8021	8028	8035	8041	8048	8055
64	8062	8069	8075	8082	8089	8096	8102	8109	8116	8122
65	8129	8136	8142	8149	8156	8162	8169	8176	8182	8189
66	8195	8202	8209	8215	8222	8228	8235	8241	8248	8254
67	8261	8267	8274	8280	8287	8293	8299	8306	8312	8319
68	8325	8331	8338	8344	8351	8357	8363	8370	8376	8382
69	8388	8395	8401	8407	8414	8420	8426	8432	8439	8445
70	8451	8457	8463	8470	8476	8482	8488	8494	8500	8506
71	8513	8519	8525	8531	8537	8543	8549	8555	8561	8567
72	8573	8579	8585	8591	8597	8603	8609	8615	8621	8627
73	8633	8639	8645	8651	8657	8663	8669	8675	8681	8686
74	8692	8698	8704	8710	8716	8722	8727	8733	8739	8745
75	8751	8756	8762	8768	8774	8779	8785	8791	8797	8802
76	8808	8814	8820	8825	8831	8837	8842	8848	8854	8859
77	8865	8871	8876	8882	8887	8893	8899	8904	8910	8915
78	8921	8927	8932	8938	8943	8949	8954	8960	8965	8971
79	8976	8982	8987	8993	8998	9004	9009	9015	9020	9025
80	9031	9036	9042	9047	9053	9058	9063	9069	9074	9079
81	9085	9090	9096	9101	9106	9112	9117	9122	9128	9133
82	9138	9143	9149	9154	9159	9165	9170	9175	9180	9186
83	9191	9196	9201	9206	9212	9217	9222	9227	9232	9238
84	9243	9248	9253	9258	9263	9269	9274	9279	9284	9289
85	9294	9299	9304	9309	9315	9320	9325	9330	9335	9340
86	9345	9350	9355	9360	9365	9370	9375	9380	9385	9390
87	9395	9400	9405	9410	9415	9420	9425	9430	9435	9440
88	9445	9450	9455	9460	9465	9469	9474	9479	9484	9489
89	9494	9499	9504	9509	9513	9518	9523	9528	9533	9538
90	9542	9547	9552	9557	9562	9566	9571	9576	9581	9586
91	9590	9595	9600	9605	9609	9614	9619	9624	9628	9633
92	9638	9643	9647	9652	9657	9661	9666	9671	9675	9680
93	9685	9689	9694	9699	9703	9708	9713	9717	9722	9727
94	9731	9736	9741	9745	9750	9754	9759	9763	9768	9773
95	9777	9782	9786	9791	9795	9800	9805	9809	9814	9818
96	9823	9827	9832	9836	9841	9845	9850	9854	9859	9863
97	9868	9872	9877	9881	9886	9890	9894	9899	9903	9908
98	9912	9917	9921	9926	9930	9934	9939	9943	9948	9952
99	9956	9961	9965	9969	9974	9978	9983	9987	9991	9996

Chapter 1

1.
   a. $1.40 \, g/cm^3$
   b. $11.0 \, g/cm^3$
   c. $1.40 \, g/L$
2. Pb 47.5 grams, Fe 444 grams, Fe heavier
3. 48.0 grams H_2O
   75.8 grams CCl_4
   648 grams Hg
4.
   a. $25.8 \, cm^3$ HCl
   b. $16.4 \, cm^3 \, H_2SO_4$
   c. $24.0 \, cm^3 \, HNO_3$

5.
   a. 4
   b. 3
   c. 3
   d. 2
   e. 2
   f. 4
   g. 3
   h. 2
   i. 3
   j. 5
   k. 4
   l. 4
   m. 4
   n. 4

6.
   a. 29
   b. 32.9
   c. 7.16
   d. 0.1809
   e. 55.35

7.
   a. 11.21
   b. 7.3
   c. 150
   d. 13.31

8.
   a. 9.8
   b. 2.4
   c. 32
   d. 0.0028
   e. 16
   f. 0.0007
   g. 35.9
   h. 64

9.
   a. 56
   b. 1.6
   c. 2.32
   d. 2.5

10. 1.36 grams
11. 3380 grams
12. $3.00 \times 10^3 \, cm^3$
13. 2.74 grams
14.
   a. 3×10^{-5}
   b. 8×10^6
   c. 5.5×10^7
   d. 2×10^{-3}
   e. 7×10^{-6}
   f. 6.5×10^4
15.
   a. 1×10^{-6}
   b. 3×10^9
   c. 2×10^1
   d. 3×10^1
   e. 2×10^{-2}
   f. 4×10^2
   g. 4×10^5
   h. 4×10^{-3}
   i. 4×10^{-2}
   j. 3×10^{-7}
   k. 7×10^{-9}
   l. 5×10^{13}
   m. 5×10^{-5}
   n. 3×10^2
   o. 3×10^{-1}
   p. 2×10^1
   q. 1×10^2
   r. 1×10^{-1}
   s. 8×10^{12}
   t. 4×10^{-2}

16. 1.674×10^{-24} gram
17. 3.349×10^{-24} gram
18. proton 1.008 a.m.u.
    electron 5.487×10^{-4} a.m.u.
    neutron 1.009 a.m.u.
19. hydrogen 1.009 a.m.u.
    deuterium 2.018 a.m.u.
20. $3.302323 \times 10^{-7} \, m$
    $5.688224 \times 10^{-7} \, m$
    $5.889953 \times 10^{-7} \, m$
21.
   a. $3500 \, cm^3$
   b. $7.5 \times 10^5 \, mg$
   c. $1.5 \times 10^{-3} \, km$
   d. $8.64 \times 10^4 \, s$
   e. $5000 \, mL$
   f. $520 \, m$
   g. $0.065 \, kg$
   h. $7.5 \times 10^{-4} \, g$
   i. $2.5 \times 10^7 \, cm$
22. $4.464 \times 10^4 \, min$
23. $1390 \, cm/s$
24. 672 test tubes
25. $17.50
26. 10 quarters
    25 dimes
27. 37 donuts
28. $70.31
29. $22.0 \, cm^3$
30. 118 grams
31. 306.2 grams
32. 1.6×10^{-5} light years
33. $3 \times 10^{-7} \, mm$
    $3 \times 10^{-13} \, km$

Chapter 2

1.			2.			3.		
	a.	Cu		a.	Cu		a.	sodium sulfide
	b.	Bi		b.	K		b.	lithium oxide
	c.	Nb		c.	Li		c.	magnesium bromide
	d.	Mg		d.	Ca		d.	chlorine(I) oxide
	e.	Ta		e.	Na		e.	nitrogen(II) oxide
	f.	Al		f.	Mg		f.	hydrogen sulfide
	g.	Ga		g.	Ba		g.	hydrogen chloride
	h.	Li		h.	Al		h.	aluminum nitride
	i.	Zr					i.	calcium fluoride
	j.	Cr					j.	potassium iodide

4.
- a. magnesium hydroxide
- b. potassium cyanide
- c. sodium hydroxide
- d. zinc cyanide
- e. calcium oxide
- f. sodium azide
- g. calcium amide
- h. potassium hydroxide

5.
- a. LiF, LiCl, LiBr, LiI, Li_2O, Li_2S
- b. NaF, NaCl, NaBr, NaI, Na_2O, Na_2S
- c. KF, KCl, KBr, KI, K_2O, K_2S
- d. NH_4F, NH_4Cl, NH_4Br, NH_4I, $(NH_4)_2S$

6.
- a. $MgCl_2$, $MgBr_2$, $Mg(OH)_2$, MgS
- b. $CaCl_2$, $CaBr_2$, $Ca(OH)_2$, CaO, $Ca(CN)_2$, CaS

7.
- a. NaOH, NaCN
- b. NH_4CN
- c. $BaCl_2$, $Ba(OH)_2$, $Ba(CN)_2$, BaO, BaS

8.
- a. sodium sulfate
- b. sodium nitrate
- c. magnesium nitrate
- d. ammonium acetate
- e. potassium perchlorate
- f. ammonium chlorate
- g. sodium perchlorate
- h. barium carbonate
- i. sodium dihydrogen phosphate
- j. potassium sodium carbonate
- k. ammonium magnesium phosphate
- l. potassium nitrite
- m. magnesium sulfate
- n. calcium hypochlorite
- o. barium nitrite
- p. barium chlorate
- q. calcium sulfite
- r. potassium bromate
- s. cadmium iodate
- t. sodium ammonium hydrogen phosphate
- u. sodium hydrogen sulfate

9.
- a. $CaSO_4$
- b. $NaNO_3$
- c. $KClO_4$
- d. $Al_2(SO_4)_3$
- e. $KClO_3$
- f. NaClO
- g. $Ba_3(PO_4)_2$
- h. $(NH_4)_2CO_3$
- i. $MgSO_3$
- j. $LiNO_2$
- k. $NaClO_2$
- l. $(NH_4)_2Cr_2O_7$
- m. $NaNO_2$
- n. $NaBrO_3$
- o. K_3PO_4
- p. Ag_2CO_3

10.
- a. titanium(II) chloride
- b. titanium(IV) bromide
- c. copper(I) chloride
- d. lead(II) iodide
- e. tin(IV) chloride
- f. copper(I) oxide
- g. chromium(VI) oxide
- h. manganese(II,III) oxide
- i. titanium(IV) oxide
- j. lead(II) oxide
- k. titanium(III) chloride
- l. nickel(II) bromide
- m. copper(II) bromide
- n. lead(II) chloride
- o. chromium(III) fluoride
- p. copper(II) oxide
- q. tin(II) oxide
- r. titanium(II) oxide
- s. iron(III) oxide
- t. manganese(III) oxide

11.
- a. $MnCl_3$
- b. $FeBr_3$
- c. $CrBr_3$
- d. $SnCl_4$
- e. $MnBr_2$
- f. SnO_2
- g. Cr_2O_3
- h. Pb_2O_3
- i. Mn_2O_7
- j. Hg_2O
- k. $FeCl_2$
- l. $CuCl_2$
- m. $SnCl_2$
- n. TiI_4
- o. NiF_2
- p. MnO_2
- q. PbO_2
- r. NiO
- s. HgO
- t. Co_2O_3

12.
- a. iron(III) sulfate
- b. chromium(II) hydroxide
- c. mercury(I) chlorate
- d. iron(II) perchlorate
- e. manganese(II) sulfate
- f. chromium(III) sulfite
- g. mercury(II) iodate
- h. lead(II) chlorite
- i. copper(II) acetate
- j. copper(I) sulfate
- k. cobalt(II) sulfate
- l. lead(II) phosphate

13.
- a. $Cu(ClO_3)_2$
- b. $Co_2(SO_4)_3$
- c. $Mn_2(SO_4)_3$
- d. $Fe(NO_3)_3$
- e. $Sn(NO_3)_4$
- f. $Co(ClO_4)_2$
- g. $Cr_2(SO_4)_3$
- h. $Fe(OH)_2$
- i. $Cu_3(PO_4)_2$
- j. $Hg_2(NO_2)_2$
- k. $Pb(NO_3)_2$
- l. Hg_2SO_4

14.
- a. iron(II) sulfate
- b. ammonium chlorate
- c. iron(II) acetate
- d. copper(II) chromate
- e. magnesium nitrate
- f. aluminum phosphate
- g. sodium sulfite
- h. calcium chlorite
- i. ammonium carbonate
- j. silver chromate
- k. barium phosphate
- l. potassium perchlorate

15.
- a. $Mg(NO_3)_2$
- b. $AgC_2H_3O_2$
- c. $Ba(ClO_4)_2$
- d. KNO_2
- e. $(NH_4)_2SO_4$
- f. $(NH_4)_2Cr_2O_7$
- g. Na_2CO_3
- h. $Ca_3(PO_4)_2$

16.
- a. dinitrogen oxide
- b. nitrogen dioxide
- c. dinitrogen pentoxide
- d. phosphorus trichloride
- e. nitrogen oxide
- f. dinitrogen tetroxide
- g. diphosphorus pentoxide
- h. phosphorus pentachloride

17.
- a. Cl_2O
- b. ClO_2
- c. CS_2
- d. ClF_3
- e. ClO_7
- f. SF_6

18.
- a. sodium chlorate, chloric acid
- b. iron(II) perchlorate, perchloric acid
- c. ammonium bromate, bromic acid
- d. magnesium iodate, iodic acid
- e. manganese(II) iodide, hydroiodic acid
- f. barium nitrate, nitric acid

g. lead(II) chloride, hydrochloric acid

h. mercury(II) bromate, bromic acid

i. zinc sulfate, sulfuric acid

j. calcium hypochlorite, hypochlorous acid

19. a. $(NH_4)_2SO_4$, sulfuric acid

b. $Ba(ClO)_2$, hypochlorous acid

c. $LiClO_3$, chloric acid

d. $CoSO_3$, sulfurous acid

e. $Hg_2(BrO_3)_2$, bromic acid

f. $Cr(NO_3)_3$, nitric acid

g. $MgCl_2$, hydrochloric acid

h. $KClO_4$, perchloric acid

20. a. magnesium carbonate

b. $MgCO_3 \cdot 3H_2O$

c. magnesium phosphate tetrahydrate

d. cobalt(II) chloride dihydrate

e. $Ca(NO_3)_2 \cdot 3H_2O$

21. a. $NaNO_2$

b. Na_2CO_3

c. Na_2SO_4

d. KOH

e. KNO_3

f. K_2SO_3

g. K_3PO_4

h. $Cd(OH)_2$

i. $CdCO_3$

j. $CdSO_4$

k. $Cd_3(PO_4)_2$

l. $AlBr_3$

m. $Al(NO_3)_3$

n. Al_2S_3

22.	**a.** $Mg(NO_3)_2$	**d.**	$BaBr_2$	**g.**	FeO	**j.**	$FeSO_4$		
	b. $MgSO_4$	**e.**	$Ba(NO_3)_2$	**h.**	$Fe(OH)_2$	**k.**	$Fe_3(PO_4)_2$		
	c. $MgCO_3$	**f.**	$BaSO_4$	**i.**	$FeCO_3$	**l.**	$FeBr_3$		
23.	**a.** $SrCl_2$	**d.**	$SrSO_3$	**g.**	$FePO_4$	**j.**	HgS		
	b. $Sr(OH)_2$	**e.**	SrS	**h.**	$HgBr_2$				
	c. $Sr(NO_3)_2$	**f.**	$Fe_2(SO_4)_3$	**i.**	$HgCO_3$				

24. a. sodium nitrate

b. sodium sulfite

c. sodium phosphate

d. potassium nitrite

e. potassium carbonate

f. potassium sulfate

g. cadmium bromide

h. cadmium nitrate

i. cadmium sulfite

j. cadmium sulfide

k. aluminum chloride

l. aluminum hydroxide

25. a. magnesium nitrite

b. magnesium sulfite

c. magnesium phosphate

d. barium nitrite

e. barium sulfite

f. barium carbonate

g. aluminum sulfate

h. aluminum phosphate

i. iron(II) bromide

j. iron(II) nitrate

k. iron(II) sulfite

l. iron(II) sulfide

26. a. barium phosphate

b. strontium bromide

c. strontium nitrate

d. strontium carbonate

e. strontium sulfate

f. strontium phosphate

g. iron(III) chloride

h. iron(III) nitrate

i. iron(III) sulfide

j. mercury(II) chloride

k. mercury(II) nitrate

l. mercury(II) sulfate

27. a. $NaOH$

b. $HgSO_4$

c. $Ca(ClO)_2$

d. $Pb_3(PO_4)_2$

e. $Al(ClO_3)_3$

f. $(NH_4)_2S$

g. Cu_2CO_3

h. Hg_2S

i. $Pb(C_2H_3O_2)_2$

j. MnO_2

k. $Mn_2(SO_4)_3$

l. Ag_2O

m. $Zn(NO_3)_2$
n. $Cr_2(SO_3)_3$

o. $(NH_4)_2Cr_2O_7$
p. Fe_2O_3

28. a. sodium acetate
b. nickel(II) nitrate
c. mercury(I) chloride
d. tin(II) phosphate
e. chromium(II) hydroxide
f. zinc chlorate
g. magnesium bromide
h. copper(I) azide

i. calcium hydride
j. barium nitrite
k. manganese(II) sulfide
l. tin(IV) nitrate
m. ammonium sulfate
n. lead(IV) oxide
o. potassium cyanide
p. cobalt(II) perchlorate

Chapter 3

1. a. 98.1
   b. 40.0
   c. 80.0
   d. 230
   e. 160
   f. 172
   g. 198
   h. 342

   i. 241
   j. 174
   k. 120
   l. 250
   m. 108
   n. 149
   o. 120

   p. 213
   q. 116
   r. 64.1
   s. 84
   t. 106
   u. 129

2. 121
3. 132
4. 180
5. 292
6. $2.17 \times 10^{-2}\%$
   or 0.0217%
7. 75.8%
8. 6.95%

Chapter 4

1. a. 69.0 grams
   b. 100 grams
   c. 122 grams
   d. 35.5 grams
   e. 350 grams

   f. 23.8 grams
   g. 306 grams
   h. 192 grams
   i. 108 grams
   j. 3.03 grams

   k. 196 grams
   l. 831 grams
   m. 111 grams
   n. 109 grams

2. a. 5.263 moles
   b. 3.60 moles
   c. 2.97 moles
   d. 4.491 moles
   e. 4.999 moles

   f. 1.186 moles
   g. 0.614 mole
   h. 2.294 moles
   i. 2.003 moles
   j. 4.476 moles

   k. 0.499 mole
   l. 0.128 mole
   m. 0.344 mole
   n. 2.35 moles

3. a. 1.20×10^{24} atoms
   b. 6.02×10^{23} atoms
   c. 1.20×10^{24} atoms
   d. 1.81×10^{24} ions
   e. 1.20×10^{24} molecules

   f. 4.69×10^{23} atoms
   g. 3.01×10^{23} atoms
   h. 1.20×10^{24} molecules
   i. 1.17×10^{24} molecules
   j. 3.01×10^{23} ions

4. a. 1.00 mole, 23.0 grams
   b. 0.500 mole, 20.0 grams
   c. 2.00 moles, 88.0 grams
   d. 0.250 mole, 5.75 grams
   e. 0.500 mole, 16.0 grams
   f. 4.00 moles, 72.0 grams

Chapter 5

1. a. Fe 69.9%, O 30.1%   c. Hg 92.6%, O 7.39%
   b. Ag 93.1%, O 6.90%   d. Na 58.9%, S 41.1%
2. 32.4% Na   4. a. N 35.0%   b. 38.5 kilograms Fe
3. a. Na 14.3%   b. N 24.1%   c. 19.9 kilograms Pb
   b. O 69.5%   c. N 29.8%   d. 105.8 kilograms Al
   c. H_2O 55.9%   5. a. 21.5 grams Mg   e. 67.54 grams Sr
6. a. 36.1%, 31.1%, 27.3%, 18.3%   7. a. 17.7 grams NH_3
   b. —, 13.9%, 24.5%, 49.3%   b. 22.9 grams CO_2
8. a. 8.46 grams Cr   9. a. 13.9 grams Pb
   b. 6.56 grams Cr   b. 21.5 grams Pb
   c. 4.44 grams Cu   c. 18.2 grams Pb
   d. 2.85 grams Cu
10. a. 15.3% H_2O 11. 1.62% S   13. Cu 11.0%, C 66.7%
    b. 84.7% $BaCl_2$ 12. a. 69.1% ClO^- 14. P 26.5%
    c. 3.70% error   b. 3.46% in bleach   15. Na 11.2%, C 41.0%
16. $Z(OH)_3$ 18. 20.0%
17. C 40.2%, N 9.38%, S 21.5%   19. 4000 metric tons Ag
20. Fe 0.699%   22. $Na_4P_2O_7$ 24. 24.2% $BaCl_2$
21. 8.33 kilograms   23. P 25.3%

Chapter 6

1. a. FeS_2 d. $K_2Cr_2O_7$ c. $Na_2S_2O_3$ b. P_2O_5, P_4O_{10}
   b. FeS   2. a. Na_2SO_3 3. a. N_2O_4 c. Fe_2O_3
   c. MnS   b. Na_2SO_4 4. a. P_2O_3, P_4O_6
5. a. $CoCl_2 \cdot 6H_2O$ 6. a. K_2CrO_4 7. a. FeO
   b. $Pb(C_2H_3O_2)_2 \cdot 3H_2O$ b. $Mg_2P_2O_7$ b. Fe_3O_4
   c. $NiSO_4 \cdot 6H_2O$ c. Sr_2SiO_4 8. $MgHPO_4 \cdot 3H_2O$
   d. $CaSO_4 \cdot 2H_2O$ d. $Na_4P_2O_7$ 9. $Na_2HPO_4 \cdot 7H_2O$
10. $NaHSO_4 \cdot H_2O$ 11. $Ca(NO_3)_2 \cdot 3H_2O$, $Ca(NO_3)_2 \cdot 4H_2O$
12. $CrCl_2$, $CrCl_3$ 14. a. CrO   c. CrO_2 15. a. $K_2Cr_2O_7$
13. $Na_2S_2O_3 \cdot 5H_2O$ b. Cr_2O_3 d. CrO_3 b. K_2CrO_4
16. MgO   18. $C_{55}H_{104}O_6$ 20. $C_{22}H_{23}O_8N_2Cl$
17. $Pb(OH)_2 \cdot 2PbCO_3$ 19. $C_6H_8O_7$ 21. $NaHCO_3 \cdot 2H_2O$

Chapter 7

1. $MgBr_2(aq) + Cl_2(g) \rightarrow MgCl_2(aq) + Br_2(g)$
2. $2Na(c) + 2H_2O(l) \rightarrow 2NaOH(aq) + H_2(g)$
3. $2KNO_3(c) \rightarrow 2KNO_2(c) + O_2(g)$
4. $Zn(c) + 2HCl(aq) \rightarrow ZnCl_2(aq) + H_2(g)$
5. $CaO(c) + 2HCl(aq) \rightarrow CaCl_2(aq) + H_2O(l)$
6. $2Mg(c) + O_2(g) \rightarrow 2MgO(c)$

7. $4Fe(c) + 3O_2(g) \rightarrow 2Fe_2O_3(c)$

8. $H_2O(l) + N_2O_3(g) \rightarrow 2HNO_2(aq)$

9. $Na_2O(c) + H_2O(l) \rightarrow 2NaOH(aq)$

10. $3Fe(c) + 4H_2O(l) \rightarrow Fe_3O_4(c) + 4H_2(g)$

11. $2KClO_3(c) \rightarrow 2KCl(c) + 3O_2(g)$

12. $2PbO_2(c) \rightarrow 2PbO(c) + O_2(g)$

13. $2HgO(c) \rightarrow 2Hg(l) + O_2(g)$

14. $2H_2O(l) \rightarrow 2H_2(g) + O_2(g)$

15. $2Al(c) + 3Pb(NO_3)_2(aq) \rightarrow 2Al(NO_3)_3(aq) + 3Pb(c)$

16. $Cu(c) + 2AgNO_3(aq) \rightarrow Cu(NO_3)_2(aq) + 2Ag(c)$

17. $2K(c) + 2H_2O(l) \rightarrow 2KOH(aq) + H_2(g)$

18. $MnO_2(c) + 4HCl(aq) \rightarrow MnCl_2(aq) + Cl_2(g) + 2H_2O(l)$

19. $Cl_2(g) + 2LiI(aq) \rightarrow 2LiCl(aq) + I_2(g)$

20. $Ca(OH)_2(aq) + 2HCl(aq) \rightarrow CaCl_2(aq) + 2H_2O(l)$

21. $3KOH(aq) + H_3PO_4(aq) \rightarrow K_3PO_4(aq) + 3H_2O(l)$

22. $2Al(NO_3)_3(aq) + 3H_2SO_4(aq) \rightarrow Al_2(SO_4)_3(aq) + 6HNO_3(aq)$

23. $Na_2SO_3(aq) + 2HCl(aq) \rightarrow 2NaCl(aq) + H_2O(l) + SO_2(g)$

24. $(NH_4)_2SO_4(aq) + 2KOH(aq) \rightarrow K_2SO_4(aq) + 2NH_3(g) + 2H_2O(l)$

25. $Pb(NO_3)_2(aq) + K_2S(aq) \rightarrow PbS(c) + 2KNO_3(aq)$

26. DD $\quad Al(NO_3)_3(aq) + 3NaOH(aq) \rightarrow Al(OH)_3(c) + 3NaNO_3(aq)$

27. D $\quad 2KClO_3(c) \rightarrow 2KCl(c) + 3O_2(g)$

28. DD $\quad 2H_3PO_4(aq) + 3Mg(OH)_2(aq) \rightarrow Mg_3(PO_4)_2(c) + 6H_2O(l)$

29. D $\quad NH_4NO_2(c) \rightarrow N_2(g) + 2H_2O(l)$

30. SD $\quad 4NH_3(g) + 5O_2(g) \rightarrow 4NO(g) + 6H_2O(g)$

31. DD $\quad BaCl_2(aq) + Na_2SO_4(aq) \rightarrow 2NaCl(aq) + BaSO_4(s)$

32. DD $\quad Fe_2O_3(c) + 3CO(g) \rightarrow 2Fe(c) + 3CO_2(g)$

33. DD $\quad 3Mg(OH)_2(aq) + 2(NH_4)_3PO_4(aq) \rightarrow$
$\qquad Mg_3(PO_4)_2(c) + 6NH_3(g) + 6H_2O(l)$

34. DD $\quad 2FeBr_3(aq) + 3(NH_4)_2S(aq) \rightarrow Fe_2S_3(c) + 6NH_4Br(aq)$

35. S $\quad 3CaO(c) + P_2O_5(c) \rightarrow Ca_3(PO_4)_2(c)$

36. DD $\quad MgCl_2(aq) + 2AgNO_3(aq) \rightarrow Mg(NO_3)_2(aq) + 2AgCl(c)$

37. DD $\quad Na_2CO_3(aq) + H_2SO_4(aq) \rightarrow Na_2SO_4(aq) + CO_2(g) + H_2O(l)$

38. DD $\quad Al(OH)_3(c) + 3HC_2H_3O_2(aq) \rightarrow Al(C_2H_3O_2)_3(aq) + 3H_2O(l)$

39. DD $\quad Pb(NO_3)_2(aq) + CuSO_4(aq) \rightarrow PbSO_4(c) + Cu(NO_3)_2(aq)$

40. SD $\quad 2Al(c) + 3CuCl_2(aq) \rightarrow 2AlCl_3(aq) + 3Cu(c)$

41. SD $\quad Fe(c) + 2AgC_2H_3O_2(aq) \rightarrow Fe(C_2H_3O_2)_2(aq) + 2Ag(c)$

42. DD $\quad Al(C_2H_3O_2)_3(aq) + 3NaOH(aq) \rightarrow$
$\qquad Al(OH)_3(c) + 3NaC_2H_3O_2(aq)$

43. SD $\quad Br_2(g) + CaI_2(aq) \rightarrow CaBr_2(aq) + I_2(g)$

44. SD $\quad Cu(c) + 2H_2SO_4(aq) \rightarrow CuSO_4(aq) + SO_2(g) + 2H_2O(l)$

45. DD $\quad 3Ca(OH)_2(aq) + 2H_3PO_4(aq) \rightarrow Ca_3(PO_4)_2(c) + 6H_2O(l)$

46. DD $\quad Mg(NO_3)_2(aq) + H_2SO_4(aq) \rightarrow MgSO_4(aq) + 2HNO_3(aq)$

47. DD $\quad K_2CO_3(aq) + BaCl_2(aq) \rightarrow 2KCl(aq) + BaCO_3(c)$

48. DD $\quad 2AlCl_3(aq) + 3H_2SO_4(aq) \rightarrow Al_2(SO_4)_3(aq) + 6HCl(g)$

49. DD $\quad Cd_3(PO_4)_2(c) + 3(NH_4)_2S(aq) \rightarrow 3CdS(c) + 2(NH_4)_3PO_4(aq)$

50. DD $2NaOH(aq) + H_2SO_4(aq) \rightarrow Na_2SO_4(aq) + 2H_2O(l)$
51. S $2Mg(c) + O_2(g) \rightarrow 2MgO(c)$
52. SD $2Al(c) + 6HCl(aq) \rightarrow 2AlCl_3(aq) + 3H_2(g)$
53. S $Na_2O(c) + SO_2(g) \rightarrow Na_2SO_3(aq)$
54. D $2H_3PO_4(l) \rightarrow P_2O_5(c) + 3H_2O(l)$
55. D $2NaClO_3(c) \rightarrow 2NaCl(c) + 3O_2(g)$
56. DD $ZnCl_2(aq) + (NH_4)_2S(aq) \rightarrow ZnS(c) + 2NH_4Cl(aq)$
57. SD $ZnS(c) + 2O_2(g) \rightarrow ZnSO_4(c)$
58. D $CaCO_3 \rightarrow CaO(c) + CO_2(g)$
59. DD $HgSO_4(c) + 2NH_4NO_3(aq) \rightarrow Hg(NO_3)_2(aq) + (NH_4)_2SO_4(aq)$
60. SD $Fe(c) + CuSO_4(aq) \rightarrow FeSO_4(aq) + Cu(c)$
61. SD $Zn(c) + H_2SO_4(aq) \rightarrow ZnSO_4(aq) + H_2(g)$
62. S $N_2O_5(c) + H_2O(l) \rightarrow 2HNO_3(l)$
63. SD $Cl_2(g) + MgI_2(aq) \rightarrow MgCl_2(aq) + I_2(g)$
64. SD $2K(c) + 2HOH(l) \rightarrow 2KOH(aq) + H_2(g)$
65. SD $2Fe(c) + 6HCl(aq) \rightarrow 2FeCl_3(aq) + 3H_2(g)$
66. DD $Co(OH)_3(aq) + 3HNO_3(aq) \rightarrow Co(NO_3)_3(aq) + 3HOH(l)$
67. SD $Br_2(g) + 2NaI(aq) \rightarrow 2NaBr(aq) + I_2(g)$
68. DD $3NaOH(aq) + H_3PO_4(aq) \rightarrow Na_3PO_4(aq) + 3HOH(l)$
69. DD $(NH_4)_2SO_4(aq) + Ca(OH)_2(aq) \rightarrow CaSO_4(c) + 2NH_4OH(aq)$
70. DD $AgNO_3(aq) + KCl(aq) \rightarrow KNO_3(aq) + AgCl(c)$
71. DD $3Mg(OH)_2(aq) + 2H_3PO_4(aq) \rightarrow Mg_3(PO_4)_2(c) + 6HOH(l)$
72. DD $FeS(c) + 2HCl(aq) \rightarrow H_2S(g) + FeCl_2(aq)$
73. DD $(NH_4)_2S(aq) + Fe(NO_3)_2(aq) \rightarrow FeS(c) + 2NH_4NO_3(aq)$
74. DD $H_2SO_4(aq) + 2KOH(aq) \rightarrow K_2SO_4(aq) + 2HOH(l)$
75. DD $Al_2(SO_4)_3(aq) + Ca_3(PO_4)_2(c) \rightarrow 2AlPO_4(c) + 3CaSO_4(c)$
76. DD $BaCO_3(c) + 2HCl(aq) \rightarrow BaCl_2(aq) + H_2O(l) + CO_2(g)$
77. DD $2AgC_2H_3O_2(aq) + K_2CrO_4(aq) \rightarrow$
$Ag_2CrO_4(c) + 2KC_2H_3O_2(aq)$
78. DD $2(NH_4)_3PO_4(aq) + 3Ba(OH)_3(aq) \rightarrow$
$Ba_3(PO_4)_2(c) + 6NH_4OH(aq)$
79. DD $Cr_2(SO_3)_3(aq) + 3H_2SO_4(aq) \rightarrow Cr_2(SO_4)_3(c) + 3H_2SO_4(aq)$
80. DD $Ca(OH)_2(aq) + 2HNO_3(aq) \rightarrow Ca(NO_3)_2(aq) + 2HOH(l)$
81. Redox a. $Cu(c) + 4HNO_3(aq) \rightarrow$
$Cu(NO_3)_2(aq) + 2NO_2(g) + 2H_2O(l)$
    DD b. $Cu(NO_3)_2(aq) + 2NaOH(aq) \rightarrow$
$Cu(OH)_2(c) + 2NaNO_3(aq)$
    D c. $Cu(OH)_2(c) \rightarrow CuO(c) + H_2O(l)$
    DD d. $CuO(c) + H_2SO_4(aq) \rightarrow CuSO_4(aq) + H_2O(l)$
    SD e. $CuSO_4(aq) + Zn(c) \rightarrow ZnSO_4(aq) + Cu(c)$
82. DD $Na_2CO_3(aq) + H_2SO_4(aq) \rightarrow Na_2SO_4(aq) + CO_2(g) + H_2O(l)$
    DD $2NaHCO_3(aq) + H_2SO_4(aq) \rightarrow$
$Na_2SO_4(aq) + 2CO_2(g) + 2H_2O(l)$ sodium hydrogen carbonate
83. SD $4FeS_2(c) + 11O_2(g) \rightarrow 2Fe_2O_3(c) + 8SO_2(g)$
84. D $2NaHSO_3(aq) \rightarrow Na_2SO_3(aq) + SO_2(g) + H_2O(l)$

Chapter 8

1.	41.6 grams	**3.**	1.96 grams	**5.**	9.19 grams	**7.**	8.36 grams
2.	6.07 grams	**4.**	0.747 grams	**6.**	18.7 grams	**8.**	20.4 grams

9. 15.0 grams HCl, 20.1 grams H_2SO_4

10. 39.4 grams Fe (20% inert), 40.9 grams Fe (10% inert)

11. 70.5 grams Zn   **12.** 13.9 grams $CuSO_2 \cdot 5H_2O$

13. 0.5102 mole and 134.1 grams of $Mg_3(PO_4)_2$

14. 0.455 mole

15. 52.0 grams $Mg_3(PO_4)_2$, 26.2 grams CO_2, 10.7 grams H_2O

16. 38.6 grams $MgCO_3$ **19.**   **a.**   94.1 grams SO_2

17. 11.6 grams O_2 (trioxide)   **b.**   26.5 grams H_2O

     19.4 grams O_2 (pentoxide)   **c.**   47.2 grams H_2O

18. 0.0196 mole Al, 0.0294 mole Zn   **20.** 18.0 grams H_2O

21. 1.06 grams $Na_2S-Hg(ClO_3)_2$ **22.** 16.6 grams MgO

     2.07 grams $Na_2S-Cu(NO_3)_2$ 13.8 grams Mg_3N_2

     1.52 grams $Na_2S-Bi(C_2H_3O_2)_3$ **23.**   **a.**   147.0 grams H_2O

     2.13 grams $Na_2S-Sn(NO_3)_4$ **b.**   137.8 grams H_2O

24. 5.11 grams NaOH   **29.** 19.4 metric tons

25.   **a.**   1.93 grams $CaCl_2$ **30.** 90.2% Ag

     b.   0.0348 mole $AgNO_3$ **31.** 313 moles

     c.   2.86 grams $Ca(NO_3)_2$ **32.** 469 grams limestone

26. 354. grams air   **33.** 742.24 kilograms H_2SO_4

27. 1420 grams $ZnCl_2$ soln   **34.** 667 kilograms coal

28. 0.884 mL   **35.** 1530 kilograms

Chapter 9

1. 16 000 Pa,
10 700 Pa

2.   **a.**   106 cm³
    b.   48.2 cm³
    c.   472 cm³
    d.   127 cm³
    e.   2.90 cm³
    f.   0.982 dm³

3. 125 kPa

4. 266 cm³

5.   **a.**   25.0 m³
    b.   16.7 m³
    c.   100.0 m³

6. 2.03 dm³

7. 211 kPa

8.   **a.**   47.4 cm³
    b.   69.9 cm³

    c.   128 cm³
    d.   220. cm³

9. 75.3 cm³

10. 53.6 kPa

11. 94.96 kPa

12.   **a.**   294 cm³
    b.   67.3 cm³
    c.   91.0 cm³
    d.   324 cm³
    e.   2.64 dm³
    f.   27.4 cm³

13. −6°C

14.   **a.**   20.0 m³
    b.   5.00 m³

15.   **a.**   552 cm³
    b.   213 cm³

    c.   111 cm³
    d.   69.8 cm³
    e.   177 cm³

16.   **a.**   173 cm³
    b.   109 cm³
    c.   42.8 cm³
    d.   280.0 cm³

17. 548 cm³

18. 41.9 cm³

19. 331 kPa

20. 7.91 m³

21. 2.93 g/dm³

22. 2.96 g/dm³

23. 312 K or 39°C

24.   **a.**   36.4 cm³
    b.   295 cm³

c. 83.7 cm^3 25. a. 1.67 g/dm^3 30. 546 K or 273°C
d. 147 cm^3 b. 1.64 g/dm^3 31. a. 1040 dm^3
e. 114 cm^3 26. 1.88 g/dm^3 b. 755 dm^3
f. 1.31 dm^3 27. 2.74 mg/cm^3 c. pressure
g. 275 cm^3 28. 50.0 cm^3 32. 797 K or 524°C
h. 237 cm^3 29. 45.0 kPa   33. 1.15 × 10^{10} cm^3

Chapter 10

1. a. 2.23 moles   e. 3800 grams   4. a. 1.52 g/dm^3
    b. 0.0446 mole   f. 5.33 grams   b. 0.714 g/dm^3
    c. 0.290 mole   3. a. 89.6 dm^3 c. 0.759 g/dm^3
    d. 0.670 mole   b. 131.0 dm^3 d. 3.17 g/dm^3
    e. 0.112 mole   c. 8.91 dm^3 5. 1.980 g/dm^3
    f. 0.0893 mole   d. 189.0 dm^3 6. 1.639 g/dm^3
2. a. 14 300 grams   e. 56.0 dm^3 7. 63.8 grams SO$_2$
    b. 4.75 grams   f. 24.3 dm^3 8. 128 grams HI
    c. 0.250 gram   g. 157 dm^3 9. 16.0 grams CH$_4$
    d. 589 grams   h. 6.14 dm^3 10. 87.4 grams PF$_3$

11. 44.33 grams N$_2$O   14. 4.71 dm^3
12. a. 0.0298 mole, 0.954 grams O$_2$ 15. a. 9.45 dm^3 H$_2$
     b. 0.141 mole, 6.22 grams CO$_2$ b. 10.3 dm^3 H$_2$
     c. 0.0893 mole, 1.52 grams NH$_3$ c. 10.5 dm^3 H$_2$
     d. 0.205 mole, 13.1 grams SO$_2$ 16. 0.00989 mole N$_2$,
13. a. 73 700 cm^3 H$_2$ 17. 58.1 g/mol   0.277 grams N$_2$
     b. 46 900 cm^3 Cl$_2$ 18. 269 g/mol   21. 46.3 g/mol
     c. 128 000 cm^3 CH$_4$ 19. a. 1.43 g/dm^3 22. 51.5 grams
     d. 267 000 cm^3 NH$_3$ b. 1.26 g/dm^3 23. 12.5 grams
                              20. 30.9 grams   24. 28.8 g/mol air

Chapter 11

1. 1370 cm^3 5. 3110 cm^3 9. 16.6 g   13. 16.8 g   17. 1210 dm^3
2. 3360 cm^3 6. 8.04 g   10. 31.9 dm^3 14. 4460 cm^3 18. 189 dm^3
3. 1880 cm^3 7. 1560 cm^3 11. 4350 cm^3 15. 3.64 g   19. 76.7 kg
4. 35.5 g   8. 3130 cm^3 12. 7.67 dm^3 16. 1110 dm^3

Chapter 12

1. 150 cm^3 2.80 dm^3 SO$_2$ 11. a. 0.268 mol   c. 812 cm^3
2. 30.0 cm^3 7. 119 dm^3 air   b. 9.64 g   d. 896 cm^3
3. 90.0 dm^3 H$_2$ 20.0 dm^3 NO   c. 0.536 mol 13. a. 52 500 cm^3
    30.0 dm^3 N$_2$ 8. 100 dm^3 d. 12.0 dm^3 b. 36.2 g
4. 25.0 cm^3 9. 1480 dm^3 e. 13.4 dm^3 c. 1.34 mol
5. 119 cm^3 10. 37.5 dm^3 12. a. 2.96 g   d. 250 000 cm^3
6. 1.40 dm^3 CO$_2$ 179 dm^3 air   b. 1.16 g   e. 134 g

Chapter 13

1. NaOH limiting
2. $AgNO_3$ limiting
3. NaBr limiting
4. a. 0.114 mol
   b. 3.86 g
   c. 5090 cm^3
   d. 5580 cm^3
5. a. 3.60 g $CaCl_2$ in excess
   b. 0.206 mol
   c. 16.9 g
6. N_2 limiting 24.0 dm^3 NH_3
7. a. 0.274 mol
   b. 1.65 × 10^{23}

c. 6940 cm^3
d. 7000 cm^3
8. a. 20.0 dm^3
   b. 39.3 g
   c. 32.1 g
9. a. 0.134 mol
   b. 4.82 g
   c. 39.8 g
10. 10.1 g from $MgCrO_4$
    13.9 g from $MgSO_4$
11. N_2 limiting
    7.99 g NH_3
12. a. 2.44 g excess H_3PO_4
    b. 2.86 g
    c. 0.106 mol

d. 10.2 g
e. 3560 cm^3
f. 3.37 L
13. a. 37.4 g
    b. 0.556
    c. 6170 cm^3
    d. 6820 cm^3
    e. 16 200 cm^3 air
14. 17.5 dm^3
15. red
16. 200 cm^3 H_2O vapor
    50 cm^3 O_2 remaining
17. 60 cm^3 N_2 in excess
    40 cm^3 NO

Chapter 14

1. 484 kJ
2. 0.216 kJ
3. 93.3 kJ
4. 143 kJ

5. a. 21.9 kJ
   b. 32.1 kJ
   c. 21.1 kJ
   d. 10.9 kJ

e. 4.81 kJ
6. a. 4360 J
   b. 958 J
   c. 61.9 J

d. 813 J
e. 2550 J
7. 10 900 J
8. 114 200 J

Chapter 15

1. a. −3 kJ
   b. 1.4 kJ
   c. −30 kJ
   d. −422 kJ
   e. −358 kJ

2. a. 82.2 kJ
   b. −690 kJ
   c. −124 kJ
   d. −114 kJ
   e. −1317 kJ

3. a. −151 J
   b. −451 J
   c. 167 J
   d. −557 J
   e. 128 J

4. a. −456 kJ
   b. −140 kJ
   c. −245 kJ
   d. −42.9 kJ
   e. −192 kJ

Chapter 16

1. a. 0.625M
   b. 0.250M
   c. 1.21M
   d. 1.00M
   e. 0.800M
   f. 0.500M
2. a. 41.6 g
   b. 421 g
   c. 71.0 g
   d. 134 g
   e. 48.9 g
   f. 630 g

3. 7.85 g, 0.048M
4. a. 1.00 dm^3
   b. 4.00 dm^3
   c. 0.333 dm^3
   d. 20.0 dm^3
   e. 0.200 dm^3
   f. 12.8 dm^3
5. 417 g $Al(NO_3)_3 \cdot 9H_2O$
   0.741M
   0.741M Al^{3+}
   2.22M NO_3^-
6. a. 1.0

b. 3.0
c. 1.0
d. 3.0
e. 1.0
f. 3.0

7. a. 0.400N, 0.200M
   b. 2.00N, 2.00M
   c. 0.400N, 0.200M
   d. 3.00N, 1.00M
   e. 1.33N, 0.667M

8. a. 2.00N
   b. 0.200M
   c. 0.200N
   d. 1.50M
   e. 1.50M
   f. 0.500N
   g. 2.00M
   h. 4.50N
   i. 0.500M
   j. 0.600N
   k. 1.50M

9. **a.** 2.03 g, 2.03 eq, 4.06M, 4.06N
   b. 20.0 g, 0.500 mol, 5000 cm^3, 0.100N
   c. 261 g, 3.00 eq, 3000 cm^3, 0.500M
   d. 148 g, 1.00 mol, 1.33M, 2.67N
   e. 49.0 g, 1.50 eq, 250 cm^3, 6.00N
   f. 0.143 mol, 0.858 eq, 143 cm^3, 1.00M

10. **a.** 32.0 g
    b. 100 g
    c. 72.0 g

11. **a.** 25.0%
    b. 9.09%
    c. 20.0%

12. **a.** 146 g
    b. 102 g
    c. 180 g

13. 26.7 g, 0.435M

14. 7.67M

15. 4.59 mol, 9.17M

16. 6.02×10^{23} molecules
    46.1 g, 58.4 cm^3

Chapter 17

1. **a.** right   **e.** right   **i.** right   **m.** left
   b. left   **f.** left   **j.** left   **n.** no change
   c. left   **g.** right   **k.** right   **o.** right
   d. no change   **h.** left   **l.** no change   **p.** left

2. 217

3. 0.0313M

4. $H_2 = 0.0400M$
   $I_2 = 0.0400M$
   $HI = 0.320M$

5. 6.61

6. $CO_2 = H_2 = 0.0668M$
   $CO = H_2O = 0.0260M$

7. $H_2 = 0.015M$
   $I_2 = 0.215M$
   $HI = 0.370M$

8. one half the original

9. $H_2 = I_2 = 0.228M$
   $HI = 1.54M$

10. $PCl_3 = 0.0295M$
    $Cl_2 = 0.0295M$
    $PCl_5 = 0.0205M$

Chapter 18

1. 400 cm^3
2. 6.25 cm^3
3. 8.00 dm^3
4. 0.800N
5. 0.300M
6. 0.400M
7. 282 cm^3
8. 2.93M
9. **a.** 330 cm^3
   b. 1110 cm^3
   c. 436 cm^3
   d. 681 cm^3
   e. 1130 cm^3
10. **a.** 25.0 cm^3
    b. 12.5 cm^3
    c. 16.7 cm^3
    d. 33.3 cm^3
    e. 8.33 cm^3

Chapter 19

1. **a.** 2.00m **d.** 1.30m
   b. 2.40m **e.** 0.111m
   c. 1.67m **f.** 1.33m

2. **a.** 252 g   **d.** 18.3 g
   b. 22.5 g   **3.** 684 g
   c. 900 g   **4.** 6.77×10^{23}

5. 620 g, 6.02×10^{24} molecules

6. 17.8%

7. $-3.72°C$, 101.02°C

8. 1.86°C, 0.512°C

9. 80.7 g

10. **a.** $-3.72°C$, 101.02°C
    b. $-3.71°C$, 101.02°C
    c. $-3.72°C$, 101.02°C

11. 1980 g, 1770 mL

12. 180 g/mol, $C_6H_{12}O_6$

13. 46.0 g

14. 46.0 g

15. **a.** 7.31 g
    b. 14.6 g
    c. 21.9 g
    d. 29.3 g

16. **a.** 250 g
    b. 500 g
    c. 1000 g

17. **a.** 3.94%
    b. 4.08%
    c. 5.06%

18. **a.** 1.00m
    b. 0.80m
    c. 1.09m

19. $-2.49°C$, $84.1°C$

20. $28.5°C$, $189°C$

21. 160 g

22. 255 g

23. 110 g/mol

24. 43.5 g/mol

25. 138 g/mol, $C_8H_{10}O_2$

26. 218 g/mol, $C_{10}H_6N_2O_4$

Chapter 20

1.
a. $2Na + 2H_2O \rightarrow 2Na^+ + H_2 + 2OH^-$
b. $6H^+ + 2PO_4^{3-} + 3Mg^{2+} + 6OH^- \rightarrow Mg_3(PO_4)_2 + 6H_2O$
c. $Ba^{2+} + SO_4^{2-} \rightarrow BaSO_4$
d. $3Mg^{2+} + 6OH^- + 6NH_4^+ + 2PO_4^{3-} \rightarrow$
$Mg_3(PO_4)_2 + 3NH_3 + 6H_2O$
e. $2Fe^{3+} + 3S^{2-} \rightarrow Fe_2S_3$ g. $2Al + 3Cu^{2+} \rightarrow 2Al^{3+} + 3Cu$
f. $CO_3^{2-} + 2H^+ \rightarrow CO_2 + H_2O$ h. no reaction

2.
a. 1.6×10^{-5}
b. 1.7×10^{-5}
c. 6.16×10^{-10}

3. $H_3O^+ = 0.0042M$
$C_2H_3O_2^- = 0.0042M$
$HC_2H_3O_2 = 1.0M$

4. 0.42%

5.
a. 7.90×10^{-4}
b. 1.80×10^{-5}
c. 1.85×10^{-5}
d. 6.05×10^{-10}

6. $0.56M$ **8.** a. $2.54 \times 10^{-3}M$

7. $0.035M$ b. $2.24 \times 10^{-3}M$

Chapter 21

1.
a. pH 4, pOH 10
b. pH 12, pOH 2
c. pH 9, pOH 5
d. pH 2, pOH 12

2.
a. $1 \times 10^{-3}M$

b. $1 \times 10^{-6}M$
c. $1 \times 10^{-2}M$

3.
a. $1 \times 10^{-11}M$
b. $1 \times 10^{-10}M$
c. $1 \times 10^{-8}M$

4.
a. pH 11.4, pOH 2.6
b. pH 2.30, pOH 11.70
c. pH 0.82, pOH 13.18
d. pH 1.32, pOH 12.68
e. pH 12.5, pOH 1.5
f. pH 10.2, pOH 3.8

5.
a. $H_3O^+ = 3.162 \times 10^{-3}M$
$OH^- = 3.162 \times 10^{-12}M$
b. $H_3O^+ = 6.329 \times 10^{-9}M$
$OH^- = 1.580 \times 10^{-6}M$
c. $H_3O^+ = 1.585 \times 10^{-11}M$
$OH^- = 6.310 \times 10^{-4}M$
d. $H_3O^+ = 1.995 \times 10^{-5}M$
$OH^- = 5.013 \times 10^{-10}M$
e. $H_3O^+ = 2.512 \times 10^{-10}M$
$OH^- = 3.981 \times 10^{-5}M$
f. $H_3O^+ = 1.995 \times 10^{-4}M$
$OH^- = 5.012 \times 10^{-11}M$

6.

	pOH	H_3O^+	OH^-
a.	11.2	$1.6 \times 10^{-3}M$	$6.3 \times 10^{-12}M$
b.	10.5	$3.2 \times 10^{-4}M$	$3.2 \times 10^{-11}M$
c.	7.8	$6.3 \times 10^{-7}M$	$1.6 \times 10^{-8}M$
d.	5.5	$3.2 \times 10^{-9}M$	$3.2 \times 10^{-6}M$
e.	11.0	$1.0 \times 10^{-3}M$	$1.0 \times 10^{-11}M$
f.	9.8	$6.3 \times 10^{-5}M$	$1.6 \times 10^{-10}M$
g.	6.2	$1.6 \times 10^{-8}M$	$6.3 \times 10^{-7}M$
h.	3.5	$3.2 \times 10^{-11}M$	$3.2 \times 10^{-4}M$

8.
a. 11.1
b. 2.88
c. 3.03
d. 1.74
e. 5.62
f. 10.5

9.
a. 4.4×10^{-10}
b. 1.8×10^{-5}
c. 1.8×10^{-5}
d. 1.8×10^{-5}

		pOH	H_3O^+	OH^-
7.	a.	13.00	$1.00 \times 10^{-1}M$	$1.00 \times 10^{-13}M$
	b.	11.10	$1.26 \times 10^{-3}M$	$7.94 \times 10^{-12}M$
	c.	2.90	$7.9 \times 10^{-12}M$	$1.3 \times 10^{-3}M$
	d.	12.80	$6.31 \times 10^{-2}M$	$1.58 \times 10^{-13}M$
	e.	5.60	$3.98 \times 10^{-9}M$	$2.51 \times 10^{-6}M$
	f.	1.00	$1.0 \times 10^{-13}M$	$1.00 \times 10^{-1}M$

Chapter 22

1. a. $0.300M$ **2.** $2.40M$ **b.** 20.0 mL **c.** 3.60%
   b. 15.0 mL **3.** 21.41 mL **c.** 8.80 mL **7.** 6.82 grams
   c. $2.50M$ **4.** 2.92 grams **d.** 54.0 mL **8.** 7.21 mL
   d. 17.5 mL **5.** a. 6.00 mL **6.** a. $2.01M$ **9.** $0.600N\ H_3PO_4$
10. a. $0.880N$, $0.930N$, $0.908N$ **b.** 34.2 g/L $0.200M\ H_3PO_4$
    b. 52.9 g/L, 55.9 g/L, 54.6 g/L **11.** a. $0.171M$ **d.** $0.333M$
    c. 5.29%, 5.59%, 5.46% **b.** 41.2 mL **e.** 12.5 mL
    d. Trial 3, 1.11% error **c.** 30.0 mL **f.** $1.80M$
12. 1.28 grams **16.** $0.980N$ **c.** 1.49 grams
13. 333 mL **17.** 20.3 mL **19.** 0.76 g/L
14. 12.0 mL **18.** a. 0.213 grams **20.** 9.80 mL
15. $0.667N$, $0.333M$ **b.** 140 mL

Chapter 23

1. a. 1.50×10^{-16} **d.** 1.53×10^{-72} **13.** a. $3.98 \times 10^{-10}M$
   b. 4.90×10^{-9} **e.** 5.27×10^{-14} **b.** $3.54M$
   c. 4.14×10^{-11} **f.** 1.00×10^{-25} **c.** $1.03 \times 10^{-6}M$
   d. 2.96×10^{-16} **7.** a. $2.51 \times 10^{-17}M$ **14.** a. no, 2.50×10^{-7}
   e. 3.63×10^{-9} **b.** $1.08 \times 10^{-5}M$ **b.** yes, 2.25×10^{-11}
   f. 2.82×10^{-13} **c.** $5.83 \times 10^{-6}M$ **c.** no, 1.08×10^{-30}
2. a. $2.51 \times 10^{-18}M$ **d.** $1.49 \times 10^{-9}M$ **15.** $1.15 \times 10^{-8}M$
   b. $3.97 \times 10^{-4}M$ **8.** a. $8.91 \times 10^{-4}M$ **16.** 2.95×10^{-3} g/200 mL
   c. $2.61 \times 10^{-9}M$ **b.** $1.17 \times 10^{-3}M$ **17.** yes
   d. $1.61 \times 10^{-3}M$ **c.** $3.07 \times 10^{-2}M$ **18.** 3.83 grams
3. a. $1.35 \times 10^{-5}M$ **d.** $2.14 \times 10^{-6}M$ **19.** 2.10×10^{-11} g/mL
   b. $1.81 \times 10^{-9}M$ **e.** $1.00 \times 10^{-1}M$ **20.** yes, ion product
   c. $1.81 \times 10^{-8}M$ **f.** $6.91 \times 10^{-7}M$ $= 4.17 \times 10^{-7}$
4. a. $1.11 \times 10^{-2}M$ **g.** $1.44 \times 10^{-4}M$ **21.** $7.94 \times 10^{-8}M$
   b. $5.50 \times 10^{-4}M$ **9.** a. 3.94×10^{-2} mg/100 mL
   c. $5.50 \times 10^{-2}M$ **b.** 1.72×10^{-3} mg/100 mL
   d. $3.71 \times 10^{-3}M$ **c.** 2.10×10^{-6} mg/100 mL
5. a. $6.54 \times 10^{-5}M$ **d.** 41.1 mg/100 mL **22.** AgCl
   b. $7.00 \times 10^{-10}M$ **e.** 0.227 mg/100 mL **23.** $5.4 \times 10^{-5}M$,
   c. $1.06 \times 10^{-6}M$ **f.** 3.34 mg/100 mL 0.054%
6. a. 1.07×10^{-51} **10.** AgI
   b. 4.43×10^{-27} **11.** $PbSO_4$
   c. 4.57×10^{-18} **12.** yes, $PbCO_3$

Chapter 24

1. $2Cr(c) + 3Sn^{4+}(aq) \rightarrow 2Cr^{3+}(aq) + 3Sn^{2+}(aq)$
2. $2Al(c) + 6H^+(aq) \rightarrow 2Al^{3+}(aq) + 3H_2(g)$
3. $Zn(c) + 2Ag^+(aq) \rightarrow Zn^{2+}(aq) + 2Ag(c)$
4. $6NO_3^-(aq) + S(c) + 6H^+(aq) \rightarrow 6NO_2(g) + H_2SO_4(aq) + 2H_2O(l)$
5. $Br_2(l) + SO_3^{2-}(aq) + H_2O(l) \rightarrow 2Br^-(aq) + SO_4^{2-}(aq) + 2H^+(aq)$
6. $5Fe^{2+}(aq) + MnO_4^-(aq) + 8H^+(aq) \rightarrow$
   $Mn^{2+}(aq) + 5Fe^{3+}(aq) + 4H_2O(l)$
7. $Cu(c) + SO_4^{2-}(aq) + 4H^+(aq) \rightarrow Cu^{2+}(aq) + SO_2(g) + 2H_2O(l)$
8. $3Cu(c) + 2NO_3^-(aq) + 8H^+(aq) \rightarrow 3Cu^{2+}(aq) + 2NO(g) + 4H_2O(l)$
9. $2MnO_4^-(aq) + 5S^{2-}(aq) + 16H^+(aq) \rightarrow$
   $2Mn^{2+}(aq) + 5S(c) + 8H_2O(l)$
10. $CuS(c) + 2NO_3^-(aq) + 4H^+(aq) \rightarrow$
    $Cu^{2+}(aq) + 2NO_2(g) + 2H_2O(l) + S(c)$
11. $2NO_2(g) + ClO^-(aq) + H_2O(l) \rightarrow 2NO_3^-(aq) + Cl^-(aq) + 2H^+(aq)$
12. $6Fe^{2+}(aq) + Cr_2O_7^{2-}(aq) + 14H^+(aq) \rightarrow$
    $6Fe^{3+}(aq) + 2Cr^{3+}(aq) + 7H_2O(l)$
13. $2MnO_4^-(aq) + 10Cl^-(aq) + 16H^+(aq) \rightarrow$
    $2Mn^{2+}(aq) + 5Cl_2(g) + 8H_2O(l)$
14. $6IO_3^-(aq) + 5H_2S(g) \rightarrow 3I_2(g) + 5SO_3^{2-}(aq) + 3H_2O(l) + 4H^+(aq)$
15. $H_2SeO_3(aq) + 4Br^-(aq) + 4H^+(aq) \rightarrow Se(c) + 2Br_2(g) + 3H_2O(l)$
16. $BrO_3^-(aq) + 2MnO_2(c) + H_2O(l) \rightarrow$
    $Br^-(aq) + 2MnO_4^-(aq) + 2H^+(aq)$
17. $3H_2S(g) + 2NO_3^-(aq) + 2H^+(aq) \rightarrow 3S(c) + 2NO(g) + 4H_2O(l)$
18. **a.** $+0.66\,V$ **c.** $+0.54\,V$ **e.** $+1.21\,V$
    b. $+1.66\,V$ **d.** $+0.74\,V$ **f.** $+0.13\,V$
19. $3AsH_3(g) + 4ClO_3^-(aq) \rightarrow 3H_3AsO_4(aq) + 4Cl^-(aq)$
20. $2HNO_2(aq) + 2I^-(aq) + 2H^+(aq) \rightarrow 2NO(g) + I_2(g) + 2H_2O(l)$
21. $2MnO_4^-(aq) + 5H_2O_2(aq) + 16H^+(aq) \rightarrow$
    $2Mn^{2+}(aq) + 5O_2(g) + 8H_2O(l)$
22. $3MnO_2(c) + ClO_3(aq) + 6OH^-(aq) \rightarrow$
    $3MnO_4^{2-}(aq) + Cl^-(aq) + 3H_2O(l)$
23. $6Br_2(l) + 12OH^-(aq) \rightarrow 10Br^-(aq) + 2BrO_3^-(aq) + 6H_2O(l)$
24. $3N_2O_4(aq) + Br^-(aq) + 6OH^-(aq) \rightarrow$
    $6NO_2^-(aq) + BrO_3^-(aq) + 3H_2O(l)$
25. $3H_2PO_2^-(aq) + 2SbO_2^-(aq) + OH^-(aq) \rightarrow$
    $3HPO_3^{2-}(aq) + 2Sb(c) + 2H_2O(l)$
26. $2CrO_2^-(aq) + 3ClO^-(aq) + 2OH^-(aq) \rightarrow$
    $2CrO_4^{2-}(aq) + 3Cl^-(aq) + H_2O(l)$
27. $2Cu(OH)_2(c) + HPO_3^{2-}(aq) \rightarrow$
    $Cu_2O(c) + PO_4^{3-}(aq) + 2H_2O(l) + H^+(aq)$
28. $3HS^-(aq) + IO_3^-(aq) + 3H^+(aq) \rightarrow I^-(aq) + 3S(c) + 3H_2O(l)$
29. $N_2O(g) + 2ClO^-(aq) + 2OH^-(aq) \rightarrow$
    $2Cl^-(aq) + 2NO_2^-(aq) + H_2O(l)$

30. $H_2SO_3(aq) + MnO_2(c) \rightarrow SO_4{}^{2-}(aq) + Mn^{2+}(aq) + H_2O(l)$
31. $IO_4{}^-(aq) + 7I^-(aq) + 8H^+(aq) \rightarrow 4I_2(g) + 4H_2O(l)$
32. $2CrO_4{}^{2-}(aq) + 6I^-(aq) + 16H^+(aq) \rightarrow$
    $2Cr^{3+}(aq) + 3I_2(g) + 8H_2O(l)$
33. $4Cr^{2+}(aq) + O_2(g) + 4H^+(aq) \rightarrow 4Cr^{3+}(aq) + 2H_2O(l)$
34. $H_3PO_3(aq) + 2NO_3{}^-(aq) \rightarrow$
    $PO_4{}^{3-}(aq) + N_2O_4(g) + H_2O(l) + H^+(aq)$
35. $Cr_2O_7{}^{2-}(aq) + 3HNO_2(aq) + 5H^+(aq) \rightarrow$
    $2Cr^{3+}(aq) + 3NO_3{}^-(aq) + 4H_2O(l)$
36. $Sb_2O_5(c) + 4I^-(aq) + 10H^+(aq) \rightarrow 2Sb^{3+}(aq) + 2I_2(g) + 5H_2O(l)$
37. $3H_2SO_3(aq) + IO_3{}^-(aq) \rightarrow 3SO_4{}^{2-}(aq) + I^-(aq) + 6H^+(aq)$
38. $2NO_3{}^-(aq) + 2SO_2(g) + H_2O(l) \rightarrow$
    $N_2O_3(g) + 2SO_4{}^{2-}(aq) + 2H^+(aq)$
39. $2SbO^+(aq) + 2HClO(aq) + H_2O(l) \rightarrow$
    $Sb_2O_5(c) + 2Cl^-(aq) + 4H^+(aq)$
40. $2NO_3{}^-(aq) + 3H_2S(g) + 2H^+(aq) \rightarrow 2NO(g) + 3S(c) + 4H_2O(l)$
41. $5TeO_2(c) + 2BrO_3{}^-(aq) + 14H_2O(l) + 2H^+(aq) \rightarrow$
    $5H_6TeO_6(aq) + Br_2(g)$
42. $I^-(aq) + 2HClO_2(aq) \rightarrow IO_3{}^-(aq) + Cl_2(g) + H_2O(l)$
43. $Bi_2S_3(c) + 2NO_3{}^-(aq) + 8H^+(aq) \rightarrow$
    $2Bi^{3+}(aq) + 2NO(g) + 3S(c) + 4H_2O(l)$
44. $S(c) + 2HNO_2(aq) \rightarrow H_2SO_3(aq) + N_2O(g)$
45. $2NO(g) + 3H_5IO_6(aq) \rightarrow$
    $2NO_3{}^-(aq) + 3IO_3{}^-(aq) + 5H_2O(l) + 5H^+(aq)$
46. a. $+0.59\,V$ b. $Cl_2(g) + Br^-(aq) \rightarrow Br_2(l) + Cl^-(aq)$
     b. $-0.29\,V$ c. $Cu^{2+}(aq) + H_2(g) \rightarrow H^+(aq) + Cu(c)$
     c. $-0.34\,V$ e. $Zn(c) + Pb^{2+}(aq) \rightarrow Pb(c) + Zn^{2+}(aq)$
     d. $+0.90\,V$
     e. $-0.63\,V$

Chapter 25

1. $0.373\,mol\ e^-$
2. $2.90 \times 10^4\,s$
3. 3.29 grams
4. 164 grams
5. 140 grams
6. 216 grams
7. 5.97 mol
8. 268 s
9. 0.721 A
10. $0.522\,dm^3\,O_2$
    $1.04\,dm^3\,H_2$
11. 54.4 grams
    $50.1\,dm^3$

12. a. 0.373 mol Na
       $4.18\,dm^3\,Cl_2$
    b. 0.187 mol Ca
       $4.18\,dm^3\,Cl_2$
    c. 0.124 mol Al
       $4.18\,dm^3\,Cl_2$
13. 1290 min
14. 193 min
15. 58 200 s
16. 6.41 A
17. a. $CoCl_2$
    b. $Fe(NO_3)_2 \cdot 6H_2O$
    c. $8.36\,dm^3$ from both

18. 0.0563 grams
19. a. 0.378 grams Zn
       0.00386 mol Fe
    b. $0.0648\,dm^3$
    c. $0.0702\,dm^3$
       0.341 grams
    d. 1120 C
    e. $0.0116\,mol\ e^-$

Chapter 26

1. **a.** $^{208}_{82}Pb$ **c.** $^{235}_{92}U$ **e.** $^{5}_{2}He$ **g.** $^{8}_{3}Li$
   b. $^{210}_{82}Pb$ **d.** $^{14}_{6}C$ **f.** $^{40}_{19}K$ **h.** $^{238}_{92}U$

2. **a.** $^{7}_{3}Li + ^{1}_{1}H \rightarrow 2^{4}_{2}He$

   b. $^{3}_{1}H + ^{2}_{1}H \rightarrow ^{4}_{2}He + ^{1}_{0}n$

   c. $^{14}_{6}C \rightarrow ^{14}_{7}C + ^{0}_{-1}e$

   d. $^{9}_{4}Be + ^{4}_{2}He \rightarrow ^{12}_{6}C + ^{1}_{0}n$

   e. $^{14}_{7}N + ^{4}_{2}He \rightarrow ^{18}_{8}O + ^{0}_{+1}e$

   f. $^{26}_{12}Mg + ^{1}_{0}n \rightarrow ^{27}_{11}Na + ^{0}_{+1}e$

   g. $^{59}_{27}Co + ^{2}_{1}H \rightarrow ^{61}_{27}Co + ^{0}_{+1}e$

3. $^{214}_{82}Pb \rightarrow ^{214}_{83}Bi + ^{0}_{-1}e$

   $^{214}_{83}Bi \rightarrow ^{214}_{84}Po + ^{0}_{-1}e$

   $^{214}_{84}Po \rightarrow ^{210}_{82}Pb + ^{4}_{2}He$

4. **a.** $^{22}_{11}Na \rightarrow ^{22}_{12}Mg + ^{0}_{-1}e$, beta

   b. $^{66}_{29}Cu \rightarrow ^{66}_{30}Zn + ^{0}_{-1}e$, beta

   c. $^{208}_{84}Po \rightarrow ^{204}_{82}Pb + ^{4}_{2}He$, alpha

   d. $^{27}_{14}Si \rightarrow ^{27}_{13}Al + ^{0}_{+1}e$, positron

Chapter 27

1. **a.** 3,4-dimethylhexane
   b. 2,3,4-trimethylhexane
   c. 2,2,3-trimethylpentane
   d. 3,4,5-trimethylheptane
   e. 2,2-dimethylbutane
   f. 3,4,5-trimethylheptane
   g. 3,3-diethylhexane
   h. 2,3,4-trimethylhexane

2. **a.** 2-methylpentane
   b. 2-methylbutane
   c. 2,3-dimethylpentane
   d. 3-ethylpentane
   e. 2,4-dimethylpentane
   f. 2,3-dimethylpentane
   g. 3-methylpentane
   h. 2,3-dimethylpentane

3. **a.** heptane
   b. 2,4-dimethylpentane
   c. 2,2,3-trimethylbutane

   d.
   $$CH_3CH{-}CHCH_2CH_3$$
   with CH_3 on first carbon, CH_3 on second carbon, and CH_3 group

   e.
   $$CH_3CH_2CCH_2CH_3$$
   with CH_3 substituent

   f. 3-methylhexane
   g. 2,2-dimethylpentane

4. **a.** 2-pentene
   b. 1,2-dimethylbenzene

   c. cyclohexane
   d. phenylethyne
   e. cyclobutene

5. **a.** $CH_3CH_2C{\equiv}CCH_2CH_2CH_3$

   b.

   c. $CH_3{-}\overset{CH_3}{\underset{CH_3}{C}}{-}CHCH_2CH_2CH_3$

   d. $CH_2{=}CHCH{=}CH_2$

   e.

6. **a.** 1-chloropentane
   b. 1-chloro-3-methylbutane

   c. $CH_3\overset{Cl}{C}HCH_2CH_2CH_3$

   d. $CH_3\overset{Cl}{\underset{CH_3}{C}}CH_2CH_3$

   e. 3-chloropentane
   f. 2-chloro-3-methylbutane

g.

$$CH_3CH_2\underset{\underset{\displaystyle CH_3}{|}}{\overset{\overset{\displaystyle CH_3}{|}}{C}}HCH_2Cl$$

h.

$$CH_3\underset{\underset{\displaystyle CH_3}{|}}{\overset{\overset{\displaystyle CH_3}{|}}{C}}CH_2Cl$$

7.
a. 1-bromo-3-ethyl-3-methylpentane
b. 1-butene
c. 4-methyl-2-pentene
d. 3-methyl-1,4-pentadiene
e. 3,3-dimethyl-1-butene
f. chlorobenzene
g. 2-pentene
h. 2-methyl-2-butene
i. 2,3-dimethyl-2-pentene
j. 2,4-dimethyl-1,4-pentadiene
k. 2,3,3-trimethyl-1,4-hexadiene
l. 1,4-dibromonaphthalene

8. a. $CH_3CH_2CH = CHCH_2CH_2CH_3$

b.

c. $HCCl_3$

d.

$$CH_3\overset{\overset{\displaystyle Cl}{|}}{C}HCHCH_2CH_2CH_3$$

e.

f.

g.

h. $CH_3\underset{\underset{\displaystyle Br}{|}}{C} = \underset{\underset{\displaystyle CH_3}{|}}{C}CH_3$

9. a.

$$CH_3CH_2\overset{\overset{\displaystyle Cl}{|}}{C}HCH_3$$

b. $CH_3CH = CHCH_3$

c. $CH_3\overset{\overset{\displaystyle CH_3}{|}}{C}H - \overset{\overset{\displaystyle CH_2CH_3}{|}}{C}HCH_2OH$

d. $CH_3\underset{\underset{\displaystyle CH_3}{|}}{C}CH_2\overset{\overset{\displaystyle O}{\|}}{C}\underset{\underset{\displaystyle OH}{}}{}$

e. $CH_3\overset{\overset{\displaystyle CH_3}{|}}{C}HCH_2\overset{\overset{\displaystyle O}{\|}}{C} - \underset{\underset{\displaystyle CH_3}{|}}{\overset{\overset{\displaystyle CH_3}{|}}{C}}CH_2CH_3$

f. $CH_3C \equiv CCH_2C \equiv CCH_2CH_2CH_3$

g.

h. $CH_3CH_2 - O -$

i. $CH_3CH_2CH_2CH_2OH$

j. $CH_3CH = \overset{\overset{\displaystyle CH_3}{|}}{C}CH_2CH_3$

k. $CH_3\overset{\overset{\displaystyle CH_3}{|}}{C}HCH_2\underset{\underset{\displaystyle CH_2CH_3}{|}}{C}H\overset{\overset{\displaystyle O}{\|}}{C}H$

l. $CH_3\underset{\underset{\displaystyle CH_3}{|}}{C}H - \underset{\underset{\displaystyle OH}{|}}{\overset{\overset{\displaystyle CH_2CH_3}{|}}{C}} - \underset{\underset{\displaystyle CH_3}{|}}{C}HCH_2CH_3$

m. $CH_3CH_2\overset{\overset{\displaystyle Cl}{|}}{C}HCH_2\overset{\overset{\displaystyle CH_2CH_3}{|}}{C}H - \underset{\underset{\displaystyle CH_3}{|}}{\overset{\overset{\displaystyle CH_3}{|}}{C}}H\overset{\overset{\displaystyle O}{\|}}{C}\underset{\underset{\displaystyle OH}{}}{}$

n. 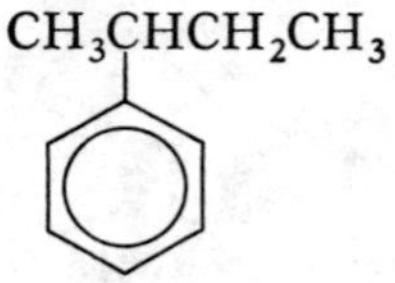 CH₃CHCH₂CH₃

o. 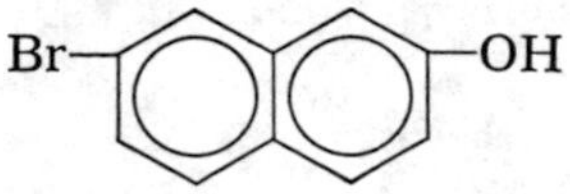 Br—⬡⬡—OH

p. COOH
⬡
Br

10. **a.** 2-methyl-3-pentanol
    b. 2-methyl-3-pentanone
    c. 3-methyl-1-butene
    d. butanal
    e. 4,4-dimethyl-1-pentanol
    f. 3-methyl-3-ol-1,4-hexadiene

11. **a.** 1-chloro-2-methylbutane
    b. 1-bromo-2,3,3-trimethylbutane
    c. bromocyclopropane
    d. 3-chloropentane
    e. 2-methyl-2-butanol
    f. 3-bromo-2-pentene

12. **a.** CH₃CH₂OH, ethanol; alcohol
       CH₃OCH₃, dimethylether; ether

       CH₃CH₂CHO, propanal; aldehyde

                  O
                  ‖
    b. CH₃CCH₃, propanone; ketone

    c. 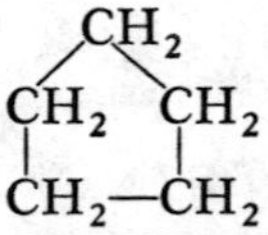   CH₂
           CH₂   CH₂   cyclopentane; cycloalkane
           CH₂—CH₂
           CH₃CH=CHCH₂CH₃, 2-pentene; alkene

Index